Michael Bragg

RDF 1

THE LOCATION OF AIRCRAFT BY
RADIO METHODS 1935 – 1945

MICHAEL BRAGG

HAWKHEAD PUBLISHING

FIRST PUBLISHED IN HARDBACK
IN 2002 BY HAWKHEAD PUBLISHING
6 HAWKHEAD ROAD PAISLEY PA1 3NA

BRITISH LIBRARY CATALOGUING IN PUBLICATION DATA

A CATALOGUE RECORD FOR THIS BOOK IS AVAILABLE
FROM THE BRITISH LIBRARY.

IBSN 0 953154 40 8

Typesetting by Hawkhead Publishing

Printed by Gilmour Print 01294 850217
www.gilmourprint.co.uk

With love and remembrance of
my mother and father and the
late Mrs Janie Elliott

CONTENTS

ACKNOWLEDGEMENTS

MY very first action in researching this book was to write to the Air Historical Branch of the Ministry of Defence regarding advice on seeking Air Ministry records. My letter was answered by Mr E.A. Munday, who not only directed me to Volume 4 of the Air Ministry Signals Series entitled *'Radar in Raid Reporting'*, but also sent me photocopies of the introductory chapters. I consider that I was very fortunate to be made aware of such an important book at an early stage of my research.

The next step was to arrange for a 'Help' notice to be placed in the magazine *'Air Mail'*, the journal of the RAF Association, for which many thanks to the Secretary, that produced a number of replies from ex–RAF and WAAF who had worked on CH and CHL stations. Some of their narratives are contained at the end of the book and I thank them all for their immediate answers to my many questions.

By a pleasant stroke of luck I made early contact with other radar enthusiasts, in particular Ian Shaw from Cambuslang, Glasgow, and Ian Brown from Peebles, both in Scotland and within reasonable car and telephone distance; a great deal of information has been discussed and sites visited that has enhanced the accuracy and quantity of my research.

Also living nearby in Glasgow is Charles McKay, an expert on the personalities and organisation of the Royal Air Force, who had an instant reply to all my queries and Ian Macdonald of The Gleniffer Press, who made me aware of the trials and tribulations of writing a book and the vagaries of the publishing world. I must also thank the Chief Librarian of Renfrewshire Council and his staff at the Central Library in Paisley, who had the burden of processing my many requests for books, John Begg for providing a 1938 copy of Keen's *Wireless Direction Finding*, Len Thomas, the West Chain expert, Stan Sheppard for details of the Electric Calculator and Mike Dean, MBE, who supplied both information and enthusiasm.

Other individuals who must be thanked for their replies to my frequent letters are Len Wilson from the Orkney Islands, Mr Roger Bridgman, the Curator of Communications and his staff of the Science Museum, Mr P. Elliott, the Keeper of Research and Information Services at the Royal Air

Force Museum at Hendon, and Mr A. Doyle of the Civil Aviation Authority Library at Gatwick.

Thanks are also due to the Controller of Her Majesty's Stationery Office for permission to use extracts from the Public Record Office, the Ordnance Survey and RDF/Radar Bulletins, the Trustees of the Tizard Papers at the Imperial War Museum for extracts from Sir Henry Tizard's Diary and Papers, and the Civil Aviation Authority for extracts from NOTAMs. Extracts from Mr A.F.Wilkins' papers deposited in Churchill College, Cambridge, are by kind permission of the Keeper of the Archives and Mrs Nancy Wilkins. I am also greatly indebted to Mr James S. Farrior, of Florida, USA, for his narrative and assistance in preparing a balanced view of the Civilian Technical Corps organisation and to Mr J.S. Goulden for the Pevensey auction papers and his discussions on 'Willie' and 'Oswald' on papers supplied by Mr W. Slack.

The author has made every effort to trace copyright owners and any omissions will be rectified in subsequent reprints. He is also responsible for any errors in the technical material and the interpretation of political events.

Last but certainly not least, my thanks are due to my twin brother, Ted Bragg, for his forbearance and patience in editing the many drafts of this book while in the years of preparation.

INTRODUCTION

WHEN Great Britain declared war on Germany on 3 September 1939 the radar chain, although not complete, was in position to perform its unique defensive function – blunting the element of surprise. Enemy aircraft could be detected approaching the southeast and the east coasts of England and Scotland when over 100 miles away while fighters and crews remained on the ground until they were within striking distance. What a difference just five years had made: in 1934 inland flying patrols were the cornerstone of air defence; they placed an almost intolerable demand on men and machines with successful combats, or even the detection of hostile machines, a matter of chance and good fortune.

But 1934 was also a year of the greatest concern for the Air Staff for three very good reasons: the rising speed of aircraft had rendered the current sound detection system obsolescent and, unless a new technique was evolved of which at present there was no sign, the next war would be lost, the Air Ministry was not in control of air defence research and there were unmistakable signs of political unrest in Germany. Yet within five years a system of outstanding technological and operational complexity for its day had been built and commissioned by the Air Ministry, already overburdened by the need for an urgent and massive expansion of the military potential of the Royal Air Force.

The letters RDF were adopted in 1935 to conceal the existence of radar and were intended to have no special significance. It was then so secret that everyone involved, from the civilian scientists, civil servants and RAF personnel in the Air Ministry, to the RAF and the WAAF on the stations, had their backgrounds checked by Military Intelligence (MI.5) before employment. The early researchers were forbidden to retain technical notes and diagrams and RDF matters were not allowed to be discussed over public telephone lines or referred to in non-secret correspondence. Research was directed mainly on RDF1, the Chain Home (CH) ground stations, to ensure that the RAF had an effective air defence system in the shortest possible time, but RDF2, airborne interception of the bomber, was given an early start in expectation of the immense problems that had to be overcome.

The outbreak of the war and indeed for its duration, continued to demand intensive effort in research and development of a wide range of radars. First was the Chain Home Low (CHL) stations that were hurriedly installed with makeshift equipment along the east coasts of England and Scotland during 1939/40 to detect low flying aircraft attacking shipping during the day and dropping magnetic mines at night.

Both chains were vital in assisting Fighter Command to defeat the German Air Force in September 1940, in what is known as the Battle of Britain, the result of which forced the Germans to switch from day raids on military objectives to night bombing of civilians. These attacks, almost unopposed by air or ground defences, caused much anxiety as few enemy aircraft were shot down. Urgent moves were taken to speed up the effective night interception of enemy bombers by the introduction of Ground Control Interception (GCI) stations that were independent of the existing CH and CHL chains; there was direct radio telephone contact with the pilot of the intercepting fighter.

The introduction of 10 centimetric wavelength equipment in 1941/42 revolutionised both air and ground operations with freedom from enemy jamming and the ability to locate down to sea level. Towards the end of the war, in a last ditch stand for survival by Germany, when pilotless aircraft and rockets were directed mainly on London and the Home Counties, the full range of radar equipment was in place to provide the maximum assistance to fighters and anti-aircraft guns.

The history of radar in comparison with other aspects of the growth of re-armament before and during World War Two has been very poorly served. Cabinet historians considered that it was 'too diffuse and unwieldy'; the Air Ministry produced seven volumes of Signals history that include a wealth of detail of radar history from 1935 to 1945 but were classified until 1972. These documents conform to strict guidelines of all official histories; to record facts, drawing from them the lessons of the future, not to award credit to individuals or to pass judgement on government policy.

Of the thousands of books published about deeds and exploits in the wartime RAF, only a handful mention the ground chains and then only at the time of the Battle of Britain. Some emphasise the airborne radars that enabled the war against Germany to be intensified and brought to a quicker conclusion than contemplated; there is a measure of fascination about the cut and thrust of electronic aerial warfare. The few books that have been published on radar history make a contribution to the overall picture usually from a narrow specific point of view, either as a civilian or Service person;

the sheer magnitude of the spread of radar from 1940 to 1945 prohibits any one from covering, even in outline, the complete story.

This book gives an informative account of the beginning of radar and the building of the ground chains. The story is told directly, as one that needs very little comment, by the participants themselves from extracts of contemporary correspondence from official files in the Public Record Office. It covers the actions of individuals and departments under pressure for results in the few remaining peacetime years; in wartime they were faced with the task of organising an enormous expansion of equipment and personnel, coupled with rapid and continuous advances in technology and changing enemy tactics.

Where possible the story is told in chronological order with the majority of chapters covering one year. Some technical detail is unavoidable in dealing with the subject of radar but it has been kept to the absolute minimum, as have details of the many committees which were so essential in keeping the three Services in touch with developments. The vast amount of equipment that played such a significant part in the defence of the United Kingdom has vanished completely, suffering the usual fate when unwanted – sold to the highest bidder for scrap metal. Only a few items of early experimental radar now remain in contrast to the care and devotion that has been given to many surviving aircraft of the period.

The whole of the ground chains was an engineering undertaking of the most formidable kind ever undertaken in the world in so short a time by government departments and this great achievement has never received the recognition it deserves. Without their timely appearance, the history of World War Two would certainly have had to be rewritten to include a successful enemy invasion, which would have been only the second in nearly a thousand years of English history, and the occupation of the United Kingdom by German civil and military forces.

Chapter 1   1914 to 1934

FOR centuries past the English – and later the British – have fought battles on foreign soils leaving the civilian population with no direct confrontation with the destruction and horror of war. The first ever flight across the English Channel – by Frenchman Louis Blériot, who flew from Calais to Dover Castle in 37 minutes on 25 July 1909 – was perhaps looked upon by many, if not all, as a completely innocent endeavour unconnected with any hostile intentions. This blissful ignorance ceased in a very small way when, during the Great War (1914-18), a German aeroplane flew over Dover, in Kent, in December 1914, and dropped a bomb – into the sea. This scarcely noticed event was followed by a series of determined and organised nightly air raids on civilians by German airships called Zeppelins.

The first was on 19 January 1915 on Great Yarmouth and King's Lynn in Norfolk, when four people were killed; both towns were undefended with no 'blackout'. London's first air raid was on 31 May, when over 120 tons of bombs were dropped, with a further two on 7 September and the following night. Bombing missions were also widespread over England, as far away as Lancashire and Cheshire, and were carried out with absolute freedom from interception. The effect on the civilian population was mainly psychological and, perhaps more worrying to the government, caused much dislocation of munitions production.

Defence against the airships was, at first, totally absent as guns and aircraft were at the battle fronts in France and Belgium, and although the ground defences improved during 1915, only one of the 37 Zeppelins that crossed the coast was damaged. With a very slow speed, some 40mph as compared to the aeroplane, which was twice as fast, the Zeppelins, whose 4,000lb bomb loads were released indiscriminately, had the great advantage of a superior height of 10,000 to 15,000ft, that could not be reached quickly by defending aircraft.

In 1916 a Home Defence Squadron was formed and the BE2C fighter modified from a two to a single seater, enabling it to climb higher and faster, to take on more fuel and fitted with incendiary ammunition, an innovation that had a lethal effect on the Zeppelin's hydrogen filled gas bags. So effective was the use of aircraft that by November 1916 the raids had all but ceased. Twenty one airships had been shot down, many to the delight of civilians who, during a raid, were on the streets eagerly waiting for the sudden massive glow in the sky that heralded the burning by fire of the hated enemy.

After a lull of seven months, the air raids recommenced but this time in daylight. The first one was by 21 giant twin engine Gotha biplanes which, unable to find London because of the cloudy weather, bombed Folkestone, in Kent, on 25 May 1917 killing 95 people and injuring 192. Only one bomber was shot down by an intercepting force of over 70 aircraft. The first daylight bombing raid on London took place on 13 June watched by crowds unaware that they were looking at hostile aircraft, and whose bombs would kill 162 and injure 432; 90 fighters accounted for only one enemy bomber.

There was a second London raid by Gothas on 7 July, mainly on the City and the East End that killed 54 people and injured 190, causing a public outcry at the obvious lack of air defence; the dismal record was repeated with 95 fighters destroying just one bomber. There were no planned air raid precautions; the first sign that enemy aircraft were nearing the capital was the sight of a policeman on a bicycle blowing a whistle or swinging a bell and wearing a placard worded 'Take Cover'. Shelters were the nearest railway arches or the 'Underground' railway stations, enabling Londoners to seek the safety of the platforms. A significant dimension had been added to modern warfare by the Germans and one that was to have an horrific backlash for them 25 years later, the bombing of defenceless civilians.

What had alarmed the War Cabinet was the huge escalation of the bombing, from that of the Zeppelins, which were now an easy prey to a single fighter, to the new tactics of enemy bombers flying over London, sometimes in formation with almost complete impunity. A hastily convened committee was ordered by the War Cabinet on 11 July to report in days on (a) Home Defence against air raids and (b) the Air Organisation. London was now thought to be a special case demanding exceptional measures, it being possible that in the next 12 months the capital might, through bombing attacks, become part of the battle front line.

The committee consisted of only two persons, Prime Minister David Lloyd George and General Jan Christian Smuts, who had come to London to represent South Africa at the Imperial Conference in March 1917 and had subsequently joined the War Cabinet. He was at first reluctant to undertake the investigation because it involved questions on which there had been strong political controversy, but accepted when the Prime Minister agreed to deal with all the repercussions that might arise. The committee heard from representatives of the Admiralty and the War Office that there were four agencies contributing to the defence of London: (1) the Royal Naval Air Service working under senior naval officers, (2) the Observation Corps, mostly of infantry soldiers, often elderly and not specially qualified, (3) various incomplete units or machines of the Royal Flying Corps allocated to Home Defence and (4) anti-aircraft guns of the War Office, the last three operating under the orders of the Home Defence HQ, the only connecting link.

Smuts' Report on Home Defence was in front of the War Cabinet by 19 July 1917 and was immediately approved and implemented: the appointment of a senior Army officer of first rate ability for executive command, to be followed quickly by the addition of three squadrons, which would be trained to fly in formation. The latter recommendation had arisen from a report circulated by the Ministry of Munitions on the poor showing of air defence over London on Saturday 7 July:

> "Our machines were not in formation when in the air and even when they attempted to concentrate they did not come under a unified command in the air, nor had they been trained to fight. The result was that their very spasmodic or guerrilla attacks failed to make an impression on the solid formation of the enemy, and the damage that was being done by our superior numbers of first class Royal Flying Corps machines was negligible. We have investigated the circumstances in some detail, and I am informed that the reason why greater results were not achieved was that some of the pilots were not accustomed to the new machines that they were flying, certain machines were not used due to missing parts and there were a number of defective shells." [1]

Under the direction of Major-General E.B. Ashmore, the defence of London was immediately improved to the extent that daylight bombing had ceased by the end of August. In circumstances that had a parallel in 1940 the German Air Force resumed night raids on London in September until their conclusion in May, 1918.

Smuts' proposals for the Air Organisation took a little longer for approval; it was not until 17 August 1917 that it was considered by the War Cabinet, and the reason was Whitehall wrangling over separation of the naval and military wings of the Royal Flying Corps, which had been created by Royal Warrant on 13 April 1912. On 1 July, 1914, as if to emphasise its independence the naval wing had been renamed 'The Royal Naval Air Service'. The early part of the Great War saw two quite distinct air services with divergent ideas and in wasteful competition for men, machines, airfields and equipment. There was frequent pressure for the combination of both Services, a Ministry of Aeronautics being suggested, but in February 1916 the government's answer was to set up a joint War Air Committee with functions to co-ordinate and advise. Without any executive power the Chairman, Lord Derby, resigned within a few weeks and the committee was dissolved. It reappeared as an Air Board under Lord Curzon but, as it had no more power than its predecessor, it soon ran into conflict with the Admiralty and the War Office, both of which strongly resisted any interference on matters of air policy. The political voices that had long clamoured for a unified air Service were to hear what they already knew; the aeroplane had reached the stage where it demanded its own department to meet the growing dominance it was to have on matters of war. Smuts put his foresight on paper. In his view, air developments had been such that the time was approaching when aircraft would cease to be merely ancillary to naval and military operations:

> "The day may not be far off when aerial operations with their devastation of lands and destruction of industrial and populous centres on a vast scale may be the principal operations of war, to which the older forms of military and naval operations may become secondary and subordinate...But to secure the advantages of this new factor....we must create a new directing organisation, a new Ministry and Air Staff which could properly handle the instrument of offence and equip it with the best brains at our disposal." [2]

He recommended that an Air Ministry be formed as soon as possible to control and administer all matters in connection with air warfare of every kind, and to prepare for the amalgamation of the two air Services. But there was powerful opposition to the change as it was thought that such a move should not occur in time of war. Sir Douglas Haig of the War Office was one member of the Cabinet who exerted his influence to delay the decision, but without success. The War Cabinet accepted the report in principle on the 24 August and set up an Air Organisation Committee under General Smuts to detail the merger and the Parliamentary legislation.

The government announced in the House of Commons on 16 October that a Bill would shortly be introduced (8 November) to set up an Air Ministry, with Lord Rothermere as the Air Minister and it received the Royal Assent on 29 November. His main task before he resigned on 23 April 1918 was in organising the unification of the RNAS and the RFC into a single new service – the Royal Air Force – announced on 1 April 1918. The function of the new ministry would be the recruitment and training of personnel, the collection of intelligence, the initiation of air plans and the provision of fighter squadrons but air operations were to remain with the War Office.

The Air Staff and other senior appointments at the Air Ministry were high ranking officers who had transferred from the Navy and the Army; Major-General Hugh Trenchard was appointed Chief of the Air Staff (CAS) on 18 Jan 1918. There were, however, strong disagreements by political figures of the day on the formation of the Air Ministry that forced Trenchard to resign the following April. The post was taken by Major-General Sir Frederick Sykes on 13 April 1918 but on Winston Churchill's appointment at the beginning of 1919 as the Secretary of State for Air and War, Trenchard was reinstated as the CAS from 31 March 1919. It was not until 4 August that new rank designations were introduced into the RAF, Trenchard now an Air Vice Marshal and a week later an Air Marshal.

With the Armistice in November 1918 and the Treaty of Versailles in 1919, air defence rapidly disappeared for economic reasons, and because France was then not seen as a potential enemy. The politicians of the day had ignored Smuts' visionary advice that:

> "...it is important that for winning the war we should not only secure Air predominance but secure it on a very large scale, and having secured it in this war we should make every effort and sacrifice to maintain it for the future. Air supremacy may in the long run be as important a factor in the defence of the Empire as sea supremacy." [2]

In the UK the RAF was drastically reduced from 53 operational squadrons to seven (overseas from 132 to 21 squadrons) with what remained by 1920 eventually grouped into two main areas, inland and coastal, each under the control of an Air Officer Commanding. By 1922, however, there was growing government concern that whereas RAF aircraft could be counted in 'tens' those of France were in 'hundreds', the difference between the two forces of defence and offence being sufficient for them to put forward a scheme for 23 squadrons. The new Labour government of 1924 announced the rebuilding of the Royal Air Force, and by a decision the following year to initiate a major expansion to 52 squadrons for completion by 1928.

25 squadrons were in service by 1925 but the political climate had changed again in that the completion date was made a victim of the 'ten year rule'– there would be no war for the next ten years. It was not long before it was realised by those intent on forcing the pace of re-armament that the politicians were 'extending' the rule year by year, the completion date being moved to 1930, then 1935, and finally to 1938. But in 1932, when the RAF was still ten squadrons short of completion, the rule was abandoned in the face of growing international tension.

The first expansion of the RAF produced a new organisation on 1 January 1925, the Air Defence[s] of Great Britain (ADGB, the [s] was dropped later), with the Air Officer Commanding-in-Chief reporting direct to the CAS. From headquarters at the Air Ministry and, from 1 June 1926 at Hillingdon House, Uxbridge, Middlesex, the ADGB controlled bomber and fighter squadrons. The latter operated in the Aircraft Fighting Zone which, by 1933, was centred on London but not over it, was 15 miles wide and 150 miles long that stretched from Duxford in Cambridgeshire, round the east and south of London to Devizes near Salisbury Plain, in Wiltshire. Ten sectors each defended a 15 mile front 35 miles from the coast, this distance being chosen to allow the fighters, which took 15 minutes to reach 14,000ft, to be ready to intercept the enemy bombers flying over the coast that had been reported by the Observer Corps. There were two Artillery Zones, one defending London and the other the approaches; both could be lit by searchlights for night fighting.

Annual exercises were held on a modest scale to evaluate the effectiveness of interception, with a small wooden hut outside Hillingdon House as the Operations Room. The plotting system differed little from the Great War; a web of telephone lines was connected to Observer Corps posts, gun and searchlight stations and aerodromes that formed sub-controls, which were connected by telephone lines to the Operations Room. There, plotters with headphones sat round a large table on which was fixed an Ordnance Survey map, overmarked with 10km squares with 1km markers, ten of which formed a lettered 100km square (the Cassini or Military Grid). Aircraft flying over the country were reported every half minute to sub-control, which recorded their positions on the map and passed them to the plotters, who marked out the course with coloured counters.

In October 1927 the ADGB made an application to the Air Ministry for the sum of £1,000 to provide a larger Operations Room, which was in addition to the cost of removing the existing telephone equipment, and re-installation for which £500 would have to be approved by Signals. The letter was forwarded to the Director of Operations from the Signals branch signed by a Flight Lieutenant V.H.Tait (by 1942 an Air Vice Marshal, the Director-General of Signals). Tait conveyed the information that the Operations Room had been installed two years previously at considerable cost, (the telephone work alone costing £728) and had only been used twice for training sessions. Moreover, it had been slightly modified in telephone arrangements as a result of an ADGB exercise with further modifications as a result of that year's exercises. Tait suggested that:

> "Unless there are some strong reasons which are not put forward in the letter, it seems in view of the limited experience which has been gained, premature to consider moving the Operations Room at a cost of £1,500." [3]

The Director agreed and appended a hand-written note on the file: 'Dead as a doornail!...the whole proposal has been dropped.'
Trenchard was most energetic in creating the foundations of the Royal Air

Force on which future Chiefs of the Air Staff and Secretaries of State were so expertly able to build upon. For the RAF to survive against those politically and militarily wanting to dismember the third Service, he knew that he had to place it beyond their reach. One such move that had to be taken quickly was his assertion that it was the right of the RAF to have the prime responsibility for defence against hostile attacks not only from the air but also from the sea, but the latter was too revolutionary even to be considered. The reaction of the Admiralty and the War Office can be imagined; the prestige of the capital ship was at its peak and the Army was unwilling to part with an organisation that had had some success.

As a result of continual disagreement, the government of the day finally conceded that in principle the Air Ministry should take over air defence from the War Office but gave no specific details; the two departments had to agree on the transfer terms. The responsibility for the financing, provisioning and the manning of AA guns and searchlights remained with the War Office but with the anomaly of not having the power to order firing of the guns; that passed to the Air Ministry, which was now in operational control. The all important function of air defence research, however, was retained by the War Office with the Air Ministry represented on the Inter-departmental Acoustical Research Committee.

The experiments on the location of aircraft were exclusively based on the detection of sound from their engines. An attempt to increase the listening distance of the human ear for the detection of aircraft had been carried out by the Army in 1917 at the front line in France to assist gun batteries. Two pairs of wooden trumpets were arranged vertically and horizontally and connected to the ears of the observer, resulting in a threefold increase in range coupled with a broad indication of direction. At home, trials had begun just before the end of the war for the detection of enemy aircraft engaged on night bombing when they were crossing the coast. Some measure of success had been achieved by the placing of a microphone into the centre of a concrete slab and connected to loudspeaker amplifying equipment situated in the vicinity of AA guns.

After the war the War Office continued using acoustic techniques at the Air Defence Experimental Establishment (ADEE) at Biggin Hill, Kent, but the political view at this time was that there would never be another war in Europe and, as a consequence, there was a severe shortage of funds with near stagnation in development. By the middle of the 1920s the microphone in the centre of the concrete slab had evolved into a 20ft (6m) diameter spherical mirror made of reinforced concrete. The observer operated controls a short distance in front of the mirror that moved a small 'trumpet' microphone across its face and he listened with a tiny stethoscope style earphone. But the observer was out in the open and exposed to the weather with the disadvantage that as he was facing the mirror he was unable to see any approaching aircraft.

In December 1926 the Air Ministry were informed by the ADGB that the mirror was unsatisfactory as there were large errors in azimuth and elevation and a pressing need for operational improvements. The mirror diameter was increased to 30ft (9m) with a small control room underneath where the operator could sit down in comfort to manipulate controls that moved the microphone vertically and horizontally; the track of an aircraft could now be followed. A second operator telephoned the information to the control room, a wooden hut at Hythe. Air exercises had shown that the longest range achieved, about 8 miles (13km), was very dependent on atmospheric conditions and considerably reduced by fog and mist.

ADEE did not confine experiments to the detection of aircraft as there had been trials to evaluate the speed of aircraft by sound. A report dated January 1929 described one such scheme laid out across the Romney Marshes that comprised 32 microphones, each set in a 15ft (4.5m) diameter concrete disc, in two lines eight miles long and three miles apart, connected to a control room at Newchurch.

The theory was that an approaching aircraft would be picked up by the first line of microphones with sufficient amplification to light a lamp and, as the aircraft approached the second line, another lamp would be lit. The delay time between the lighting of the second lamp compared to the first could be used to calculate its speed to within three to four miles per hour. ADEE were hopeful that the system would also give the course of the aircraft to about five degrees.

All these results were made available to the Air Staff but none was found favourable. A letter from the ADGB to the Air Staff summarised the work in a few well-chosen words:

"Acoustical research [is] conducted without any definite plan, by scientific officers who have been employed on the task for ten years without producing anything of practical value, which the A.O.C.-in-C. is prepared to accept for reproduction as part of the defence of the country." [4]

This patronising attitude of the RAF to the Army experiments was due to the differing aspects of air defence: the Army was only concerned with the shooting down of enemy planes by AA guns before they crossed the coast so an eight mile range was considered adequate; the RAF needed much longer to give extra time for the standing patrols to be in position. Dissatisfied with the performance of the 30ft mirror the Air Ministry wrote to the War Office in April 1927 to put forward their proposals for the development of a new mirror with three main objectives: (a) the detection of hostile aircraft 25 miles from the coast with approximate bearing, (b) when ten miles away the approximate height, speed, bearing and numbers, (c) and exact indications when over the coast. In July they replied that a detection range of 25 miles could be obtained with a mirror having dimensions of 200ft (61m) in length, which would cost about £3,000, but they regretted not being able to build it as no funds were available. The Air Ministry offered £1,000, the agreed arrangement that they paid one third of the building costs, but the War Office again declined to accept the responsibility for constructing the mirror and firmly declared that funds would not be available, even in 1928. The Air Staff commented:

> "A curious situation [has arisen] as the War Office cannot put up funds for the 200ft mirror, yet in war [the RAF] may find that a tool essential to their needs has not been provided owing to a lack of funds in another state department." [5]

Trenchard viewed the matter with the greatest concern as he considered that the War Office were trying to duck out of its responsibilities and land the Air Ministry with additional costs. In a strongly worded memo circulated to all heads of departments, he wrote on 23 April 1928:

> "Proposals.... to saddle the Air Ministry votes with charges which relieve the other Service Departments of their legitimate responsibilities are to be most strongly deprecated. There are serious objections and risks in such departures, apart from the fact that it provides critics, parliamentary and public, with material for unfavourable comparison between the total expenditure on Air votes and the number of effective aircraft, there is a less apparent but more serious danger arising therefrom. If in the course of carrying out our responsibilities in various parts of the world we offer, as the major user, to pay for defences whether material or personnel, which normally are appropriate to and paid for by the Army, then the time will inevitably come when the Army will as a corollary press to pay for their Army co-operation squadrons. Such pressure, if successful, would in my opinion prove a fatal blow to the Air Service. It must be remembered that the surrender to the Navy of their claim to pay for the Fleet Air Arm nearly wrecked the Air Force six years ago. I must impress upon all concerned the great importance of bearing the above in mind. Failing to appreciate its importance may be disastrous. After ten years experience I am convinced of the truth of this." [5]

With deadlock between the two departments and Trenchard's opposition, the only way the matter could be resolved was by higher political direction from the Committee of Imperial Defence (CID), which had been formed in 1904 to remove the conduct of wars from the military in the War Office, to the civilians in the House of Commons. Chaired by the Prime Minister of the day, it was responsible for the defence not only of the United Kingdom but also the Dominions and the Colonies. In April 1928 the Cabinet, through the CID, ordered that the money should be provided but the two departments had to agree on what and which should pay. There was a last desperate effort by the War Office to force the Air Ministry, which had absorbed the Observer Corps, to take over immediately all the existing research and development of the mirrors and disc systems; the 200ft mirrors would be of no operational use to the Army as the 30ft mirrors were quite adequate. The Air Ministry refused. The Air Staff were already doubtful whether the 200ft mirror would ever meet their expectations, but they did not want to suggest that assumption to the War Office 'as they might seize it as an excuse for curtailing the experimental work'. It was not until October that the argument was finally settled, with agreement that they should both equally share the cost of the 200ft mirror, now estimated to be £5,200. The Treasury gave sanction on 21 December 1928.

The mirror, designed to the calculations of Dr W.S.Tucker, the Director of the Acoustics Department at ADEE, was 200ft (61.5m) in length, 26ft (8m) high, in the shape of an arc of 158 degrees and made of reinforced concrete. Construction began in January 1929, half a mile from the shore at Greatstone-on-sea, near Denge, Kent, an isolated place not far from Dungeness. The position of the mirror was significant; if a war was to be declared then the RAF, not the Army, would use the mirror operationally, so in which direction would enemy aircraft appear? As politicians of the day were of the opinion that the French would become belligerent, the direction of the mirror was fixed for due east, northern France.

The mirror was completed by June 1930 and, as soon as all the builder's equipment was removed, a fence was placed round the adjacent area; it was, according to ADEE,

"...essential to prevent casual picnickers and potential journalists from getting near the focus of the mirror and observing its properties." [6]

The 200ft and two adjacent 20ft and 30ft mirrors were on a 30 acre area in the middle of a large expanse of scrub land that at first did not appear to be of any significance. There was no doubt some astonishment when the War Office received a letter in December 1931 from a Mr R.B.Burrowes that he had personally signed for the payment of £11,000 for about 271 acres except for the mirror site and the access road, which was Army property. The land was to be bought by the Royal Society for the Protection of Birds as it formed the only known ground for the Kentish Plover and, as his savings were only £8,000, and his pension only £139 a year, would the Army consider donating £1,000? There is no indication in the file of any money being paid to Mr Burrowes, but it is likely that his request was ignored as he persistently watched Army personnel to ensure that there was no trespassing on his property. Indeed, in May 1934, he did spot a tent outside the mirror area and asked for £10 a month rent that was reduced by mutual consent to £4.

The War Office was constantly made aware of the danger that Mr Burrowes, through lack of funds, could be forced to sell back the birds' preserve to the developer, a Mr C. E. Andrews, who wanted to build houses and roads up to the boundary. At the same time it was making strong efforts through the Treasury Solicitors' Department to prevent the development of a holiday camp and bungalows along the coast road from Littlestone, but without success. By February 1932 the holiday camp had been built and taking visitors. The Army commented:

> "The camp goes to bed early, and ordinary conversation does not effect the microphones, but if a band started up then matters would be different. If the motor road continued south along the coast, traffic would develop and would definitely interfere with the mirror and put it out of action." [6]

The civilian noise element was a direct indication that the successful siting of a 200ft mirror was totally dependent on obtaining a large expanse of land in front of it with listening rights, a factor that would add materially to the cost. (The Denge mirror site continued to cause concern; the blow fell in April 1935 when ADEE were informed that the developer had repurchased the bird sanctuary and contacted the War Office with an immediate option to buy but this offer was not taken up. In January 1936 the problem was resolved by a proposal to take down the 200ft mirror and re-erect it on 90 acres of land to be purchased from the Southern Railway southwest of the present site. But before any action could be taken, radio had overtaken 'sound' for air defence so the mirror remains at Denge to this day.)

In early 1933 the Army had made a number of flight trials using RAF aircraft, which confirmed that the range of the mirror was 25 miles but only in good weather. Unexpectedly, the microphones were greatly affected by wind noise, which was reduced to some degree by the erection of canvas screens carried by pulleys on a rail fitted to the two flanks of the mirror. In June 1933 two RAF officers and 15 men arrived at Hythe to begin three weeks' training on the complete mirror system, the 20ft mirror at Abbots Cliff (mid Folkestone and Dover), the 30ft mirror at Hythe (south of Folkestone) and the 30ft and 200ft mirrors at Denge, to be followed immediately by a three day air exercise to include day and night flying.

The operation of the 200ft mirror was essential to the success of the exercise; in front was the focal gallery where 20 microphones were fitted covering an arc of 100 degrees in five degree steps. In operation, the microphones, acoustically tailored to respond to the sound of enemy bombers, were manually switched one at a time to a loudspeaker amplifier to ascertain the direction of the incoming aircraft. There were also two listeners on the forecourt with a telephonist reporting observations to the Operations Room, a temporary wooden hut to one side of the mirror. When the direction of the enemy aircraft had been decided the information was then passed to the Hythe control room, which directed the bowl mirror operators to search a specific part of the mirror. These mirrors were so spaced that by using doctored maps to allow for the slow speed of sound it was possible to use standard triangulation techniques to provide 'fixes', which were telephoned to ADGB.

The RAF were able to operate the system with ease as the training was primarily to locate single aircraft. During the exercise, however, formations had been used, together with a flying boat that was regarded as a friendly patrol, but which caused a distracting effect when they all came within microphone pickup resulting in highly confusing sounds. The average performance of the mirrors could not be judged because of the wide fluctuations in range caused by variable weather conditions: at night time it was noted that there was less interference from road traffic noises.

Despite the inconclusive results, the ADGB forwarded a proposal to the Air Staff that a scheme should be considered for the Aircraft Fighting Zone to be backed up with forty 30ft bowl and twenty-seven 200ft strip mirrors, to be placed from St Alban's Head, near Swanage on the southwest coast, to the area of the Wash along the east coast of England. As it was understood that funds were unlikely to be available for such a large scheme (over £60,000) and that the Treasury would insist on a trial system, it was submitted to the CAS that a pilot scheme, known as the Thames Estuary Mirror Scheme (TEMS), comprising two 200ft mirrors and eight 30ft mirrors should be provided. To reduce costs the CAS suggested a reduction to four 30ft mirrors but this was later amended to seven by the War Office on technical advice from ADEE.

Treasury approval was granted in February 1934 but only for the positioning of the mirrors, which was done at great speed by a combined RAF/Army committee. But the location of the 200ft mirrors was proving very frustrating for as the months passed there appeared to be no area in the vicinity of Clacton (Essex) in the north or Reculver Bay (Kent) in the south that did not have noise from cars and motorbikes with the inevitable beach huts producing loud sounds from portable radios. Landowners were asking for what the War Office called 'grotesque sums' for listening rights so by the end of 1934 the final sites for the 200ft mirrors had still not been found.

A major ADGB Air Exercise took place on 23 to 27 July 1934 that covered the sound mirrors. 33 Bomber Squadron was specially detailed to simulate raids from the direction of France to give practice to the 200ft mirror personnel; aircraft were heard from between 10 to 20 miles but there was unexpected man-made interference. The first was caused by ships in the English Channel moving across the front of the mirror, which then picked up the noise of the propellers. The second, and much more serious, occurred during the exercise when 'enemy' aircraft were approaching the mirror head-on; an Imperial Airways airliner flew across it causing complete disruption of the incoming signals. The ADGB report noted:

"Little or no use of early warning from the mirrors this year-much of the information reported the approach of civil aircraft. Again [this] raises the question of serious interference by our own aircraft, and also the effect of decoy aircraft sent out by the enemy with the deliberate intention of confusing the mirrors." [7]

The conclusion reached was that the 200ft mirror provided early warning of 20 to 25 miles but was very susceptible to jamming, would be useless when patrolling aircraft were in the vicinity by day, and only be of value at night. The basic limitation of the mirrors was the speed of sound. An aircraft flying at 300mph would have travelled 2½ miles or completely changed direction before being detected. A War Office letter to the Air Ministry had summarised the situation as early as November 1929:

"I hope you fellows realise that our results can never be very accurate for the simple reason that the sound takes a whole minute to travel 12½ miles in still air... and is often deflected from its original source." [4]

Events across the Continent were beginning to cause anxiety for political stability. In January 1933, Adolf Hitler had risen to power and by October had withdrawn Germany from the Disarmament Conference and the League of Nations. In March 1934 the Air Staff were informed that the government had decided that a war with France was unlikely and that recent developments indicated such a possibility with Germany.

A five year plan was proposed for the Air Ministry and the War Office to change and re-orientate the home defences from facing France to pointing towards Germany. The possibility of German aircraft flying over neutral territory had to be allowed for, with Belgian aerodromes being occupied after the first few months of a war. In addition to the expected air raids on London, which had to be regarded as the first primary objective of the enemy, there was the probability of attacks on the industrial areas of the Midlands, Yorkshire, Lancashire and the Tyne and Tees.

The plan was based on the recognition that the range of certain German aircraft exceeded 900 miles and, from northwest Germany, the towns of Southampton, Birmingham, Manchester and Newcastle were now within reach; if German bombers illegally flew over the Low Countries then the whole of England and possibly Glasgow would be under threat. As the Admiralty had requested that Portsmouth and Southampton be defended by the RAF, the southern defences opposite France were retained by the Air Staff. To ensure that the proposal to back up the Aircraft Fighting Zone with sound mirrors was viable, approval was eventually given by the Treasury in December 1934 for work to commence immediately on the TEMS plan. The Air Staff were of the view that they could confidently plan for air exercises to be ready for June 1936 although by May 1935 there was still indecision over land purchase near Clacton and Reculver Bay.

On 14 August the Superintendent of ADEE was advised that the Air Ministry had called a temporary halt to the mirror constructions with the reason not yet officially communicated to the War Office. On 19 August a top secret letter from the Air Ministry was delivered by hand to the War Office for the Army Council that stated:

> "Pending further consideration of the results of experiments with radio detection they desire to suspend *temporarily* the construction of the Thames Estuary Mirror Scheme." [8]

This news was most unsettling to the Army and the officer in charge of the scheme wrote to his superior:

> "It is disturbing that the Air Ministry should, without informing you, have brought to an apparently advanced state a system of location which is claimed to be superior to acoustic methods. Not only does the Air Ministry well know of the War Office heavy acoustical commitments by virtue of its active membership of the InterServices Acoustical Committee and of our own committees, but their D.S.R.'s [Director of Scientific Research] department is kept in close touch with all the activities of A.D.E.E. In view of the potential effect of radio detection on the Army Council's own policy, we submit that there is a clear case for asking the Air Council to communicate details of the methods developed. As no information has been passed to us we are unable to hazard a guess as to what the repercussions it may have on sound generally." [8]

By September there was still no information from the Air Ministry that prompted a reaction from ADEE to the War Office:

> "I hope also that we shall soon be vouchsafed some information as to the reason for the delay as a prolonged unblissful ignorance will have an unfortunate effect on our staff ." [8]

The War Office wrote again to the Air Ministry that they were anxious to resolve the matter as the continuing delay would have repercussions especially from the Post Office, which was pressing for them to release space at Faraday House in London that had been earmarked for the mirrors' telephone termination equipment. The Air Ministry replied on 7 November that they had considered all the repercussions and were extending the suspension of operations until March 1936. The War Office wrote on 20 December to the Superintendent of ADEE:

> "The Air Ministry have not answered because they are pursuing another hare; privately, we are convinced that it will not be caught easily and therefore the mirrors are by no means dead. We are not likely to abandon the mirrors for years, they are the only means we have of co-ordinating early warning with close A.A. gun defences and are likely to remain so." [9]

To show their confidence in acoustic methods, the War Office had completed a 200ft mirror built of local stone near Valletta in Malta, continued with a survey for four around Gibraltar and obtained financial approval for two for Singapore. Two more letters came from the Air Ministry extending the suspension with the final dispatch on 26 August 1937:

> "I am commanded by the Air Council to inform you that they have finally decided to abandon the Thames Estuary Mirror Scheme." [8]

Possibly there was some surprise and amusement at the Air Ministry and the War Office when the *Sunday Pictorial* published on 10 March 1935 details of what were called 'Acoustic Ears' that would make surprise air raids impossible. The article explained that listening posts were to be established on the east and southeast coasts, which in the event of an enemy air raid on London, would give an alarm long before hostile planes were in range of the most powerful lens. The special correspondent continued:

> "I understand that the system involves the use of a new invention by means of which sound is made visible. In other words, it will be possible to see the approach of hostile aircraft long before they are in the line of vision...Acoustic ears will act with equal efficiency in daylight or darkness, and by the vibrations set up it will be possible to tell the type, and therefore the nationality of aircraft. Surprise attacks, should the invention come up to expectations, would thus be rendered almost impossible." [8]

REFERENCES

1 MUN5/134/1000/116	2 AIR2/7842	3 AIR2/1225	4 AIR16/316
5 AIR2/1195	6 AVIA7/2764	7 AIR2/1398	8 AVIA12/133
9 AVIA46/53			

Chapter 2   1935

IT is often said that in moments of crisis in our history, a man of greatness is in the right position at the right time. One such person was Henry Thomas Tizard (later Sir Henry). He had joined the Army in 1914 and quickly transferred to the Royal Flying Corps where he became a first class pilot and, because of his background, was involved with all the scientific aspects of military flying. When he left the Army in 1919 he was the Controller of Research and Experiment with the rank of Lieutenant Colonel.

His civil appointments remained in the field of science and aeronautics where his influence soared far and wide. In 1920 he undertook the task of co-ordinating the scientific work of the defence and civil departments, and for two years from 1927 he was the Permanent Secretary at the Department of Scientific and Industrial Research (DSIR). He knew everyone in the field of aviation research, what they were doing and where. One appointment which he treasured from 1929 to 1942 was that of Rector of the Imperial College of Science and Technology in London.

Because of his incomparable standing in the aviation world he was able to persuade the Air Ministry to obtain Treasury approval for the post of a Director of Scientific Research (DSR), which he then declined to accept as he considered that the proposed salary was too low. The post was then offered to the existing Deputy Director, Harry Wimperis, whose qualifications were about on par with Tizard, a first class degree at Cambridge (Tizard's from Oxford). He had joined the Royal Naval Air Service as an experimental officer and took up flying with a keen interest in bomb sights and improvements in flying instruments. Both men were rare – scientists, each with a pilot's licence.

For reasons that members of the Air Council were unable to find out at a later date, the DSR was excluded from research into telegraphy, telephony and armaments and had no department to 'direct': his duties were more in line as an adviser to the Air Staff. His personal assistant was A.P.Rowe, a young scientific officer who frequently deputised for Wimperis at committee meetings. It was not long before Rowe was aware of Army air defence projects and, as an observer at the various test trials, the limitations of the acoustic mirrors. He was also a close watcher of the political picture that was developing in Europe and, conscious of the possibilities of a warlike situation arising that could involve the United Kingdom, he called for all the files on air defence and found a mere total of 53. In a memo to Wimperis he put forward his view that unless science evolved a new technique of aiding air defence the next war could be lost if it started within ten years.

From time to time Wimperis was required to investigate claims of a 'death ray' invention but in all cases they were found to be just short of fraudulent.Wishing to know more about the effect of radio power on the human frame, he decided to meet Professor A.V.Hill, an eminent physiologist, and on 15 September 1934 they had lunch at the Athenæum, Wimperis' club. He made notes of the conversation:

> "A human body subject to radiant energy will be affected by it and the nature of the response will depend on the frequency. Energy on a wavelength of 100 metres [3 MHz] would, if sufficiently concentrated, raise the temperature of the human body receiving it; if the rise in temperature so caused was 5 degrees Centigrade or more, the recipient would be incapacitated. If the frequency could on the other hand be got as low as 200 cycles per second, [Hz] the pain caused – by a sufficient supply of energy – would be so intense as to be quite unbearable. If at the other extreme end of the scale the frequency and energy could be got into the range of hundreds of millions of cycles per second, [Hz].... then, (with adequate energy), the skin would be burnt off. (In a laboratory experiment on these lines the skin was burnt off the tail of a rat). Against this, it may be that the human body when contained in a metal monocoque fuselage would be wholly or partially protected: and in that event it would be necessary to explore whether the energy could be raised sufficiently to fusing metal parts. The amount of energy necessary can be predicted; but its means of radiation may have yet to be discovered." [1]

It was at this point in time, 1934, that many voices were being heard both outside and inside Parliament of the need for a scientific approach to air defence. Tizard was one of them and, with Winston Churchill – who was now out of office and a backbencher – and his scientific adviser, Professor F.A.Lindemann, they were all pressing the government for action.

It is very likely that Wimperis had already made an unofficial approach to Tizard on the possibility of him chairing a committee together with the names of those whom Tizard wanted to serve with him. There can be no question that his action was unique in that it was virtually unknown, in those days, for any of the three Services to enlist the aid of outside top scientific figures to solve exclusive military problems. On 12 November 1934 he signed a long memo the opening sentence of which was certainly thought provoking:

> "When one looks back on the stupendous technical advances of the last 50 years one cannot but wonder what equally striking advances can possibly lie ahead of us in the next equal period of years...." [1]

(Today we are fully aware of those advances and, like Wimperis, we can only wonder what the next fifty years will bring in terms of scientific achievement.) His memo was mainly concerned with the defence of cities against hostile aircraft that was becoming increasingly inadequate because of improvements in their range and speed:

> "We need, therefore, to intensify our research for defence measures and no avenue, however seemingly fantastic, must be left unexplored. The idea of a ray of energy to put the engine ignition out of regular action has often been proposed, but it suffers from the vital defect that it is easy to screen the ignition leads and plugs... There remains to consider the effect of this radiation on the human body." [1]

He indicated that his notes of his talk with Professor A.V.Hill had been placed in the file and that there were certain possibilities revealed for the future, if not for the present, which would need careful watching. A scientific survey was proposed:

> "...with two or three scientific men specially collected for the purpose: their findings may sometimes prove visionary, but one cannot afford to ignore even the remotest chance of success: and at the worst a report that at the moment 'defence was hopeless' would enable the Government to realise the situation and know that so far retaliation was the sole remedy,– if such it can be called. I would submit....that the formation of such a body be now considered." [1]

Wimperis proposed that Tizard should be the chairman with additional scientific expertise from Professors A.V.Hill and P.M.S.Blackett, who was a distinguished physicist; his assistant A.P.Rowe would act as the secretary with himself to represent the Air Ministry. The terms of reference for the committee had to be sufficiently wide to cover all possible developments and Wimperis suggested it might be:

> "To consider how far recent advances in scientific and technical knowledge can be used to strengthen the present method of defence against hostile aircraft." [1]

His memo was placed in the file for the attention of the Air Member for Supply and Research (AMSR), the Chief of the Air Staff (CAS), the Secretary, and the Secretary of State, and in that order. This procedure ensured that the Secretary of State was able to see all the actions and comments of intervening officials, all of whom had the power to suggest amendments. Wimperis' immediate chief was Air Marshal Sir Hugh C.T.Dowding, who since 1930 was the Air Member for Supply and Research with total responsibility for technical progress in the Royal Air Force. On passing the file to the CAS, Air Chief Marshal Sir Edward Ellington, Dowding wrote:

> "I agree generally. Possibly the terms of reference of the committee might be criticised as being so wide as to approach to infinity, so far as the labours of

the committee are concerned; but the presence of D.S.R. [Wimperis] should suffice to confine its researches to what he considers to be practical." [1]

The CAS wrote: "I agree to this proposal to set up a Committee as suggested by the D.S.R." with even shorter responses of "I agree " from the Secretary, Sir Christopher Bullock and the Secretary of State for Air, the Marquess of Londonderry. In the incredibly short time of nine days the formation of the committee had received ministerial approval and on 11 December the letters of invitation were ready for signature by Londonderry. Professor Hill replied on the 13th that he would first have to seek the approval of the Royal Society, where he was working as a research professor, and Professor Blackett on the 14th that he had much pleasure in accepting the invitation. Tizard's reply was on the 18th with his usual characteristic modesty:

"I shall be very glad to serve as chairman...I am doubtful whether I can be of real use but I am very willing to try." [1]

The official name was the Committee for the Scientific Survey of Air Defence but it quickly became known as the Tizard Committee such was his reputation in government circles. Wimperis was aware that 'his' committee was only answerable to the Air Ministry, was without any executive power and could be viewed by others to be of a slightly doubtful legitimacy as air defence was still in the hands of the War Office.

Lindemann had corresponded with the Secretary of State about the appointment of a committee to investigate the possibilities of defence against air attack. At the beginning of December 1934 he wrote again of his apprehension over night bombing which:

"constitutes the greatest menace to the future of Western civilisation. It can be carried out by ordinary, possibly mass produced machines; it requires a minimum of skill in the pilots; damage from explosives, poison gas and above all incendiary bombs may be immeasurable: and finally, so far as I can gather, there exists at present no means of prevention which is even approximately adequate. Carried out ruthlessly on a large scale it might paralyse all endeavours to resist and compel the country to abject surrender." [1]

He mentioned Stanley Baldwin's speech on air defence on 10 November 1932 which included the most quoted of all quotations on air defence – 'the bomber will always get through'.

Lindemann presumed that as the RAF could deal with the day bomber, Baldwin's quote referred to night bombers, and his complaint was that it was generally understood that the quotation had the approval of the Air Ministry. His view was that an antidote had always been found for every offensive weapon and he saw no reason to suppose that aircraft would be the only exception; it was a defeatist attitude. He did not think that a purely Air

Ministry committee would be adequate and urged the setting up of a small committee of scientists and Service representatives, with an independent chairman (a man of the type of Lord Weir) to report directly to the Prime Minister:

> "Its task should be to find a method for preventing bombers and especially night bombers from reaching their objectives." [1]

The CAS was required to advise Londonderry on a suitable reply to Lindemann. Ellington wrote a memo to the DCAS and Dowding asking for their views on Lindemann's letter:

> "I suggest that the first thing the Secretary of State should do is to disabuse Professor Lindemann of the idea that Mr. Baldwin's remark.... had the approval of the Air Ministry...I think it should also be explained to Professor Lindemann that, far from accepting such a thesis as Mr Baldwin's, the Air Ministry and the War Office believe that a defence is possible...." [1]

Dowding replied to the CAS that Lindemann's proposal to set up a committee had already been anticipated by the DSR and he thought it desirable that it should start its existence within the Air Ministry so as to avoid the protracted triangular negotiations that a combined committee would involve:

> "...[and] it would suffice to put Professor Lindemann in touch with it when it is formed." [1]

Londonderry took that advice and Lindemann was asked to join the Tizard Committee, which he initially refused to do. Much to the discomfort of the Air Staff, Lindemann had certainly put his finger on their greatest fear, the destruction of cities and high civilian casualties because of intractable problems in the interception and shooting down of the night bomber. Taken literally, Baldwin's famous and oft repeated remark implied that every bomber would get through, but for the Air Ministry the question was how many could be shot down; the situation did not inspire confidence in the ability to win a war. In the 1934 air exercises the interception of bombers over London showed that in daylight only two bombers out of five were intercepted, a figure that would not improve as the speed of the bomber was rapidly approaching that of the fighter, ie, it could not be overtaken.

In early January 1935 Wimperis telephoned Robert Watson Watt, the Superintendent of the Radio Research Department of the National Physical Laboratory (NPL), at Slough, in Berkshire. Watson Watt recalled the occasion some ten years later:

> "Early in 1935 Mr. H.E.Wimperis asked me to call at his office. He made it clear on my arrival that he was not consulting me in any way officially, but as a friend with some expert knowledge in whose judgement and discretion he could rely. He then asked me for my opinion on the practicability of proposals of the type colloquially called Death Rays, i.e., proposals to produce structural damage or

functional derangement in enemy aircraft or crew. I gave an off hand opinion [that it was impractical] but I promised a qualitative examination." [2]

On his return, Watson Watt passed a short note to A.F.Wilkins, a scientific officer, for him to calculate the radio energy required to raise 75kgm of water by 2 deg. C in ten minutes from a distance of 600 metres. Wilkins deduced at once that the question of the practicability of the 'death ray' had risen again and this was confirmed by Watson Watt, who added that the Air Ministry had asked the DSIR on its probability. He then asked Wilkins if he had any suggestions to make on how the presence of aircraft approaching the coast could be detected. Wilkins replied that he knew that aircraft re-radiated enough energy on a 5 metre wavelength to give appreciable 'beating' on a receiver when flying near the aerial. In a memo on his connections with early RDF, Wilkins wrote:

"I do remember clearly that Mr. Watt indicated that it was also his proposal that this phenomenon of re-radiation should be used as a means of detecting aircraft..." [3]

and that he was aware that Watson Watt had suggested to others that by using pulses and re-radiation it ought to be possible to achieve results superior to those being obtained with sound-locators; it was well before he was asked for the 'death ray' calculations.

The first meeting of the Tizard Committee was held at the Air Ministry, Adastral House, Kingsway, London, on 28 January 1935, to discuss its terms of reference and a memorandum on air defence. Agreement was reached that the main problem would be the detection of the position of enemy aircraft. Excellent results had been obtained at 10,000ft in directing searchlights by 'trumpet' style sound locators but, in a few years' time they would be ineffective due to increasing aircraft speeds and advances in the art of silencing; it was of the greatest importance to examine other methods. One possibility was the infra-red radiation emitted directly or indirectly by aircraft but a detailed discussion was deferred to a later meeting. The likelihood of detecting short wave electromagnetic radiation reflected from the metal surfaces of an aircraft using a ground wave source was also considered. Wimperis told the committee that Watson Watt had prepared a memo on the defence use of short wave radio and that he considered that there was some hope of detection by these means. It was decided that further discussion should be given to this possibility after his memorandum had been circulated.

Watson Watt's reply to Wimperis conveyed the impracticability of a 'death ray' as the basic power required to be emitted from a single dipole was almost five million kilowatts, a figure derived from calculations made by Wilkins. For an effective beam a stacked 1 metre aerial array reduced the radiated power to 300kW, but to date the maximum radiated power on that wavelength was only 25 watts. The figures were based on the proviso that the aeroplane would need to be in the ray for ten minutes to produce the effect, but Watson Watt thought that one minute would be more realistic – but this factor immediately raised all the calculations ten fold and rendered the scheme outside practical limits. He completed the double demolition of the 'death ray' as a potent weapon by stating that the metal frame of the aircraft would provide an effective shield for the crew and engine. If Watson Watt had ended his letter at this point it would have been satisfactory to Wimperis as his query had been expertly answered, but Watson Watt had given thought to the question that had not been asked:

> "Meanwhile attention is being turned to the still difficult but less unpromising problem of radio-detection as opposed to radio-destruction, and numerical considerations on the method of detection by reflected radio waves will be submitted when required." [4]

This sentence must be considered as the beginning of radar in this country because it gave Wimperis and the Tizard Committee a head start; without it there would have been months, if not years, of delay while the feasibility of using radio techniques was being investigated by the Royal Aircraft Establishment (RAE). With hindsight we now know that a later start even as short as six to nine months of the development of radar could well have been fateful to the outcome of the Battle of Britain.

It is not clear when Wimperis received the 'death ray' memo but at the first committee meeting on 28 January the minutes convey that he had knowledge of its content. Rowe had returned it to Wimperis on 4 February with a memo that copies had been circulated to the committee, that he had checked the arithmetic and that the 'formidable figures' appeared correct for the assumptions made. He added:

> "Mr. Watson Watt refers in his last paragraph of his memo to detection by radio beams and offers to submit calculations if required. There appears to be an urgent need for an investigation....[of an] alternative to sound." [4]

Wimperis replied the next day instructing Rowe to ask Watson Watt to report on the detection method so that the committee could consider it before he was interviewed. He sent his letter on 6 February:

> "Dear Mr. Watson Watt, In your recent memorandum to D.S.R. on the possible uses of radio beams for air defence, you kindly offered to provide a quantitative estimate on the possibilities of detection as distinct from destruction. Mr. Wimperis has asked me, as secretary of the committee that is investigating these questions, to ask you whether you would be good enough to provide

these further data. Your recent memorandum [on the death ray] has been circulated to members of the Committee and when your notes of detection have been circulated it is intended to arrange for you to meet the Committee. Yours faithfully, A.P.Rowe." [4]

Watson Watt replied to Rowe on 12 February. His second memo 'The Detection of Aircraft by Radio Methods' clearly indicated the phenomenon of reflection, as fields of one millivolt per metre were readily attainable and rose to ten millivolts per metre as the aircraft passed overhead at heights under 20,000ft. These fields were about ten thousand times the minimum required for commercial radio communication so that large factors of safety were in hand. Using pulse techniques in use at the Radio Research station, the distance between the aircraft and the transmitter could be measured; the use of two or more receivers would enable its position to be found and, by means which could be made partially or wholly automatic, the height and plan position. The concept of a chain of stations, and the option of using continuous wave should there be an unexpected flaw in the use of pulse, was discussed.

In concluding his memo, Watson Watt added two innovations; the identification on the cathode ray tube display of the intercepting fighter fitted with a keyed resonator aerial (that would cause the echo to increase and flash), and direction to the point of interception by radiotelephone without reference to ground features. The most important aspect was that the returned radio wave was sufficiently strong for measurements to be made. In fact so strong, that in the covering note to Rowe he wrote:

"It turns out so favourably that I am still nervous as to whether we have not got a power of ten wrong, but even that would not be fatal. I have therefore thought it desirable to send you the memorandum immediately rather than to wait for close re-checking." [5]

Wimperis sent the memo to RAE for an expert opinion by the Radio Department, which expressed the view that the principles were sound and believed that the phenomena would be of sufficient magnitude to be useful. Practical evidence was given in one of their reports a year previous or so in which reflections from aircraft had been noticed on a wavelength of 2½ metres, and an article in the Bell *Telephone Journal* of 1933 that also referred to the reflections of radio waves from aircraft flying at considerable distances. As RAE had not been asked about the detection of aircraft, the fundamental indications of reflected waves were not given any importance. The mistake in the calculations suspected by Watson Watt was found and corrected. (Rowe later wrote that if it had not been so preoccupied with development at the expense of research it was likely that RAE would have produced a radio based system without resorting to outside help.)

The sequence of events, from Wimperis meeting Watson Watt in early January to the receipt by Rowe of his second memo dated 12 February on the detection of aircraft by radio methods, after the first meeting of the Tizard Committee, is clearly shown in Air Ministry files, which have been available at the Public Record Office since 1972, and to official historians without any restriction. Few authors have written the correct version of events but repeated the incorrect information found in other books. The cardinal error occurs with the Tizard Committee's first meeting where it is stated that (1) the committee should seek the advice of Watson Watt on aircraft detection, or (2) that the committee considered Watson Watt's idea and suggested that he should pursue it, or (3) that the committee should consult Watson Watt on the 'death ray', or (4) that Watson Watt appeared at the first committee meeting and discussed his proposal, or (5) that Professor Watson-Watt in February 1935 explained to a technical sub-committee that the detection of aircraft by radio might be feasible and proposed that it should be tested. None of these statements is true as an examination of the minutes of the first meeting will reveal. In all these versions there is no mention of Wimperis; indeed, one book suggested that it was Tizard himself who set up the committee, but how he was able to do that without being an Air Ministry official was not explained.

Watson Watt's memory was certainly at fault when interviewed by Cabinet historians on 26 January 1945, by saying that he had prepared a memo on the possibilities of detecting aircraft by reflected waves that was taken to the first meeting of the Tizard Committee. Rowe also had a memory lapse when interviewed in December 1944 by incorrectly stating:

"The Tizard Committee had some ideas about the possibility of a ray that would stop internal combustion engines and a letter was written to Mr. Watson Watt enquiring about the possibility, a step of the greatest importance when the committee called for information about the possibility of Mr. Watson Watt's work being used in regard to defence against air attacks. The committee were anxious to have the theory of the detection of aircraft by radio methods tested by a practical demonstration." [6]

Watson Watt's second memo was discussed in detail by Wimperis and Tizard with him (at the Athenaeum) and concluded with Wimperis agreeing to seek approval for £10,000 for experiments. But this was a considerable sum in 1935 and required the consent of Dowding; his post had been split and he was now the Air Member for Research and Development (AMRD). Wimperis wrote to Dowding the next day, 15 February:

"Mr. Watson Watt has put before the Committee [note that some historians have incorrectly assumed that it was the first committee meeting, it was, of course, the 'committee' meeting at the Athenæm], a memorandum which describes a novel and promising method of detecting the approach of hostile aircraft by radio. I have discussed this with Mr. Tizard....and we are in agreement that it is desirable that immediate steps should be taken to try this out with actual aircraft. In fact Mr. Tizard, acting on behalf of the Committee, is desirous of putting the matter forward as a definite immediate recommendation...I propose that we should immediately obtain Treasury authority for calling on the N.P.L. to assist us in this experimentation; the cost not to exceed £10,000 including the salaries of the staff thus seconded." [5]

Dowding replied to Wimperis on 17 February:

"My only hesitation in asking for an immediate authority to spend up to £10,000 on this project is that it is purely defensive and if we go 'all out' for this immediately, some offensive device, which may be in the offing, may have to take a back seat. [The Treasury had already agreed to a similar sum in December 1934 for the development of the Spitfire fighter prototype]. The detection of aircraft by Radio methods, if successful, would be a very great improvement on detection by acoustical methods, and might enable accurate AA gun fire to be directed against an invisible aircraft. There are great advantages, and money must undoubtedly be found to follow up the suggestion, but has the Committee yet considered what it would wish to recommend in the way of research into offensive methods..." [5]

Dowding had asked Wimperis whether it was possible to check the calculations with an air experiment using the pulse equipment at Slough. ('These scientists can do anything with figures' he had been heard to say.) Wimperis replied:

"There would be some loss of secrecy in carrying out this experiment since many more would be aware of what was being done than were engaged on this particular test." [5]

There was also some doubt expressed by Watson Watt and Wilkins about the capability of the Slough equipment; the long pulse length of about 200 milliseconds, the poor envelope shape and the peak transmitter power that did not exceed 1kW. Echo returns had been obtained from the vast mass of the ionosphere but no one knew for sure what the size of the reflection would be from such a tiny object as an aeroplane. Wilkins was of the opinion that there was insufficient time to modify the transmitter and he suggested to Watson Watt that it was not essential to use pulse as a continuous wave transmission would show a comparable effect.

The principle of aircraft re-radiating radio signals had been known for some time. Wilkins knew the Post Office engineers who had carried out test trials from 15 to 18 December 1931 of a two way 5 metre radio link from Dollis Hill to Colney Heath that was near the de Havilland aerodrome at Hatfield. The Post Office *Radio Report No 223* published on 3 June 1932 included a lengthy description of the interference produced by aircraft flying in the vicinity of the receiving aerial at Colney Heath. Several pages of tables were produced that specified the time and level of interference, the height of the aircraft, distance from the aerial, whether biplane or monoplane, military or civil and registration markings. The report added that there was no interference when aircraft were not in the vicinity of the receiving aerial and gave as the only possible explanation of the phenomena that it was a result of the directly received wave being re-radiated from the aircraft. It was observed that for the 5 metre wavelength used, the strainer struts in some aircraft would be approximately the correct length for a half wave dipole. The Post Office engineers regarded the effect as a nuisance and were, of course, not concerned with aircraft detection; the lesson for them was that receiving stations should not be sited near airfields.

Wilkins' interest was the statement that in some cases of 'interference' the signal level meter needle made considerable 'swings', a very positive sign that the effect of a reflected wave from metal aircraft was certainly measurable. His first calculation used a wavelength of 50 metres that was sufficiently close to the wing span of an RAF bomber acting as a half wave dipole, the highest known radio output power of 50kW and a distance of 15km (9 miles) between the aircraft and the aerial. The second showed that a better field could be produced with 7 metres and 15kW of power, but it was decided that an air test would meet with a better chance of success if carried out on the longer wavelength. These calculations by Wilkins have not survived.

Much has been written about the Daventry Experiment that Watson Watt admitted had arisen through Dowding's distrust of the arithmetic. Wilkins was responsible for its success, an anxious task as for some unexplained reason there was no time for a dummy run. This is surprising in view of what might have happened or not happened if it had been inconclusive; it is certain that progress would have stalled until further trials had been undertaken to the satisfaction of Dowding.

Wilkins' unofficial contact with the BBC engineers at the Daventry transmitter station, and his knowledge of the direction and field strength of the radiated aerial pattern, which had been measured at Slough, enabled him to decide on the position of the van, the compass heading and the aircraft height. There was another factor in favour of Daventry; the wavelength of the BBC transmitter was 49.8 metres. The test was simple in outline: to fly an aircraft through the centre of the transmitted beam and a sensitive radio receiver on the ground would indicate on a cathode ray tube any changes due to reflections produced by the movement of the aeroplane.

On the afternoon of 25 February, Wilkins and his driver, Dyer, set off from Slough for Weedon village, just off the A5, six miles from the Daventry masts. He recalled:

"The site was previously selected by [using] a map and we were lucky to find a suitable field which the owner was prepared to let us use. We installed the aerials, [two sets of horizontal dipoles about 12ft (4m) above the ground spaced 100ft (32m) apart] and decided to risk leaving them in position while we found a hotel for the night. After dinner when we returned to the site to test the apparatus, the aerials were intact." [7]

The aerials were connected to a battery operated twin channel receiver with a cathode ray tube display which had been developed at Slough for the investigation of long distance short wave propagation. Each receiver was connected to a dipole but one of the receivers had a phase shifting device inserted between it and the aerial; the theory to be tested shortly was that both aerials would pick up the ground wave but due to the distance apart they would not be identical. With a small modification to the receiver and rotating the phase shifter, the deflection caused by the ground wave would be reduced to a small spot in the centre of the CRT screen; the effect of the ground wave on the display would be cancelled. The receivers remained sensitive and when a reflected ray was received the state of balance was upset producing a deflection on the screen.

The work took longer than expected and was made laborious as there was no lighting provided inside the van. It was well past midnight when Wilkins finally found himself connecting up the several hundred volts from accumulators for the cathode ray tube by the light of matches struck and held by the driver. Only a few minutes remained before the BBC transmitter, radiating an unmodulated 10kW carrier, closed down at 0100, an extension specially arranged for Wilkins, but within that short time the ground wave cancellation was shown to be effective. One disappointment was the failure of the pen recorder, which was provided to measure the movement of the CRT beam, as it had not survived the journey from Slough and there had been no time to investigate.

Ready to leave, the aerials were disconnected and left in the field with trust that they would be there in the morning but the driver was unable to move the van which was found to be firmly frozen to the ground. Fortunately, a shovel was stowed inside the tool locker so they were able to free the van and return to the hotel in the early hours of the morning.

By 0800 the next day Wilkins and the driver were checking that all was well before the arrival at 0930 of Watson Watt and Rowe, who was acting as the Air Ministry official observer. The driver was then asked to leave so that he could not see what was happening on the tube display. Wilkins readjusted the phase shifter slightly so that the centre dot was changed into a small vertical line to indicate that the two receivers were in operation. Wimperis had arranged with RAE, which was conducting a series of airborne radio equipment tests, for an aircraft to fly over the Daventry masts at 6,000ft and then proceed in a southerly direction on a specific compass heading for a distance of twenty miles, which would take the aircraft over the van, and then to retrace forward and backwards until 1030. At 0945 the aircraft, Heyford bomber K4030 piloted by Fl/Lt R.S.Blucke with technical officer W.T.Davies, was heard and Wilkins has written:

> "On the first approach it flew well away to the east, [and] no re-radiated signals were detected. The second approach [was] nearer the beam axis and still some way off with a small rhythmic beating detected. As the aircraft subsequently flew off to the south good beats were observed." [7]

No doubt with a great sense of relief to those on the ground, the next runs were closer to the van, of which the crew were unaware, but not over it as intended, with easily detectable beats obtained for periods of 2.0., 4.0 and 4.3 minutes. When the aircraft passed nearly overhead the green line oscillated approximately between lengths of ½ inch (13mm) and 1˜ inches (32mm). By assuming the aircraft speed of 100 miles per hour and by observations from the van it was estimated that a detection range of eight miles had been achieved. Watson Watt was quick to impress upon Rowe of the big improvements that would arise with high power transmitters, sensitive receivers, suitable aerials and wavelengths. Wilkins wrote:

> "No visible signs of excitement. I was highly elated and not a little relieved that all the calculations that I had made were not far off the mark." [7]

Rowe's scientific training enabled him to see that the experiment was one of detection only and that the location of the aircraft had not been attempted. He wrote next day to Wimperis a concise report of the demonstration. He concluded:

> "It was demonstrated beyond doubt that electromagnetic energy is reflected from the metal components of an aircraft's structure and that it can be detected. Whether aircraft can be accurately located remains to be shown. No one seeing the demonstration could fail to be hopeful of detecting the existence and approximate bearing of aircraft approaching the coast, at ranges far in excess of those given by the 200ft sound mirrors...." [5]

An authoritative description of the Daventry Experiment appeared as early as 1958 in Watson Watt's book *Three Steps to Victory*, yet many accounts that have been published after that date are in some degree of error, from the minor to the ludicrous. The common errors are: (1) the date which is usually given as 26 February with the implication that there was no preparatory work needed the day before, (2) the number of people involved, which varies from Rowe with two assistants in a van to Watson Watt, Wilkins, Rowe and a driver that mysteriously gains a fifth person at the end of the experiment. One official version stated that Dowding was there. As recently as 1998 a book stated that Rowe and Wilkins were the only observers and gave the date as 25 February, (3) the display on the cathode ray tube is described as a blip suddenly appearing, or, a straight line that bends when the aircraft is over the van, or a blip that crosses from left to right across the tube face that could be used to follow the aircraft tracks. One account suggested that those present were expecting 'death rays' and were disappointed at the result. Another that the bomber fired Very lights over Daventry, made one run then flew back to base; Rowe went back to London and the Treasury handed over the money the next day. (4) An American government publication that recorded their invention of radar had a small mention of the British contribution: 'Mr Watson Watt began his researches some years before the war using as his headquarters a hut and truck near Daventry, the headquarters of the BBC; his wife was his first assistant.'

It may be relevant to mention that the calculations and the experiment were only to prove the phenomenon of reflection of radio energy from a metal surface for which the use of continuous radio frequency waves was perfectly adequate. But if used for detection there would be difficulties (in 1935) when more than one ship or aircraft was detected because of the complexity of the returned wave and total jamming would be a simple operation: Watson Watt had no intention of using it. His work at the NPL on reflections from the ionosphere had shown that the use of pulses clearly separated the down-coming waves from the upper layers and, using a time base for the cathode ray tube display, the order of arrival of two or more echoes was easily indicated.

The disadvantage of using pulse is the minute fraction of the transmitted power that is returned to the receiver, 10^{-17}. That is why it was essential to use the highest attainable transmitter output power, the largest aerial and the most sensitive receiver. Another factor was an economic one; in 1935 a 10 metre wavelength 350 kW pulse transmitter was a practical proposition, one producing continuous power was not. Immediately after the experiment Watson Watt sent a revision of the 12 February memo to Wimperis that rectified the arithmetical error and added features, such as the use of cathode ray direction finding (CRDF) equipment and the need to develop wavelengths below 10 metres to ensure complete freedom from long distance jamming. The title was changed to 'The Detection and Location of Aircraft by Radio Methods'.

On 4 March Wimperis wrote to Dowding advising that the preliminary experiment, which he desired should be carried out, had confirmed the calculations upon which the scheme was based. He added:

"We now have, in embryo, a new and potent means of detecting the approach of hostile aircraft, one which will be independent of mist, cloud and nightfall and at the same time be vastly more accurate than the present methods in the information provided and the distances covered. I picture the existence of a small number of transmitting stations which between them will radiate the entire sky over the eastern and southern parts of the country, using a wavelength of 50 metres. This radiation will cause every aircraft to act as a secondary oscillator (whether it wishes to or not) and the secondary radiation will be received by a number of local receiving stations (equipped with cathode ray tube displays) dotted around the coast such as the acoustical mirrors might have been under the old scheme. These receiving stations would thus obtain continuous records of bearing and altitude of any aircraft flying in the neighbourhood, (including those still 50 miles out at sea) and deduce course and ground speed. Mr. Watt ...considers the system to be almost, if not quite impossible, to jamb by hostile aircraft action ..." [5]   (note the use of the word 'jamb', now obsolete and replaced with 'jam'.)

The next day Dowding spoke to Wimperis about the possibility of radio being used in an offensive capacity and he replied that in principle he thought it could be. In Dowding's memo to Secretary Bullock, approving the request for £10,000 (later amended to £12,300) he added that the reply of Wimperis had removed his last hesitation in cordially endorsing his recommendation. Secretary Bullock, already aware from Wimperis of the need for action, wrote to the Treasury the next day, 6 March:

"I am writing to you [Sir N.V.Nind Hopkins] now because we want to get as a matter of extreme urgency, sanction to go ahead with an interim recommend-ation, which the Tizard Committee have put forward for the experimental exploration of a new and, at first blush, very promising method of detecting and measuring the approach of hostile aircraft by radio...." [5]

By 12 March Treasury sanction had been received but only on the understanding that detailed financial costs had to be submitted and approved before proceeding. The speed of events in what was high level government decision making was quite extraordinary. It was just a month since Wimperis had got his glimpse of Watson Watt's second memo, the Daventry Experiment had followed within 14 days and Treasury approval for the experiments just two weeks later. Wimperis' astuteness in assuring Dowding that there was a possibility of an offensive capability of the new technique, when clearly there were no such indications whatsoever at the time, was obviously the result of an earlier talk with Watson Watt. If the answer had been in the negative or had conveyed an element of doubt, Dowding may well have delayed his endorsement. What was certain was the Treasury reluctance to agree to a figure for payments to the members of the Tizard Committee; that needed further consideration! There were only three members of the committee entitled to payment, Tizard and the two professors, but it was not until May that it was agreed that the fees would be ten guineas (£10.50p) each for the first ten meetings then five guineas (£5.25p) a meeting to a maximum of £200. By today's standards very small amounts for men who had the power to recommend the spending of millions of pounds.

In the meantime, Watson Watt and Wimperis had visited Air Ministry property on the island of Orfordness, on the Suffolk coast, and had agreed that it was a suitable place for the experimental work to begin; it was barren and isolated but had the back up and the security of an RAF station that operated the nearby bombing range. On 20 March, following Treasury approval, Watson Watt and other members of the Slough Radio Station, accompanied by two Works officers, inspected the island, their principal task to find buildings that could be made habitable from those that had remained after the end of the Great War, but were in a dilapidated state. They also decided where the aerial footings were to be placed for the three sets of 75ft (23m) guyed lattice masts, one set for the transmitting array and the other two for the receiver and the spaced heightfinding aerials.

At the Air Ministry, Wimperis, anxious that the project should not be delayed by finance branches being held to peacetime procedures for competitive tendering, obtained the approval of the Secretary of State to have a meeting of the departmental heads to ensure swift action. Only one item was outside their control – electricity – the existing island supply was insufficient so there was a wait for the local electricity company to cable over a three phase supply.

The Tizard Committee sat frequently. The second meeting on 21 February was at the ADGB headquarters at Uxbridge to discuss air defence and the third on 4 March was primarily a long discussion with Army chiefs on the limitations of anti-aircraft fire control. On the fourth meeting on 18 March two Admiralty scientists and a naval officer were interrogated on the detection of aircraft. At sea no instruments were used as observations were made by officers on duty using X7 power binoculars; under questioning it was admitted that it was not possible to estimate height. Further, it was not known by the Admiralty what the chances were of detecting an aircraft on a clear day. Wimperis commented that he had heard that often the first indications of an enemy air attack was the splash of bombs, but the Navy said that the first line of defence was not against aircraft but submarines.

The fifth meeting on 29 March was mainly a long debate on the merits of sound detection with the final word that the mirrors had reached the limit of economical size and that no important increase of range by sound locators could be expected in the future.

On 10 April Watson Watt was interviewed during part of the sixth meeting. He said that his proposals for the detection and location of aircraft were the result of fundamental research at Slough. The height of the ionosphere was determined by the difference between the times of travel of short duration pulses from the transmitter and those reflected from the ionosphere; a visual indication of the time difference, and therefore the range, was displayed on a cathode ray tube. The height of an aircraft could be obtained indirectly by measuring the angle of incidence of the returned wave as it met the ground. The responses of two horizontally spaced aerials applied to the plates of a cathode ray tube that were at right angles to each other gave an ellipse pattern from which the angle could be obtained. He was certain that by employing the technique of 'floodlighting' by radio waves, secondary radiations would be received from aircraft that could be located.

He proposed the use of a 50 metre wavelength that had the advantage of existing high output power, ease of direction finding and a suitable cover for the experiments. The alternative would be beam transmissions, which were possible using a wavelength as low as 5 metres, but there was a double disadvantage in that the transmitter and receiver were far from fully developed. When asked for assistance for AA guns and fighters Watson Watt replied that he thought that a 7 metre wavelength would probably be used for the more accurate detection of the angles of radiation, which was unobtainable with 50 metres, and he added that ships could possibly be located and their courses plotted at 20 miles.

Watson Watt had been asked by Wimperis about the viability of a 'death ray', not that of aircraft detection, but he had followed further the line of reasoning that even if such a ray were possible, the difficulties of using it to find one aircraft, let alone more than one, would be like using a telescope; valuable time would be lost in searching for the target and there was the danger of nearby high radiation levels. His proposal was the substitution of the telescope with 'floodlighting', which allowed all the aircraft to be seen together in a radio field of about a quarter of a sphere with means of obtaining range, direction and height which were already in use, but not before used collectively. Thus the basis of the location equipment was already in existence at Slough, but in a very primitive form that needed much more development.

Watson Watt was very aware of the need to provide for the Services as quickly as possible an adequate radio-based defence system using existing technology as there was no time for research. He never claimed to have invented radar, indeed, without the approach by Wimperis and subsequent events he would have been unaware of the problems of air defence that would normally have been confined to the Air Ministry and dealt with by RAE. He would have remained unknown as one of the many scientists who perform a diligent, if unexciting, lifetime in government service.

Although the formation of the Tizard Committee had been announced in the House of Commons its advisory status did not satisfy its persistent critics, and continual pressure on the government eventually produced results, a CID Air Defence Research sub-committee which was formed on 10 April and held its first meeting the next day. As would be understood from its terms of reference it had political power:

> "It was to undertake control of research into, and experiments in connection with, new methods or the improvements of existing methods of defence against hostile aircraft." [8]

Fortunately for the work beginning at Orfordness, Tizard was a member and Sir Philip Cunliffe-Lister the chairman, who, from 8 June, became the next Secretary of State for Air.

In May the Tizard Committee issued its first interim report that summarised the progress of the first seven meetings, which had been devoted to the taking of evidence from military and civil experts, on the existing and contemplated means of countering air attacks. They reported that the Vickers predictor used with AA guns was useless against dive bombers ... that it was unlikely that radio means would be available in the near future for the destruction of aircraft...the limit of technical advances for listening devices had been reached...there would be no material improvement on the warning time given by the 200ft sound mirror ... the result of the Daventry Experiment was much beyond expectations ... hostile aircraft might be detected and approximately located by radio methods between 60 miles (96km) to 70 miles (112km) from the coast in five years' time ... and the committee had reason to hope that it would also be the ideal means in the future for effecting interception and the control of AA guns.

There were frequent phone calls to Works from those waiting at Slough on the progress of renovation at Orfordness which appeared to be taking up precious time that could be used for experiments. On 13 May, A.F.Wilkins, E.G.Bowen, L.H.Bainbridge-Bell and two assistants left the radio station with a modified ionosphere receiver and a newly built transmitter contained in two 10 ton RAF lorries, which were ferried over the River Ore by the local RAF detachment the next day. Impatient at the delay in Works erecting the 75ft masts, Watson Watt obtained 60ft (18.5m) masts from Slough which were rigged with simple half wave dipoles in a direction that covered the sea and land so as to ensure the maximum flying time of test aircraft. Within seven days of their arrival on the island and using makeshift power supplies, the transmitter and receiver were producing the usual ionosphere returns. This confirmed the effectiveness of the new transmitter with the pulse width reduced from 200μsec to 30 μsec to ensure an acceptable minimum range, and the output power raised from 1kW to an estimated 60kW (later found to be no greater than 15kW when a more accurate calculation was used for measuring peak pulse power). By 5 June echoes from stray aircraft from 13km (8 miles) to 30km (18 miles) were being frequently obtained, sufficient for Watson Watt to agree to a special demonstration to be laid on for the benefit of the Tizard Committee members, but with a warning that he was unable to offer a guarantee as to what could be shown.

The ninth meeting of the committee was held at Orfordness on 15 June that enabled the members to be prepared for a demonstration with a special test flight laid on – a Vickers Valentia flying at 15,000ft to give the longest flying time without the crew using oxygen. To the dismay of Watson Watt and his research staff, unusually excessive radio interference and an overhead heavy thunderstorm caused high levels of receiver noise that all but prevented the few plots from being seen. A curve connecting range and time on the basis of the pilot's log was drawn at the conclusion of the test and it was found later that the few observations were in good agreement with the aircraft's log book.

The flight was repeated the next day but there was no improvement in the weather or the atmospherics. The basic soundness of the operation did not escape Tizard, however, who reported later that he had witnessed certain experiments that had been successfully carried out under very adverse weather conditions. For the researchers it was a major setback but at least the susceptibility of 50 metres to heavy thunderstorms had been found early on, rather than later; a decision was made to try a lower wavelength. Two identical flights were made, one using 50 metres on 8 July and 26 metres the next day, which was expected to reduce the echo size because of the wavelength change. But the lower receiver noise had allowed the amplification to be increased that extended the range from 37km (24 miles) to 45km (27 miles).

The day-to-day experiments were carried out under the general supervision of Wilkins, who was primarily concerned with the accurate measurement of smaller angles of incidence, which determined the lowest level of height finding. Other work was directed to see if the echo could indicate the type of the aircraft by using Wallace, Bristol, Seal and Vildebeeste aircraft but there appeared to be no definite relation between echo and aircraft size. Within two months the maximum detected range of 64km (40 miles) to 80 km (50 miles) was reached, fixed by the height of the aerials; to double the range to 100 miles the mast height would have to be increased to 200ft (61.5m). The discussion on the need for 200ft masts coincided with one of Rowe's fortnightly visits on 16 July when he witnessed a demonstration of a Bristol R120 aircraft flying from RAF Bircham Newton to Orfordness and back at a height of 15,000ft. On the outward run the receiver amplification was reduced to eliminate noise. Clear echoes up to 40km (25 miles) were conspicuous at a glance and, by increasing the receiver gain, echoes up to 53km (32 miles) were seen. On the return run Watson Watt detected the aircraft at 60km (36 miles), Rowe at 50km (30 miles) and accurate ranges were recorded to a minimum distance of 8km (5 miles).

Watson Watt took the opportunity before Rowe went back to London to impress on him that it was now certain that the work had an important scientific application, and that qualified staff must be provided. He visualised a chain of stations around the country at 20 mile intervals on a 26 metre wavelength that would reduce the possibility of jamming from ground stations and he was sure that the height and bearing problems would be resolved. In his report to Wimperis the next day Rowe mentioned that Watson Watt could see echoes up to 67km (40 miles) all verified by an examination of the pilot's log book, a standard feature after every test flight. The clarity of the echoes certainly made an impression on Rowe:

> "One month has elapsed between the first attempt at detection, witnessed by the Committee, and the demonstration of 16 July. It would be difficult to exaggerate to the Committee the advance made in this short interval. There is no relation whatever between the results of the two demonstrations." [9]

On 24 July an unexpected happening occurred during a flight with a single Wallace aircraft whose echo had disappeared from the screen at 34 miles. The observers were waiting while the aircraft was turning round and preparing for the return trip when an echo suddenly appeared at 20 miles, began to waver, split, then finally disappeared: there appeared to be no technical reason for such an unexpected short duration echo. Wilkins wrote:

> "the echo was probably from a formation of three aircraft that split into what was clearly an echo from a single aircraft, and another echo beating rhythmically from a formation of two aircraft." [7]

When the pilot of the Wallace was phoned later he confirmed that at the beginning of his return flight he saw a formation of three Hawker Harts that had strayed into the flight path – one had flown away suddenly and then followed by the other two aircraft. This confirmed the observers' theory that the shape of the echo provided an indication of the number of aircraft. In July, an air defence exercise was held to determine the effectiveness of 'safety corridors' whereby friendly bomber aircraft could leave and enter the country without being fired upon by friendly fighters. The report stated that it had been shown very clearly the vital necessity of ensuring that the defences knew in sufficient time beforehand when the bombers were about to use the corridors, as a failure to fully circulate the information on one occasion had resulted in the friendly bombers being attacked. Interception had not been forgotten; a third of the day raids had not been intercepted, which rose to nearly two thirds at night, but the night exercises were unrealistic because the War Office had failed to provide searchlight crews. The writer added:

> "It must be remembered that the performance of none of our aircraft bears much resemblance to that of aircraft with which an enemy, and, we hope, ourselves, will conduct the next war. It is a fallacy to suppose that a FURY intercepting a HART can be compared to the fighter of the future intercepting a bomber of the future." [10]

Several flights were made by Heyford and Virginia aircraft through the Acoustic Mirror Zone along the south coast of England and, as in previous years, civil aircraft were in the vicinity and Service aircraft came within range of audibility when not actually engaged as raiders. These conditions made it quite impossible for the listeners, who were operating by sound alone, to judge what should be reported and what should not. The result was that although the mirrors never failed to give early warning of aircraft approaching the coast 10 to 15 minutes before they actually crossed it, action could seldom be taken until confirmatory plots were received by direct observation. In a summary to the ADGB it stated what was already known:

> "In war, however, the mirrors would be reliable up to the limit of their range but, unfortunately, that range is not great enough in the case of really fast moving aircraft, to give the Commander of the Home Defence Forces a warning that is early enough to enable him to conserve his forces." [10]

Direction Finding (D/F) is nearly as old as radio itself for the directional properties of a single vertical aerial were well known by the turn of the 20th century and the ability of two or more aerials that were half a wavelength apart to provide direction finding was patented in 1899. In those days there was no prospect of an aerial being turned because of the dimensions required for wavelengths of thousands of metres. But in 1907 two Italian pioneers of direction finding, E. Bellini and A.Tosi, invented without doubt a most outstanding device that enabled two loops (four vertical aerials) to be 'electrically' turned 360 degrees by remote control; it was given the name of goniometer from the Greek words *gonio*/angle and *metron*/ measurement. As the principle was independent of wavelength the gonio dominated the design of D/F sets for over fifty years. Also in 1907 an American, Lee de Forest, patented the triode radio valve; amplification was now possible of detected radio signals, the first step of many that were destined to change the world of communications to unknown heights.

Position fixing technique of the day was based on three widely separated D/F stations measuring the bearing of a ship or aircraft that was transmitting a radio signal. Due to measuring inaccuracies the three lines intersected the position in the shape of a tiny triangle, hence the name 'triangulation'. But enemy aircraft would approach the shores in radio silence. Watson Watt's scheme was to use the system in reverse, ie, transmit from the ground and obtain the reflected range from two or more receiver stations which would pass the plot to a control room to obtain the 'fix'. But if there were two or more aircraft and widely spaced then an element of doubt would arise with two or more echoes on the screen, unless the receiver stations were absolutely sure that the echo under observation was from the same aircraft. But he decided that range cuts, as the scheme was known, even with the possibility of ambiguity, would suffice and be a better proposition to adopt it now rather then wait for further research, which he estimated might take all of five years.

The fourth meeting of the ADR sub-committee on 25 July, having read the interim reports on the work at Orfordness through the Tizard Committee, recommended:

"That the location and detection experiments had already produced results to justify the initiation of executive action on radio methods and locations...Service departments should examine the position and formulate plans for the establishment of the radio location and detection methods both as regards equipment and personnel. A letter conveying the committee's appreciation should be sent to Mr. Watson Watt for the excellent work that he has carried out." [8]

The rapid results of what were investigations into the unknown were made by Wilkins and Bowen and two assistants working on the island seven days a week from 0850 to 1830 with extensions in the evening and at weekends when Watson Watt was there. During the summer Wilkins and his team had been concentrating on improving the measurement of the angle of incidence, that had overloaded the receiver requiring modifications. Progress was slow but gradually the angle was reduced from five to half a degree which represented about a lower limit of 5,000ft. Increasing the radiated power was the next step with a reflector behind the single dipole array and improvements to the transmitter. Tests were also made on 8 metres but the results were inconclusive and eventually abandoned so as to concentrate the work on 26 metres. Watson Watt submitted an interim report for the Tizard Committee outlining what had been achieved in only two months. It was, he was careful to add;

> "obtained with a transmitter capable of some improvement, a receiver capable of considerable improvement and an aerial system capable of a great improvement." [1]

In proposing a chain of receiver stations from the Wash to Dover each flanked by a transmitter, he added that two further requirements were now immediately necessary: two receiving stations at the ends of a base line, one at Orfordness and another some 10 miles away to obtain experience on range cuts, and the provision of a large and suitable building for the accommodation of the expected special staff who could not be asked to live in the very crude housing conditions at Orfordness. To seek a suitable location Wilkins, Bowen and Watson Watt on one weekend motored north of Orfordness but without success.

At the suggestion of Wilkins, who had seen the building earlier in the year, they drove south to Bawdsey Manor and found exactly what was required; acres of land, and, what they all agreed to be of the greatest value, a 50ft (15m) increase in height over Orfordness, which was just five feet above sea level. Unbelievably, the owner had placed it on the market but so far there had been no bidders. Watson Watt wrote to Wimperis on 6 August urging the buying of Bawdsey Manor with all possible haste to solve the need for accommodation and messing required for the increase in staff necessary to extend the experimental work of height and direction finding. He added that delays of over six weeks in purchasing the manor would seriously affect research.

Wimperis acted speedily by arranging for details of the estate to be sent to him by hand from the London agents. He wrote to Dowding on 13 August to explain that further important decisions needed to be taken. The first was that 200ft masts were required to double the existing range of 40 miles and, secondly, so as to determine a suitable base line, a site some ten miles away. Watson Watt had suggested Bawdsey Manor, which was at the right distance and alignment from Orfordness, and Wimperis confirmed that a survey by road and air showed that it was the only choice. He put forward the concept of a long range detection system, apart from stations necessary across the Thames Estuary, by others suitably placed and at a convenient distance apart: Sheringham (near Cromer, Norfolk), Caister (near Great Yarmouth), Dunwich and Bawdsey (Suffolk) and Foulness, North Foreland and Hythe in Kent. He added:

> "The discovery of this means of detecting and locating hostile aircraft promised,
> if it could be successfully applied, a revolutionary improvement in the defence
> measures. Six months work has shown that success is in sight and a new step
> forward in the provision for the work is necessitated....I have discussed with Mr.
> Tizard the recommendations made in this minute and he authorises me to say
> that he strongly supports them and regards their authorisation as urgent." [1]

Dowding agreed the same day, the CAS concurred on 21 August and a
Deputy Secretary prepared a memo the next day for the Secretary of State:

> "You are of course aware of the assurances given in the House [of Commons]
> by the Prime Minister that the necessary funds for the research work of this
> [Tizard] committee will be made available, and Secretary [Bullock] took special
> steps with the Treasury to facilitate this. The [DSR's] proposals now made
> will involve additional expenditure.... Treasury authority will be required but
> on receiving your approval in principle, I anticipate no difficulty or delay in
> obtaining it, on the basis of a closer estimate from D.W.B. [Works] for the
> purchase of the property." [11]

He replied on the file in red ink the same day:

> "This must be done. Treasury are as anxious as we are to pursue this
> investigation."

He added a further instruction two days later.

> "Mr. Watson Watt's requirements on land, plant and personnel should be met
> as quickly as possible."

On 28 August, Wimperis wrote to the Director of Works of his visit with
Watson Watt to Bawdsey Manor, which they had found satisfactory in all
respects. There were 150 acres of land, adequate buildings for laboratories
and staff requiring the minimum of conversion. He asked for the Director
to ascertain on what terms the property could be obtained and how soon
possession could be given and, quoting the Secretary of State's brief minute
as authority, Wimperis concluded that he would be 'glad if the matter is
treated as urgent.' Works replied on 10 September that they had inspected
the manor and had estimated the cost of acquisition at £25,000.

If there has to be a file that is seen to initiate the chain it must be '*The
Installation of Radio Detection Stations for Defence Purposes*' which
Wimperis had opened on 2 August and enclosed the first memo for the
attention of the DCAS (Air Vice Marshal C.L.Courtney). It conveyed the
recommendation of the ADR sub-committee that the Air Ministry should
consider at once the setting up of a chain of radio detection stations for the
defence of this country from air attack.

The DCAS had discussed the proposals with the Wing Commander of
FO1 (Flying Operations) and added that he would like a name for the system

that would not immediately indicate its method of operation. In a memo to Wimperis on 23 August the Wing Commander wrote:

> "I suggest R.D.F. (a compression of R.D.[radio detection] and D/F. [direction finding]), to serve as noun, verb or adjective, as required. If you agree, will you please have the title of the file altered and we will use the initials in all future papers." [12]

After a delay of three weeks Wimperis replied to the DCAS that the initials RDF were suitable during which time the suggestion, according to Watson Watt, was a result of a discussion between him and Rowe. Much has been written about the letters RDF and if it was thought that they conveyed the impression that direction finding was the main function, then all was well, as a co-operative element was assumed in those days. The intention was that the letters RDF had no specific interpretation.

On 12 September Watson Watt wrote to the Director of the NPL that Tizard and Wimperis had suggested that a secret patent should be taken out by him to cover the proposals on which they were now working. He enclosed a draft specification:

> "I have to certify that I am the sole inventor, and that the invention did not directly arise from the official duties entrusted to me." [13]

(The patent was assigned the number 25770/35 – The chief object is to provide a means for determining the distance of a craft from a given point using a re-radiated secondary ray from the craft.)

The next sitting of the ADR sub-committee was on 16 September with the next one three months away –Watson Watt was ready. On 9 September he wrote a major report to Wimperis the gist of which was his recommendations for a chain along the coast, which would consist of transmitting and receiving stations every 20 miles (32km) but, to avoid the ambiguity of direction finding when using range cuts, an additional transmitter would be added at each receiving station. Each site would be about two miles inland, not less than 50ft (15m) above sea level and have one 200ft mast for the transmitter and two for the receiver. The maximum expected ranges were 80 miles for aircraft flying at 13,000ft, 50 miles at 5,000ft and 35 miles at 2,000ft. Height information would not be available for at least a year but the extra masts should be provided. It was visualised that plots would be sent at first to a filter room that covered three adjacent stations, the composite information then being sent to an operations room such as existed at Uxbridge.

The sub-committee made the following recommendations: (a) that a chain of stations should now be established with the object of locating aircraft approaching the coast, and the Air Ministry should proceed with the necessary executive action on the advice of the Tizard Committee as to their location and (b) it was agreed that the necessary executive action should be taken to acquire and establish Bawdsey Manor as a centre for research work and the headquarters for the construction of the chain stations.

The first recommendation is remarkable when it is understood that over £1 million would be asked for, and obtained, from the Treasury when not one station had been built or a specification issued or a prototype evaluated. There was no one on the committee that had any detailed knowledge of RDF apart from Tizard and he was totally dependent on information supplied to him by Watson Watt, who purposely underestimated progress in official papers. The one person who had the power to delay RDF was the chairman, Sir Philip Cunliffe-Lister, (later Lord Swinton), and it was his far-sightedness in this and many other matters that ensured that when World War Two began that the RAF would be in a position of reasonable military strength. Committee recommendations were the first fundamental step, but Treasury sanction was required before any action could be taken.

The next move was the preparation of a 'case', which was a detailed financial memo that was submitted to another committee, the Treasury Inter Services Committee (TISC) for approval. These rigid procedures were well known to those involved in obtaining finance from the Treasury; they had to ensure that the proposals were beyond criticism. There was one important factor that affected Works: a nail could not be driven into a piece of wood until funds had been placed in a 'Vote' that enabled work to be charged against it; any deferment in obtaining finance would extend the completion date of the chain. The first priority was to acquire Bawdsey Manor and no time was lost here for the very next day after the sitting of the ADR sub-committee, Wimperis wrote to the Director of Works:

"The meeting of the committee have decided on the purchase of Bawdsey Manor. When the minutes are received, it will be for the secretariat to obtain covering authority. At yesterday's meeting, Sir Warren Fisher [Head of the Treasury] assured us it would be given. Pending receipt of Treasury authority, I would suggest that you obtain a firm price from the vendors and the earliest possible possession date. Please treat as urgent." [11]

Works replied on the 19th:

"...that the vendor required £35,000 and will not give a figure below this. I would be glad, therefore, if you would advise us immediately the necessary sanction has been obtained to enable us to submit a firm offer." [11]

On the 20th, Wimperis wrote to Secretary Bullock through Dowding that the committee had agreed that action to acquire Bawdsey Manor should be taken immediately and that Treasury authority was needed to purchase, adapt and to man the establishment. Dowding wrote the same day:

> "The most important thing is to get immediate authority to purchase, [as] this will certainly be necessary. The adaptation, equipment and manning are more nebulous at the moment. If we can get a blank cheque for the whole, well and good. Otherwise we had better get authority to purchase as the first step." [11]

The next day Secretary Bullock issued a terse instruction to a deputy:

> "I should like this matter to be pursued urgently-verbally in the first instance - with the Treasury." [11]

On 26 September, £25,000 was obtained from the Treasury for the purchase, subject to a Works report on the building and a valuation report. The Valuer inspected the Manor on 30 September and found much to his satisfaction. On 4 October the Chief Valuer of the Inland Revenue office at Ipswich advised Works of a valuation price not to exceed £25,000. There was much discussion about the possession date as the owner, Sir Cuthbert Quilter, was finding it hard to arrange an immediate removal but eventually it was agreed that the Air Ministry would take over part of the manor, certain outbuildings and all the land on 17 January 1936 for the sum of £20,000 with complete possession by 1 June and a final payment of £5,000. It was certainly a lot longer than the six weeks that Watson Watt was expecting!

The original single dipole aerials had served their purpose in being able to allow test aircraft to be followed in front and behind so as to give the longest possible air time, but the sole function of the station was the location of aircraft in front of it; any echoes produced by aircraft behind the station would be confusing and require identification. During the autumn and winter, Wilkins was occupied with the design of transmitting aerials that reduced the back radiation, and so the back echoes, and at the same time raising the forward radiated power, which increased the height of the echoes in front of the station. Bowen complained to Wilkins that his new array was causing the transmitter to break into parasitic oscillations; when Tizard was on an unofficial visit the echo had suddenly disappeared.

The transmitter was initially designed at Slough by Bainbridge-Bell and when installed at Orfordness the development was taken over by Bowen to increase the output power and reduce the pulse width. Of startling simplicity it was a high power version of a pulsed self-oscillating circuit that was only ideal for working into a simple dipole aerial; the connection of Wilkins' array caused detuning with loss of output power. A separate oscillator stage provided the solution.

To safeguard secrecy only valves manufactured within government service could be used and these were supplied by the Admiralty from the

HM Signal School, Portsmouth. The first were NT46 triodes with bright emitter tungsten filaments and silica glass envelopes that could withstand gun fire shocks and operate at much higher bulb temperatures than ordinary glass. As pulse output is solely dependent on emission, not anode dissipation, the filament voltage was increased by ten per cent and the applied anode voltage raised to just below the internal spark-over point. There was disagreement between Bowen and Wilkins on the pulse output power as it was dependent on how the measurement was calculated; Bowen's figures were over 100kW but Wilkins' were eventually found to be correct at 20kW per pair.

The experimental work at Orfordness was only known to a few of the Air Staff because of the tight security. In October a visit was made by a wing commander from Signals who knew nothing about pulse working or the type of equipment but briefed by the DCAS to produce a report. Bad weather spoiled a convincing demonstration but he saw enough to realise that the plots had a high degree of accuracy and equal to that obtained from the RAF direction finding network. He also discerned that the effects of strong jamming signals tended to obliterate the display. He thought that the transmitter, because of its simple nature, would be difficult to stabilise within the internationally accepted limits and when told that there would be 12 such transmitters he wrote:

> "...it is quite certain that the continuous working of twelve transmitters would create uproar among Allies and Neutrals because they would eliminate a wide band in the most useful part of the spectrum over the greater part of the world. Serious complications in this respect may also be expected in peacetime..." [9]

The receiver did not escape comment:

> "Before it could be used with safety and reliability, [and] placed in the hands of the training and skill of the RAF wireless/operator/mechanic for operation and maintenance, it requires much development in the engineering sense...." [9]

It was the jamming aspect that concerned the visitor:

> "...it might be in danger of being lost in the atmosphere of pure scientific achievement...." [9]

His opinion was that the transmissions had a very marked characteristic that could not be concealed so it was easy to identify and measure the frequency; a very weak jamming signal was sufficient to destroy any useful results and a stronger one could incapacitate the RDF from any distance. It would be practically impossible to conceal the purpose of the transmissions, the present disguise under the label of 'Ionospheric Soundings' could hardly be expected to deceive foreign scientists for long and would be patently untrue when more stations came into operation. Speculation would soon produce something near the truth with the result that the organisation would become so vulnerable as to be practically useless for its intended purpose:

> "If I am correct in the above, it will be obviously unwise to start the engineering development until the possibility of jamming has been completely eliminated." [9]

The wing commander's report was in effect to give the thumbs down to the concept of RDF unless jamming was completely ineffective, which he knew as a professional radio engineer was not possible. What he did not know was that the simple jamming he had described, which he thought would incapacitate RDF, would not occur because the receiver had a wide bandwidth to preserve the shape of the incoming pulse.

Watson Watt's reply was mainly to refute the technical criticism; he was not aware of any difficulty in stabilising the frequency and the reference to 12 transmitters on separate frequencies was based on a misconception by the wing commander (who would have been unaware that pulse working could use a common frequency). He also noted the comment about development of the equipment:

> "I assume it to be the responsibility of the Air Staff to decide whether the time necessary to suit the personnel to the apparatus can be spared or whether the more rapid process of suiting the apparatus to the personnel is made necessary by urgency." [9]

He did not agree with the view that inferences by foreign scientists would make the organisation 'so vulnerable as to be practically useless' and added that:

> "it does less than justice to the expertise of those to whom the Air Council may entrust the development of the system." [9]

His trump card was that no one outside the few at Orfordness had any knowledge or experience of pulse working and, further to the point, under jamming conditions. The rapid progress in the experimental work that Wilkins had achieved had been accomplished with the observations of jamming from natural and deliberate sources as the foremost factor. Ranges of the order of 80km (48 miles) had been systematically obtained even during periods of severe signal and atmospheric interference using the simple half wave single aerials at a height of 75ft (23m).

Watson Watt had come to the conclusion that jamming from ships and distant transmitters was not a practical proposition, but there was a possibility that aircraft, which were part of a raiding force, could carry jamming transmitters, but the effect would be negligible if the ground station changed to a widely different wavelength. It does appear that in the 'fight' between

Signals and Watson Watt that he had won the first round, but it all depended on what the judges, the Tizard Committee, would declare. It was a recommendation of common sense:

"It is quite impossible in the six months from the initiation of experiments to develop a technique which was known to be free from all forms of interference and jamming. As R.D.F. is urgently required for Service use it is recommended that the 1936 chain proceed without modification." [14]

The whole episode reinforced Watson Watt's view that the Director of Signals was not on his side and had undue influence on the Air Staff.

After just four months' work, Watson Watt placed before Wimperis a proposal for a chain of 13 stations from the Wash (Norfolk) to Beachy Head (East Sussex). With the imminence of a large and highly complex technical and operational network, the Air Staff now had to decide how Bawdsey and the chain would be operated by the Royal Air Force. Dowding suggested a conference, which was held on 24 October. Recommendations were that the transmitters would be maintained by mechanics from the nearest RAF station, the grade of wireless operator/mechanic (WO/M) for the CRT observer and the plotters would be civilians, except during wartime, when airmen would be used: (Signals suggested that aircrafthand reservists would be unsatisfactory because of their low standard of intelligence.) Information on enemy aircraft should give height, position and number at a range of 60 miles with a height accuracy of ± 2,000ft, but at the coast ± 500ft. Over the sea the position should be given as bearing and distance, but Dowding suggested that plots would be more quickly effected if the sea was also covered by the land grid to give plan position. The information was to be reported every minute from the coastal station to the nearest fighter group operations room.

Additionally, the DCAS wanted a squadron leader to be appointed as a link between the civilians on research and the RAF, who were to operate the equipment. Bawdsey would be answerable to the Director of Signals with a retired officer for administration and the whole chain organisation would be under the control of Signals at Fighter HQ. Watson Watt was not at ease with this turn of events as he would be responsible to two masters, the Director of Scientific Research and the Director of Signals. He emphasised the inherent delays that would occur with split functions and their effect on progress and suggested that the RDF organisation should be separate in its own right but, as he was not an Air Ministry official, his non-technical views carried no weight.

During one of Watson Watt's weekend visits to Orfordness in November, he announced to his astonished colleagues that while on the train to Woodbridge he had devised a means of direction finding from one station; two horizontal dipoles crossed at right angles and connected to a goniometer. At the earliest opportunity Wilkins went back to Slough to make a quick test; an oscillator was connected to an aerial on the top of a telegraph pole to act as a signal source and a mobile D/F receiver driven around the tower half a mile away. The results demonstrated that the principle was sound.

Although the simple dipole and the gonio is all that is required to provide bearings, it suffers from the elementary scientific law that the dipole is equally responsive to signals front and back which, if uncorrected, introduces an error of 180 degrees. Watson Watt passed the problem to Wilkins. His solution was to place another dipole of a slightly longer length, a reflector, behind the two main dipoles that could be placed electrically 'in' or 'out' by a relay switched from the receiver. In the 'out' position the main dipoles picked up signals equally back or front but when the reflector was switched 'in' the signal pick up from the rear was greatly reduced with a corresponding increase in front. The operation was known as 'sensing'. The effect on the tube display was immediate and apparent; the echo being 'sensed' increased in height if it was seaward, decreased if it was inland. But why should inland echoes appear in a seaward looking coastal defence system? If the gonio was turned only to cover the compass range of the station then ambiguity was of no consequence. The appearance of inland echoes, however, was entirely the result of radio power leakage from the rear of the transmitting aerial, a condition not possible of elimination, only mitigation. That is why all echoes had to be 'sensed' and ignored if inland.

At the Air Ministry, Wimperis was involved in preparing a financial memorandum to set up a small group of stations to obtain technical and operational experience before work could commence on the complete chain. The Air Staff had suggested seven stations to be constructed at Dunwich, Bawdsey, Clacton, Shoeburyness, Birchington, South Foreland and Dungeness. Wimperis judged the proposal as far too ambitious, especially for a completion date of nine months, and was supported by Works, which firmly stated that it would be quite impossible in the time expected for completion to obtain the land and erect masts and buildings. With the agreement to drop Dunwich and Dungeness there was then a reasonable chance that five stations could be ready for air trials in the summer of 1936.

The scheme was costed at £68,000, made up of land £2,000, huts £4,000, power £20,000, equipment £3,500 and 11 wooden 240ft towers £38,500. The Air Council added that they were very impressed with the method of detection and with the results already obtained. They were desirous of proceeding immediately with the project so that all stations would be ready for an August 1936 exercise. There was a possible saving of £17,000 as the Thames Estuary Mirror Scheme had been suspended. The memorandum was submitted to the Treasury on 30 November and received sanction on 19 December.

The four additional locations had been provisionally selected with the aid of Ordnance Survey maps covering the areas in the vicinity of Clacton, Shoeburyness and Foulness Island (in Essex) and Faversham and Dover (in Kent). All were expected to be not too far from a reasonably flat coast with the electricity grid conveniently nearby. The siting requirements were modest: for the two transmitting stations an area for one 240ft tower and for the other three large enough for one transmitting and two receiving towers spaced by 500ft.

In early December, Wilkins and two Works officers set forth to select the sites; at Clacton two were chosen, the first one at Little Clacton, three and a half miles from the sea, 50ft above sea level, and another near the village of St Osyth. In the Shoeburyness – Foulness area, one was found at Canewdon eight and a half miles from the sea, 110ft above sea level; in the Faversham area south of the Thames Estuary at the village of Dunkirk, three and a half miles from the sea, 390ft above sea level and at Dover on Army land, part of an old aerodrome, a quarter of a mile from the sea, 400ft above sea level.

Works had the responsibility of buying the land, and that was not always an easy task in peacetime, as landowners could, and sometimes did, refuse to sell that resulted in another survey. At Clacton, where the local council advised that Little Clacton was to be developed into a municipal airport, the alternative at St Osyth was on the land of a titled gentleman, who had earlier raised fierce objections when the site for the northern 200ft acoustic mirror was being sought. At the request of Works another one was found further north at Great Bromley, a few miles east of Colchester. Wilkins supplied Works with a small plan that showed the precise positions of the towers and, at Watson Watt's request, the towers and the sites were to be surrounded by an unclimbable, palisade fence. Known as the Thames Estuary Stations, the chain consisted of Bawdsey (T and R), Great Bromley (T), Canewdon (T and R), Dunkirk (T), and Dover (T and R).

Wimperis was organising the administrative side of Bawdsey Manor. He favoured an Admin head to be appointed with the scientific work under the control of Watson Watt, who at that time was dividing his commitments between the Air Ministry and the NPL. He intended to call the Admin head the Commandant but the DCAS did not like that particular word, the retired

Air Commodore whom Wimperis had in mind declined the post and the Air Member for Personnel (AMP) queried whether such an officer was necessary. Dowding wrote to Wimperis that Watson Watt should be unhampered by administration, that he was not a servant of the Air Ministry and it was open to question whether his talents lay in other than scientific directions:

> "I am definitely of the opinion that he should not be appointed Commandant. Please discuss further with the Secretary – I will endorse any agreement." [15]

Watson Watt made his preference known to Wimperis that he wanted to manage both admin and the scientific work. At Secretary level it was finally agreed that the best course would be to appoint Watson Watt as the Superintendent with responsibility for admin and research. Wimperis' view was that;

> "...if Mr. Watson Watt is treated wholly as a Research Officer of the Air Ministry, there is no constitutional objection to [him] acting as an administrator at Bawdsey while also taking charge of research work." [15]

Air Ministry Civil had published on 10 December a NOTAM (Notice to Airmen), under the signature of Secretary Bullock, to the effect that two radio masts 250 feet in height above ground level (255 feet above sea level) are:

> "...in course of erection 350 yards S.W. of Orfordness landing ground. These new masts are situated in the centre of a group of existing masts which are 60 and 75 feet in height, and they will be lighted after erection is completed."

It was the exact place where Watson Watt was conducting the experiments.

At the close of 1935 there was certainly for Watson Watt and his staff a great measure of satisfaction in what had been achieved in nine months: the basic principles established for range, height and direction finding from a single site, a research station almost ready for occupation, the initiation of the building of five stations and an air exercise to be arranged for the following summer.

REFERENCES

1	AIR2/4481	2	AVIA53/301	3	AIR20/195	4	AIR2/4482
5	AIR2/4483	6	AVIA46/45	7	AFW PAPERS	8	CAB16/132
9	AIR20/145	10	AIR20/184	11	AIR2/4485	12	AIR2/4484
13	AVIA7/13	14	AIR20/181	15	AIR2/2724		

Chapter 3   1936

THE 17th of January was the first day of entry into Bawdsey Manor, shortly to be renamed the Bawdsey Research Station (BRS), now Air Ministry property but until June to be shared with the previous owner. The manor was possibly the most opulent building ever bought for a research station. Watson Watt's office was originally the owner's study with carved oak panelling and Spanish leather panels embossed with lions and fleur-de-lys in gold, with splendid views over the manor grounds. Watson Watt and Works had assigned rooms for official and domestic accommodation, single quarters for the staff at 7s.6d (37½p) to 15s.0d (75p) a week that included furniture, cleaning, heating and hot water but not laundry or light.

There was also the question of the manor gardens being maintained: Quilter had told Watson Watt and Wimperis that his father had employed 24 gardeners; he had managed with eleven but it was thought that five would be adequate. Works had the task of enforcing the agreement on what could be taken and what could not. They alleged that 900 tulip bulbs had been removed from the garden, together with ornamental stone work from the terrace, a brass cannon from the lawn fronting the schoolroom and a Nelson fireplace in a lounge.

The first occupant of the manor was Dr E.G.Bowen who, with one assistant, had instructions from Watson Watt (no doubt at the request of Tizard) to begin work on the near-impossible task of placing an RDF set into the confined space of an aircraft cockpit – a project that was to be one of the first stages of equipment for the Air Interception (AI) of enemy aircraft. In the commodious brick built stable block just outside the manor area Wilkins and others began the task of setting up a receiver laboratory and workshops, but with little progress as there was no electricity until early February; the manor supply was DC from a private power house.

The same month a clerical officer was posted in from RAF Cardington to organise the supply of typewriters, filing cabinets, desks, chairs, stationery and, that most important communication item, the telephone. A card had been posted to the nearest exchange, which brought a reply that there would be a delay of five months before action could be taken; almost immediately another one arrived to the effect that lines and extensions asked for would be given the highest priority – no doubt that Air Ministry Signals had spoken.

In the middle of January, at Orfordness, Wilkins had quickly arranged an air test of Watson Watt's direction finding method. With a crude set of crossed dipoles rigged between two 75ft masts and connected to a goniometer with domestic lighting flex, accurate bearings on an aircraft flying at 10,000ft for a distance of 20 miles were obtained. Wilkins was waiting impatiently for the completion of two 250ft guyed masts for the transmitter aerial and one at Bawdsey for the receiver aerials, which were finally ready in early March. It was an historic day at Bawdsey on 13 March when Wilkins conducted a test of a Hawker Hart flying at 15,000ft from Orfordness to Bircham Newton, a distance of 108km (65 miles). Wilkins recorded:

> "[We] asked the pilot to continue across the Wash to Skegness and return on the same path. [We were] able to attain a range of 130Km [78 miles] with position finding the whole way." [1]

Another major step forward occurred when Wilkins noticed that severe interference seen on the CRT display, which were reflections from the ionosphere layer and labelled Z echoes, almost disappeared when one of the open wire feeders from the receiver aerial was accidentally earthed. He found the same effect was produced by earthing the centre tap of the coupling transformer; the vertical feeders to the dipoles were picking up the interference and needed to be screened. In 1936 concentric (coaxial) cable weighed many tons per mile and was only used underground by the Post Office and quite unsuitable for fixing to the sides of a wooden tower. The eventual answer was for the research staff to make their own by using beaded copper wire pushed into standard lengths of copper piping.

In the early days it was the rule rather than the exception that the scientific staff were involved in non- scientific work and such was the sense of purpose that even Watson Watt was not averse to leaving his office and helping to make lengths of screened feeders. He was always conscious that there were too few such officers in spite of his frequent requests at every possible opportunity. There was not unlimited time for research such as was needed for mobile systems and equipment to discriminate between friendly and hostile aircraft, which was being further delayed because of the need for the BRS staff to prepare for the impending air exercise. Nothing so far had been decided on how to convey the plotting information from the estuary stations to the Operations Room at Uxbridge.

With the work clearly becoming permanent, moves were made for the transfer of personnel from the NPL to the Air Ministry. In March, the Tizard

Committee had recommended that Watson Watt be appointed full time and be given charge of research and development schemes, including those of the improvement of radio direction finding methods for defence purposes, and all technical advances to ensure automatic communication of all the data to Fighter Command and elsewhere. When the recommendation reached Dowding he wrote to the CAS:

> "I do not think that Mr. Watson Watt should be given 'charge of' anything outside Bawdsey Manor. If he were to act as an *adviser* on communication matters I would agree, but I have no responsibility for communication policy which is a matter for Signals, under you." [2]

Ellington's comment was that it was likely that Watson Watt would be given an appointment in the Air Ministry and that his ability would be more productively employed as the Superintendent of Bawdsey Manor as a full time official.

In April, Dowding relinquished his position as AMRD and three months later, on 14 July, was appointed the first Air Officer Commanding-in-Chief of Fighter Command, a part of the new structure being introduced to replace the ADGB because of the rapidly expanding Royal Air Force in preparation for war. The post was taken by Air Marshal Sir Wilfred Freeman who, like Dowding, was ex-army. He had transferred to the Royal Flying Corps in 1913, was by 1919 a Wing Commander and, after a number of senior appointments at home and overseas, the Commandant of the Royal Air Force Staff College in 1933. His comment on the transfer of Watson Watt was that action must be taken to find out his wishes:

> "So far he has not been approached and will probably be annoyed if his body is disposed of without previous reference to him." [2]

Indeed, Watson Watt's wishes were delaying the whole transfer process. He interpreted the committee's recommendation as: (a) the detection and location of enemy aircraft, the most rapid attainable positional data for such aircraft, its communication to Fighter Command and other units, its expeditious plotting by semi-automation or automatic means, and its communication to Fighter Command aircraft; (b) the provision in such aircraft of the means of direct detection and relative location of enemy aircraft to facilitate engagement without the help of ground organisations; and (c) the guidance of fighters to facilitate defence operations of such fighters and ultimate return to base.

There was no disagreement with that interpretation because it was a concise account of what was already being undertaken; in current jargon, a 'job description'. It was Watson Watt's perception of the immensity of the tasks that caused such a stir. He wanted to place on record his opinion that the proposed organisation took a too restricted view of the extent and importance of the work and its urgency, and that the measures proposed might be adequate if a period of ten years was available to resolve all the problems. He felt confident that the Air Ministry would sooner or later (only two years) find it necessary to set up a separate research department under an independent director. He proposed that the scale of responsibilities required a new Directorate of Investigations in Communications with himself as Director with a salary of £1,700 a year and, to ensure that his work was not delayed by the Air Staff, a right of access to the Secretary of State for Air. Secretary Bullock took umbrage at these proposals and made his objections known in a memo dated 23 April to the Secretary of State:

> "Frankly I can see no case for an increase... What we propose to give him is the maximum of the Superintendent's scale (£1,250) + £100 + a flat worth at least another £100 i.e., £1,450 in all....A comfortable rise of £400 in a six months' period!!...I fully realise the great importance of his work, but it is, after all, one facet (however vital) of one problem of Air Defence.
>
> Detection is no use without aircraft to operate on the information supplied, R/T communication for those aircraft, machine guns with which they can fight, etc,etc. When the whole of research (wireless, aerodynamics, ballistics, etc, etc,) is run by one Director...it seems to me it would be wholly anomalous and out of scale to make Mr. Watson Watt a Director....Sir F. Smith thinks the emoluments reasonable and A.M.R.D. sees no case for a separate Directorate...
>
> Mr. Watson Watt says that he will not like life with us so much as at the N.P.L. He is lucky he is not an Air Force officer who may be ordered to the Iraq desert or the Indian frontier...Ordinary civil servants have to go where they are told – including Heads of Departments! If you are in any doubt may I speak ? " [2]

Swinton replied:

> "I am not in doubt. He has done well in his rise in the last six months." [2]

Wimperis wrote to Freeman:

> "Mr. Watson Watt suggested his transfer to the Air Ministry for the sake of the better prosecution of his work on defence problems, and made no suggestion of this as an opportunity for a bargain on terms...On my advice Mr. Watt protected his principal invention by a secret patent, and he will, therefore, be in a firm position when any question of an award comes to be considered by the Awards Committee." [2]

On 18 May Watson Watt was advised that there were no changes in the conditions of his status or his remuneration and, in his refusal to accept the Air Ministry's offer, which he presumed was only part of the committee's recommendation, he intimated that he would seek advice from the head of the DSIR, Sir Frank Smith. On 22 May Bullock wrote privately to Smith on Watson Watt's dissatisfaction:

"From all I hear there is no doubt whatever that Mr. Watson Watt is of outstanding scientific ability...and has considerable organising powers. The last thing I should wish to do is to treat him ungenerously, but I frankly consider he is quite unduly 'on the make' and that his ideas are grossly inflated...." [2]

Smith wrote back a few days later that Watson Watt had finally agreed on the financial terms and would be satisfied with the title of Deputy Director of Scientific Research, but in an informal interview later with Freeman he was advised that the Air Council's offer would not be changed. Swinton had the last word; he wrote to the CAS:

"Mr.Watson Watt has hit upon a most ingenious and valuable discovery... that caused me to propose that Mr. Watson Watt be seconded or transferred to the Air Ministry. Mr Watson Watt can play a great part in the defence plans of the country..... his primary duty is the development of the Bawdsey experiments – that is the place he should operate." [2]

In an interview with a Principal Assistant Secretary, Watson Watt emphasised that he had been treated with a lack of courtesy in that no senior officer either in Research or the Air Staff had afforded him the opportunity of discussing the scope of his responsibilities before a decision had been reached. He anticipated considerable opposition in getting Air Ministry Signals staff, who appeared to be very conservative, to adopt his suggestions and that he apparently had no right of direct access to higher authority in order to get such difficulties removed. He reiterated his dissatisfaction with the general tenor of the decision as to the scope of his duties and to his personal status and emoluments.

In accepting his appointment as the Superintendent of the Bawdsey Research Station from 1 August, he wrote:

"...of my reluctance to end a happy and long service with the D.S.I.R. and to accept the transfer...with no interference with the wholehearted fullness of duties and responsibilities entrusted to me which is in the nation's interest." [2]

Although Watson Watt was very security minded, he was powerless to amend the might of the administration machine in other departments of the Air Ministry. One such instance was in the publication of the Army, Navy and Air Force Gazette dated 10 September in which the existence of Bawdsey as the 'Air Ministry Research Station' was revealed. It stated that Watson Watt was the Superintendent responsible for an increasing amount of important work for the Air Ministry especially in connection with radio direction finders and beacons. On the other hand it might well have been a definite ploy to associate Bawdsey with what appeared to be non-secret work and to equate the letters RDF with direction finding.

The Tizard Committee continued to consider a number of propositions that had been put forward for discussion, one for fighter aircraft to be fitted with a large rotating screw that could be switched on when the aircraft was approaching the rear of an unsuspecting enemy bomber, (committee recommendation was 'no action'). Another group of suggestions were those placed on the agenda by Professor Lindemann, now a committee member, that consisted of the dropping of aerial mines, parachute mines, short and long wire barrages on to enemy bombers from above. None of these ideas held any favour with the committee, who were no doubt relieved to be able to pass them over to RAE for comment and action.

Tizard did not confine his committee activities to the technical development of RDF. He had the advantage as an ex-military pilot of being aware that the shooting down of an enemy bomber was solely dependent on the pilot finding it without navigational assistance of any kind. As the Air Staff had already recognised that it was impossible to intercept high altitude bombers by fighters held in readiness on the ground, the only alternative was the 'standing patrol'. Fighters were sent off to a height slightly above that of the reported raiders and flew over an area lying across the anticipated approach of the enemy bombers, with changes to the line or area reported by R/T. One major disadvantage was that if the pilot could not see the ground he was unable to find or keep his patrol line.

Tizard deduced that fighter pilots would now have to develop techniques that would in time direct them to the point of interception. He had a meeting with the DCAS on 13 July to discuss and obtain his approval for the experiments. Tizard required the percentage of interceptions that could be expected by day in clear weather and the time taken to intercept from receipt of the warning of the approximate position of an enemy bomber ten minutes from the coast. Furthermore, the AI experimenters at BRS needed to know the minimum distance that an aircraft required for effective interception.

Preliminary investigations had shown that the lights of London, which were illuminating a cloud layer, had enabled a Heyford bomber flying at 6,000ft to pick up the silhouette of another Heyford flying 500ft above the cloud layer when 1½ miles away. It was proposed to install a number of floodlights in a chosen locality that would provide a greater intensity of illumination than those of London, with reports of skilled pilots required showing the possibility of this method for locating enemy aircraft flying above the clouds at night. Tizard suggested that these proposals should now take place; the Secretary of State endorsed them and he informed the CAS of the necessity for taking every step to ensure their success.

Air Commodore W. Sholto Douglas, the Director of Staff Duties, had the task of their implementation and he suggested Biggin Hill in 11 Fighter

Group to Air Vice Marshal P.B. Joubert de la Ferté, the AOC, who was in full support. Douglas had omitted to inform Dowding, who sent him a polite reminder that he had no information as to the nature of the experiments and requested to be kept informed 'of the object which it is desired to be obtained.'[3] Without RDF plots, the position of the bombers and the fighters was expected to be obtained from D/F stations with the fighters told by radio-telephone (R/T) of the changes in direction required to intercept the bombers. The experiments began on 5 August, 32 Squadron being selected for the fighters, Gloster Gauntlets, and initially 57 and 49 Squadrons for the Hind bombers. In the Operations Room there were two navigation officers, one to plot the estimated position of the bombers and the other to work out the interception course. The suggestion was soon made that it was most desirable to be provided with some form of mechanical device that would *automatically* and rapidly provide the fighter course to intercept the bomber, and the estimated time of interception knowing the wind, relative positions, track and ground speed of the fighter and bomber aircraft. The RAF officers eventually found their own solution, the practised eye, to determine in effect the angle of interception.

The Direction Finding system provided for 'Homing' was found to be of insufficient accuracy as the sectors had only one D/F station each, so the experiments continued with the use of 'dead reckoning' for navigation. Initially, the bombers were flying on a pre-arranged straight courses from an known starting point and at an agreed height; there were 26 interceptions from a total of 28 runs. The second series of tests allowed the bombers to alter their courses at will that led to frequent redirection of the fighters with delays arising from the need to work out another interception course and a consequent inability on some occasions to intercept.

As the fighters became more expert at each level of interception, the bombers were allowed to make course and height changes with, finally, a change in speed. When the fighters and bombers reached that level of proficiency, the techniques were adopted for practice by other sector stations and the interceptions carried on until the end of the year. (By the Spring of 1937 the results would show that if sectors could be supplied with the bomber positions at one minute intervals, correct to within two miles, it was then possible to direct fighters to within three miles of the bombers.)

The outcome revealed the need for each sector to have three D/F stations and the inadequacy of the fighter radio equipment; the TR9 had a maximum range of only 40 miles from the ground and 5 miles between aircraft. There were a number of RAF officers who queried the possibility of being able to get track information with such detail on enemy aircraft but Tizard remained silent in their company as the existence of RDF could not be divulged. The exercises were an essential part for the eventual use of RDF in air defence, and one example from many of the foresight of Tizard. To quote an Air Ministry publication:

> "An important feature was their freedom from undue guidance from higher authority. The operational flying problems anticipated on account of the development of radar [RDF] were allowed to work themselves out in the hands of competent men at squadron and sector level. In consequence the results of the experiments were essentially practical and well fitted for adoption by those on whom the task fell in war." [4]

Rarely mentioned even in the few published accounts of the Biggin Hill experiments, as they became known, was a most important element; the whole programme of interceptions was under the supervision of a civilian, Dr B.G.Dickens, a scientific officer, chosen by Tizard. It was the first instance of close co-operation between the civilian and the military on what was to be known in the future as Operational Research and which eventually became a dominant influence on the efficiency of war in all three Services.

The establishment of Bawdsey Research Station with names of the principal officers appeared in the Air Force List. [5]

SUPERINTENDENT   R.A.Watson Watt.

SCIENTIFIC OFFICERS   H. Dewhurst A.R.C.Sc., D.I.C.
                      J.H.Mitchell Ph.D., B.Sc.
                      L.H.Bainbridge-Bell M.C., M.A.
                      E.G.Bowen Ph.D., M.Sc.
                      A.F.Wilkins M.Sc.
                      R.W.Whelpton M.Sc.
                      H.Larnder A.M.Brit.I.R.E.
                      S.Jefferson B.Sc.

At his own request and with the approval of Wimperis, Watson Watt's qualifications of B.Sc., M.I.E.E. and F.Inst.P. were omitted.

On 6 June the Air Ministry took over the remainder of Bawdsey Manor. The previous owner had been unable to remove all his effects and to hasten matters a sale had been held on 25/26 May when a successful bid was made by the scientific staff to retain a splendid billiard table. Cabinet historians have recorded:

> "Bawdsey Manor a large late 19th Century eccentricity, built of stone faced

red brick dominated by two cupola topped towers rising from adjacent corners, woods and fields, a farm and dairy, cottages, racquet courts, and a galvanised iron chapel. Self contained, the remoteness enhanced by the river Deben which cuts it off from the main road, railway and Felixstowe. The men who worked there were young men who had gone to the N.P.L. from University, physicists rather than engineers. They were not as a body outstandingly brilliant or the cream of the country's scientists – that came later." [6]

The other end of the scale was:

"Laboratory Assistants are required at the Bawdsey Research Station. Good education with theoretical training in electricity. Practical experience of wireless receivers or of electrical testing desirable. £2 per week at age of 19 rising to a nominal maximum of £3.10s.0d [£3.50p]." [7]

The summer air exercise was primarily to show to the Air Staff that radio methods of the detection of aircraft were viable, that there were no evident operating complications or any unforeseen technical imperfections, and to show clear evidence that the expansion of the chain could proceed. Consultations with the Coastal Area of the ADGB, later Coastal Command, had begun in January for the supply of aircraft for the trials that would be in two parts; a preliminary exercise using ten aircraft to be held between the 15 and 30 May, so that any technical or operational failings could be corrected, before the major exercise with fifty aircraft to be held between 31 August and 11 September. BRS would be responsible for the design and erection of the aerials, for calibration of the three receiver sites and, to ease the workload, the NPL agreed to make the five transmitters and three receivers. Additionally, the range and direction plots would need to be converted into map co-ordinates for the Operations Room at Uxbridge. There would be no heightfinding.

Initially, much of the effort took place on the ground, where Works had to buy the land and contract out for the supply and erection of eleven 240ft wooden towers. As soon as entry was possible Works drove concrete pegs into the ground to indicate precisely where the towers had to be placed, so that the aerial arrays faced a specific direction known as the Line of Shoot. This was the line of maximum transmission of power, sensitivity and accuracy and the direction from which enemy aircraft were expected to appear; each station would be given a specific compass heading east of north. All the five estuary stations were given a Line of Shoot for Ostend, a small town on the Belgian coast. After a tower had been completed BRS required six weeks to rig the aerials and install the equipment; calibration would follow for the three transmitter/receiver sites at Bawdsey, Canewdon and Dover.

A contractor was engaged, who was well known for his ability in erecting towers, and who had given his assurance that he could meet the completion date by the end of May. However, he had underestimated the quantity of timber for the towers, each one requiring some 2,700 cubic feet of top quality British Columbian pine, some of which were 42ft in length, and arranging for the creosoting. An inspection of the five stations a week before the target date was due clearly showed that it would never be met; most of the concrete foundations had been finished but there were no completed towers with men waiting for timber. Only at Canewdon and Bawdsey was there any sign of a tower but with only the first 40ft assembled. Works wrote to Wimperis on 18 June that the contractor's organisation had failed in so many features that it was not possible to say with certainty when all the towers would be finished. Under the most favourable conditions the first tower at Bawdsey could not be ready before 25 July with the second and third towers not before the end of September. To quicken the pace the contractor was told to concentrate on the three towers for Bawdsey, Canewdon and Dover but the continuing delays began to cause disquiet for the Air Staff, who expressed doubts of the practicality of having to organise a large scale exercise in late November. By late August, as only one tower at Bawdsey was ready with the second a long way from completion and the third just appearing above the ground, work at Dover and Canewdon was abandoned and all the men sent to Bawdsey.

The date of the first exercise was fixed for 17 September with nine flying boats at 10,000ft followed ten minutes later by a single Anson. The three new receivers were all operational together at BRS but much to the puzzlement of the observers the start time had passed without the appearance of a single echo. It was only when the aircraft were within 30 miles of the coast that echoes began to appear but with unreliable bearing information. The next day saw no improvement as the reports from BRS were very few and far between with the information vague and incorrect; a repeat in the afternoon showed no improvement as the information was unusable. At BRS the anxiety can be imagined for it was abundantly clear that there were inherent technical problems so further trials were postponed. Air Marshal P.B.Joubert, now the AOC-in-C of Coastal Command, arranged to visit BRS the following Monday, the 21 September to discuss the situation.

Tizard was very annoyed at the results of the first two days for he was the head of RDF in official circles, not Watson Watt, and he had taken a professional risk by vigorously encouraging the promotion of pulse techniques to the Air Staff when not in a position to ensure complete control of the experiments. In a letter to Watson Watt on 20 September he wrote:

"To say that I was disappointed on Thursday is to put it very mildly. As you put it yourself, you have to face the fact that little progress... has been made for a year. I am surprised that you encouraged – indeed proposed – the September exercises. Unless very different results are obtained soon I shall have to dissuade the Air Ministry from putting up other stations. What particularly disturbs me is that there seems to have been a lack of good judgement on your part. You have had good results in the past, but there has been little effort to ensure that these results are repeatable, before going on to get better results... I think that it is of the utmost importance that you should find the real reason for these irregular results as soon as possible. I am sorry to write to you like this, but it will not help you if I conceal my feelings. A great deal depends on your work." [8]

There is nothing in the BRS files to establish whether the transmitter or the aerial was to blame, or the measures taken over the weekend to restart the exercise, but an unofficial and informative account of the latter can be read in *Radar Days* by E.G.Bowen. There was only one option available if the exercise was to continue and that was to use the transmitter at Orfordness that had been lying idle for months. Joubert agreed that if the re-calibration run was successful, then the exercise could restart on the Wednesday, but on a reduced scale. All appeared well for in 90 minutes over 90 reports were received with accurate range and bearing, all confirmed by the next day's results. The failure of the first two days, however, caused a degree of uncertainty that led to the more ambitious November trials being cancelled.

Eventually the results were evaluated and sent to the Air Staff, who made the inevitable adverse comments:

"It is most important that the scientists at Bawdsey should have thoroughly tested the apparatus and satisfied themselves that it was in proper working order. It is in the interest of Mr. Watson Watt and the staff at Bawdsey, that they should not attempt to run before they can walk, otherwise the indifferent results may prejudice the Services against what promises to be a very valuable aid to interception." [9]

The DCAS wrote a summary to the CAS that the object of the exercise was to enable the Air Staff to satisfy themselves that the system was sufficiently sound to justify the adoption on a more intensive scale:

"The original programme of trials was much too ambitious, construction very late with insufficient time for calibration...the results not representative of what the system can achieve; in the meantime we are not yet in a position to say that the system has proved itself in practice." [9]

The CAS disagreed and replied:

"I agree that we are not yet in a position, but the R.D.F. has proved itself in practice. When I visited Bawdsey in October, I was told that the apparatus and the personnel were not really ready for the experiments in September." [9]

The near breakdown of the air exercise was a setback to the progress of

RDF. The acceptable results of the last few days were not a sufficient basis for a document to be prepared for the signature of the Secretary of State, and submission to the Treasury, for recommending the very large expenditure necessary for setting up the chain and the training of people to use it. Another series of air trials was proposed for next January but this also began to look doubtful as the last of the eleven towers was not completed until the end of the year. The ADR sub-committee meeting on 23 November summed up the exercise results admirably in a few words:

> "[There is] justification for the assumption that R.D.F.1 is sufficiently developed to anticipate satisfactory results in the next full scale exercise." [10]

Dowding had previously agreed that the training of RAF personnel would be by Watson Watt but Freeman, his successor, was in favour of training under a Signals Officer of Fighter Command. He wrote on 28 August to the Air Member for Personnel (AMP):

> "There is every reason to suppose that the Bawdsey experiments will prove successful. If they are, I assume that in early 1937 we shall start training R.A.F. personnel in R.D.F. techniques. I suggest that training of R.A.F. personnel be undertaken by Signals Officers..." [11]

The Director of Signals wrote to the AMP:

> "With regard to the officer, he requires very careful selection owing to the special nature of the work. Of the officers with the necessary qualifications likely to be available, the following seems most suitable, F/Lt Hart, R.G., M.C." [11]

Hart (who retired as Air Marshal Sir Raymund in February 1959) was posted to HQ 11 Group (Uxbridge) on 28 November. Before long he had decided that the best place for training was at Bawdsey with the trainees placed on the strength of RAF Felixstowe for messing and accommodation; they were somewhat surprised to be told to wear civilian clothes when travelling to and from Bawdsey in obviously marked RAF transport.

The ex-ADGB Operations Room in the hut outside Hillingdon House was of no use to Dowding in Bentley Priory. On 24 September he wrote to the Air Staff outlining his proposal for a new experimental Operations Room that had been approved in principle for £500, a sum that he made clear did not cover or take into consideration the telephone services that would inevitably follow. A map table with an overlooking platform would be provided in the ballroom, at present used as a conference room, together with space in the adjoining library for a teleprinter and Meteorological and Observer Corps officers.

The Works drawings contained the instructions that the partitions were not to damage the floor or walls, that no fixing of any kind was to be made to the existing oak floor and the table was to be built up in sections for easy removal with the legs and the platform staging base to rest on felt. Plotting would closely follow that developed by the Army during the Great War in that hostile tracks began at the coast, as did the maps in the Operations Room, with track progress dependent on information supplied by the Observer Corps. There was no particular training; during exercises the Operations Room was manned by officers and other ranks that was in addition to their usual duties.

The Biggin Hill interception exercises had continued throughout the year during which it was proposed that the experiments be continued with the simultaneous interception of two raids based on the following Air Staff assumptions: a German bomber strength of 1,700 of which it was expected that 75% would be in use against the United Kingdom, some 1,280 aircraft, and of these perhaps a half, (640) for daylight raids. Only 480 of these would attack London through at least two sectors and if the daylight raids were spread over three hours some 80 enemy aircraft could be expected through each sector every hour. With an average formation strength of 15 the number expected per hour would be between five and six. With an average time from first warning to interception of 20 minutes, the Air Staff conclusions were that two interceptions must be handled simultaneously if raids were evenly distributed over each hour of the three hour raiding period.

The night interception trials had taken some time to be organised. Professor A.V.Hill had suggested that one square mile of cloud required 100kW of lighting and for the trials, carried out between the 1 and 22 October, an area of four square miles was considered to be the minimum. After a number of proposals were made as to how the 400kW of lighting could be provided, three sets of 4kW lamps units spaced one third of a mile apart were used connected to a total of 36 searchlight power units supplied by the War Office. The primary object of the experiment was to decide whether fighters could detect bombers as silhouettes; the RAE conclusions were that it was practicable to locate from below aircraft flying below an illuminated cloud cover and it was possible to attack an aircraft when it could be seen in silhouette either above or below it.

The conclusions, endorsed by Wimperis, were put to the ADR sub-committee on 23 November, who agreed that the experiments had only established scientific facts and recommended trials on a larger scale to test the practical aspects of the problem; 200 square miles was proposed at a cost of £400,000 with over two years to arrange. If successful the defence of London would require an area of 500 square miles on each side of the River Thames and for the whole country would cost £12.5 million. In July 1937 the Treasury approved the 200 square mile experiment, which was expected to be completed by September 1939, but the project was later cancelled in favour of the emerging AI.

It was through the Tizard Committee that the other two Services were informed of the existence of RDF and each invited to send a scientific officer for liaison visits, first to Orfordness and later to BRS, but the Admiralty, secretive as ever, eventually decided on independent research. In March the War Office sent Dr E.T.Paris, a Principal Scientific Officer at ADEE, to report at intervals on the possible applications of RDF, and at the end of six months he stated that it would take over two years to produce mobile sets for early warning and AA gun control. He noted:

> "...it now appears certain that Cuckoo [an early War Office name for RDF1] is a definite advance on all sound mirrors and will ultimately replace them." [7]

In October, Paris moved from ADEE and headed the Army Group at BRS to develop the existing Orfordness transmitter and receiver into a mobile version with a range of 30 miles at 10,000ft and research for greater accuracy at a shorter range. If successful, it would allow AA guns to fire at unseen targets and operate at night-time without searchlights. With hindsight, it can be recorded that the addition of Army scientific personnel then, and at a later date, was to prove of equal value to the Air Ministry and the War Office.

On 6 November a NOTAM was issued by Air Ministry (Civil), number 166, drawing pilots to the attention of changes in the Ordnance Survey Aviation maps where, among amendments such as the insertion of an explosives area symbol and the cancellation of a temporary correction, there was one insertion for an obstruction symbol and two insertions for lighted obstruction symbols as permanent corrections for radio masts. The latitudes and longitudes given were for the Bawdsey, Canewdon and Great Bromley RDF stations.

REFERENCES

1	AFW PAPERS	2	AIR2/2627	3	AIR2/2625	4	AIR10/5485
5	AVIA7/2746	6	CAB102/641	7	AVIA7/2802		

8   File HTT140 in the Tizard Papers, Dept of Documents, IWM.

9   AIR2/2585   10   CAB16/132   11   AIR2/2726

Chapter 4   1937

WATSON WATT had asked for the date of the repeat air exercise to be deferred to April so that the opportunity could be taken to convert the equipment and aerials from 26 to 13 metres; commercial and ionospheric interference would be reduced and deliberate jamming mitigated. There was also one technical advantage in that the minimum height that could be measured was lowered. There was also a radical change for heightfinding ; the two dipoles were to be horizontally spaced requiring two masts or towers, but this arrangement was not practicable for mobile operation so they were spaced vertically on one tower. Measurements were now of voltage instead of phase, a much easier task and independent of the aircraft bearing. Watson Watt had decided that only Bawdsey need be operational so as to ensure that all the scientific effort was not diluted by work at the other four stations: a second near failure was unthinkable. The exercise, however, would be a severe test for a single station providing range, direction and height, which would now be a self-contained link; there would not be a second one to provide an overlapping check.

Freeman and the DCAS (now AVM R.E.C.Peirse) had already agreed that they could safely assume that RDF would be a better proposition than sound but there did remain a slight element of uncertainty, perhaps an unsettling result of the last air exercise. However, conscious of the bureaucratic obstacles in front of them that would delay the building of the chain, Freeman acted without waiting for the results of the April air exercise. He approved the convening of a conference on 22 January to discuss the possibility of transmitters and receivers, neither of which could be 'off the shelf' and would have to be of a completely new design, being made by outside contractors. Agenda papers were supplied by the Post Office, RAE, the Air Ministry and BRS. Watson Watt stressed that secrecy was the prime factor in the supply of equipment; there would need to be separate firms for the manufacture of the receivers and the transmitters, which would have to be of the highest commercially available output power; only valves made by the Metropolitan Vickers Electrical Company (MetroVick) would be suitable. He had made private visits in 1936 to the factory at Trafford Park, Manchester, to witness tests of valves delivering over 100kW of continuous power at 6 metres. The conference favoured the manufacture of the transmitters within a research laboratory rather than a general production line, so as to preserve security. It was thought that only two companies could produce them, Standard Telephones and Cables (STC) and MetroVick but STC could not, without considerable expansion, undertake work to the value of £300,000. To complete the contract for 20 transmitters in two years the successful firm would have to devise a special organisation. Although MetroVick had very good production facilities, which had not at any time been orientated in the direction of large scale transmitter production, its factories were less vulnerable to enemy action than STC at Woolwich, in southeast London. The committee recommended:

> "If Messrs Metropolitan Vickers Ltd will give a suitable guarantee of the rate of production ... this transmitter contract should be placed with this firm...if not, the contract should be placed with Messrs Standard Telephones and Cables Ltd." [1]

A memo was passed from the DCAS to Freeman on 1 March:

> "S.T.C. have not got a self-contained research and development section like M.V. This is a serious drawback as the work would have to be done in the general shops....the same applies to Marconi. Both S.T.C. and Marconi have many international ramifications and connections." [2]

For erection of the aerials there was agreement that the Air Ministry should fabricate and install the receiving aerials but there was a difference of opinion regarding the transmitting arrays. The general view was that as they were of a fairly complicated design they should be erected by the Marconi Wireless Telegraph Company (Marconi), which had a lot of experience in that area, but this proposal was vetoed by Watson Watt. He explained that as competent observers were expecting beam transmissions, 'floodlighting' was the essential secret to be guarded right up to the last moment and it would be lost if the nature of the connections between the transmitter and the aerial were made known. The committee agreed to review the situation in six months but the meeting was never convened; BRS and later, RAE, continued to design and the Air Ministry to erect the arrays well into 1941.

The Air Ministry was represented by Wing Commander H. Leedham, an Assistant Director, who previously had been Head of the Radio Department of RAE from 1930 to 1935. Within those five years, Leedham had encouraged and educated the radio industry to undertake development work that was to be of tremendous value during the war years. Like Tizard in the aeronautical field, Leedham knew all the main commercial radio firms, their production and technical efficiency. He was of the opinion that only the Radio Transmission Equipment Company (RTE) and A.C. Cossor were capable of making the receiver. Watson Watt said that the cathode ray tube was an important part of the equipment and for that reason it was desirable that receiver construction should be placed with Cossor. The forty receivers would be made without the goniometers, which would be provided by RTE, but this arrangement was changed at a later date, possibly for secrecy reasons, in that they were also made and fitted by Cossor.

(Cossor were without any international ties, all British, a self contained manufacturer of radio valves and cathode ray tubes with a large radio and television receiver manufacturing base. When Watson Watt required cathode ray tubes for his direction finding equipment in the early 1930s he had met Leslie Bedford who was the Director of Research at Cossor and had been impressed with his expertise.)

The coastal chain had to remain operational under all conditions. Watson Watt had decided that four wavelengths were essential to remain free from severe deliberate jamming that had to be expected if and when the purpose and function of the chain became known to the enemy. He added two stringent conditions: (1) the wavelength change to take place within 15 seconds, and (2) that in the event of equipment breakdown a duplicate to take over almost immediately. Four wavelengths may appear excessive but it is indicative of the complete technical freedom enjoyed by BRS within the Air Ministry; Watson Watt's word was law as there was no one outside BRS competent enough to challenge his technical decisions. A 'take-over' attempt had been made by the Director of Signals on the grounds that RDF was radio, and searching for sites was no different from those required by HF D/F, but he was overruled.

Watson Watt thought that the whole project was not moving fast enough and in a letter of 5 February to Wimperis he put the blame fairly and squarely on the Air Ministry. He instanced a number of delays: the erection of the 250ft guyed masts at Orfordness and BRS had taken four months; the supply and erection of huts at the five estuary stations took on average eight weeks per hut whereas at Slough a similar size hut was bought on eight days delivery with seven days erection by station labour. The complete possession of Bawdsey Manor had taken ten months.

Because of the specialised nature of RDF very few components could be obtained from RAF stores depots so the majority had to be obtained from outside firms by contract action, which required the approval of the DSR for each transaction, that led to many hold-ups. Authority for local purchase was restricted to £25 for one transaction with a maximum of £100 a month and had not been increased as requested. No books had been received for the library although a grant had eventually been agreed to some three months before. The most pressing urgency was for the recruitment of scientific staff, which was greatly hampered by the official low salary scales as compared to equivalent jobs in industry. Over 60% of those whom Watson Watt had thought worth approaching had declined and many more he had not even considered because of the mediocre pay. He was to write much later of the sacrifice of personal goodwill in a continuing battle against departmental tendencies to try to operate the normal machinery at an abnormal tempo rather than introduce abnormal machinery. Typical was the reaction of the Director of Works to a suggestion that he appoint a specific officer for the co-ordination of Works services; he regretted that he could not set aside special staff for RDF but he would do all he could to help.

Freeman wrote to the DCAS on 5 February that he was doubtful at first of the wisdom of selecting Metropolitan Vickers, which had widely distributed international relations, but he was in agreement to limit their involvement to the transmission side only. He continued:

> "At the end of last year I visited the... company and had a long discussion with Dr. Fleming, who is the head of their Research Department. He satisfied me that secrecy could and would be maintained. He assured me that no foreigners were employed in his Department...Further, the Managing Director...told me that at the present time no Americans were employed at Trafford Park, nor was there a free interchange of information between his Company and the Associated Companies in other countries... [and] he was quite free to prevent representatives from foreign Associated Companies having access to all Departments at Trafford Park." [2]

Authority was obtained from the Air Council for permission to approach MetroVick and Cossor. On 6 March, Watson Watt with Wing Commander Leedham met Dr Fleming and his research staff to discuss the transmission details. It was to be no ordinary transmitter; the maximum time allowed of 15 seconds for a wavelength change ruled out the existing high power W/T designs made by STC and Marconi, which would have been relatively easy to modify for pulse working. Additionally, the transmitter had to be duplicated so that in case of a breakdown the service could be restored almost immediately, and this required a fast changeover of the four aerials between the two transmitters. MetroVick were confident that an experimental model could be completed within nine months from the date of contract followed by three transmitters every two months.

On 15 February, Watson Watt wrote to Wimperis that even if approval for the chain between Beachy Head and the Wash was received within a few months, it could not be operational until January 1939. He said that it was highly desirable to have at the earliest opportunity the working of a small group of stations rather than wait for completion of the whole chain. He proposed that the original five estuary stations be completed by the end of the year for operation by Service personnel, but with the essential difference between the original and the proposed scheme that now each station would have range, height and direction finding facilities and would be capable of combating any deliberate jamming. Known as the Intermediate stage there would be two 240ft towers, one for the receiver aerials and the other for the transmitter aerial; that arrangement would allow the station to be completed to the Final stage without interruptions. The DCAS gave his approval. This time BRS would make the five transmitters based on a design, with modifications, that was used by the Post Office at their Rugby transmitting station. Cossor would be contracted to make five copies of the Slough ionosphere receiver that had been used for the early Orfordness experiments. Installation work would continue at Bawdsey, Canewdon and Dover but extra towers were needed at Great Bromley and Dunkirk for which Treasury approval would have to be sought.

Watson Watt and Leedham visited Cossor on 9 March and they anticipated no difficulty in the design or production of the receiver, which was based on a BRS handmade pilot model for electrical and mechanical layout. Cossor were prepared to set aside special shops for pre-production work and, by limiting the assembly work to specially selected and trustworthy staff, they were satisfied that secrecy could be maintained. The receivers could be ready within 12 to 18 months from the date of contract.

In a memo to the DSR (now D.R.Pye, as H.E.Wimperis had retired on 1 March) on 10 March, Leedham outlined the talks with MetroVick and urged that requisitions for contracts be raised to cover the design and production of 20 sets of transmitters and receivers. The DSR agreed, as did Freeman, who was firmly of the opinion that the RDF scheme would not be cancelled and that it was essential to start provisioning even before the results of the air exercise were known; within five days Leedham was told by the DSR to take action. The Director of Signals advised the DCAS on 1 April:

"In forwarding the requisitions to the Director of Equipment, we will make it clear that they are liable to be recalled in the unlikely event of your deciding not to proceed as a result of the trials in April. ...Will you please say if you concur in our raising requisitions for the development and purchase of 20 sets of R.D.F. transmitting and receiving apparatus at an estimated cost of £320,000." [1]

The transmitter specification was brief with the circuit arrangements and the types of valves to be used based broadly on the discussions at BRS with MetroVick; they were, however, unwilling to accept any value of pulse output power because they had no experience on what their own valves would produce under pulse conditions or how to measure it. For specification purposes it was agreed that the continuous RF output power of the two output valves, 80 kW, would be acceptable; in use the DC supply voltage would be doubled with a corresponding increase in pulse output power. The transmitter produced between 200kW to 350 kW of pulse power depending on frequency and its enormous size produced a somewhat ridiculous story at the training schools that RDF was so secret that even MetroVick were not allowed to know that the transmitter was pulse modulated; it was built to supply continuous RF output power.

That was not the case. Dr J.M.Dodds, the designer, was taken into full confidence on the techniques of transmission and reception and the specification gave a clear and rigid definition. The pulse was to be capable of being repeated 25 or 50 times a second, amended later to include 12½ times a second, rise to 0.9 of its maximum amplitude within 1 microsecond, continue at its maximum amplitude for a period from 5 to 35 microseconds as adjusted, and fall to 0.01 of its maximum amplitude within 2 microseconds. The transmitter was the most complicated type operated by the RAF using continuously evacuated water cooled valves, which required distilled water tanks and pumps with cooling fans set in the outside blast wall.

The receiver specification was also very brief as L.H.Bedford of Cossor had visited BRS and seen the prototype receiver. There were three unusual features: (1) that it must accept a 20 volt pulse peak to peak input and recover sensitivity within 10μsecs plus the pulse width, (2) it must select one out of four pre-set wavelengths in under 15 seconds and (3) that a 50μV input should produce a 25 mm deflection on the cathode ray tube. Two receivers were required at each station with external switching for either to be connected to the four aerials. The anomaly that the transmitter specification called for a duplicate to be provided, but the receiver did not, remained undetected by Leedham's department until it was realised in July 1938 that 20 standby receivers had not been ordered or finance made available. A memo from AVM W.S.Douglas to the Director of Signals gave authority on 25 July 1938:

> "I agree a standby receiver is necessary. I am only surprised that this was not thought of before." [3]

The air exercise was planned for 19–30 April; a series of special flights across an observed area in the North Sea with three flying boats and two Anson aircraft, but the first two days' flying were abandoned because of low cloud and ice accretion. The next day's weather was sufficiently good for day and night flying to take place but, for the remainder of the exercise, many flights were modified, with some abandoned. A special flight was flown on 23 April for the benefit of the Secretary of State for Air, who was at BRS that day. A summary of the exercises indicated that most of the aircraft were reported accurately up to 80 miles, the maximum range; bearing was less so but gave a useful indication of aircraft position, the height accuracy was dependable above 8,000ft but not acceptable below 5,000ft, and the counting of the number of aircraft in a formation was unreliable. In contrast to the complete lack of technical information on the file for the September 1936 exercises, Watson Watt wrote an interim report of which this is an extract:

"The apparatus used was wholly designed and constructed at B.R.S., the working wavelength 13 metres, transmitter pulse power 40 kW, a standby receiver and transmitter available. At no time was recourse had to the standby receiver save on the morning of 23 April when it was used for easier observation by the Secretary of State and his party. The standby transmitter was used on one afternoon to enable improvements to be introduced into the main transmitter. There was no failure of transmitter components and aerials and receivers were tested every day. On no account during the exercise did interference by signals, atmospherics or ignition systems produce troublesome interference. Power radiated inland was 1% of that seaward and means for discriminating between aircraft inland and over the sea provided. The main objective was a location range of 30 miles from a formation not below 5,000 ft and over a useful sector not less than 102 degrees. The time taken for observation and the transmission of positional data, of plan position and height varied between 12 and 22 seconds, which could be reduced by practice, and by speech quality improvements on telephone lines. Preliminary experiments to facilitate raid identification systems were made late in the exercise and did show considerable promise. The need for a Filter centre is clearly established." [4]

The analysis of the air exercise had been completed by Fighter Command and circulated to the Air Staff. On 21 May, Joubert wrote to the DCAS that he wished to place on record his opinion that sufficient experience had been obtained to justify the erection of a chain of stations. He added:

"I base this view on the fact that although it is not yet possible to locate with absolute precision an aircraft or formation of aircraft flying at more than 30 miles from the coast, yet sufficient indication of enemy aerial activity can regularly be obtained up to 80 miles from the coast to facilitate very greatly the task of Fighter Command. I make this interim recommendation because I feel there is no time to be lost in carrying out further trials on a large scale and with the additional facilities for correcting observations that an increased number of Stations will provide." [5]

On 24 May the Deputy Director of Operations commented:

"In view of the expression of opinion by the A.O.C. Coastal Command, I suggest we can now instruct the Director of Signals to put in hand the completion of the R.D.F.1 chain which was recommended by the A.D.R. committee at their fifth meeting without waiting for the final report." [5]

Dowding's report dated 7 June was more reserved:

"I regard the existing achievements of the R.D.F. system as being of great value to the defence of the country in so far as they indicate generally the approach of aircraft towards our shores. This is but a fraction of the benefit which I hope we shall eventually obtain from this system, but I must emphasise that it is all that has been obtained up to the present. A general view of the charts accompanying the report shows that the average track as plotted by B.R.S. bears no recognisable relation to the track flown by the aircraft and, although there are a few exceptions to this general view, even these plots are not sufficiently accurate to enable interceptions to be attempted before the coast is reached... I think that perhaps this exercise suffered to some extent from the adoption of too ambitious a programme. The large number of machines in the air at one time in some of the exercises constituted a very high trial for a system which is really only in its infancy. The D/F system for the recognition of friendly aircraft was a complete failure. This I attribute largely to faulty liaison...but the matter is...of minor importance, since, even if the D/F system had been successful, there were no recognisable plots on the Table which the identifications could have supplied." [5]

His last paragraph was not very optimistic:

"I regret that the results of the exercise do not yet enable me to put forward definite proposals for the transfer of R.D.F. plots to the various Operations Rooms." [5]

At a later meeting in June he conceded that the results of the trials were disappointing:

"Whatever it may be capable of in the future, it is not at present capable of plotting the tracks of several formations approaching the coast simultaneously." [6]

RDF equipment was being installed at Canewdon and Dover that required the stations to be guarded by civilians, as it was peacetime, who received a weekly wage of £2.10s.7d (£2.53p), the sergeant in charge £2.19s.0d (£2.95p) with reductions if living in official accommodation. They incurred their own expenses when attending for interview and taking up the appointment, were required to work a six day 48 hour week with six days leave a year and forbidden to join associations and trade organisations.

During May one of the latest designs of transmitting arrays was rigged at Dover, an exciter curtain of six half wave dipoles behind which were two reflector curtains of equivalent dipoles to ensure that the amount of power radiated behind the arrays was at a minimum. (This research had eventually to be abandoned as many of the scientific staff were away from BRS to assist in the installation work at the five estuary stations.) The BRS riggers were duly dispatched on 5 May with the following instructions:

"The working day is from 7.45am to 5.15pm Monday to Saturday, a working week of 48 hours with 4½ hours overtime. The work is expected to be finished by May 31. The Bank Holidays of May 12 and May 17 will be worked and taken at the end of the job. Night subsistence 4s.0d (20p)." [7]

(Note. The weekly wage for a rigger was £2.8s.0d (£2.40p) with an additional 4s 0d (20p) for the charge hand.)

With the somewhat primitive aerials at Bawdsey, Canewdon and Dover, transmitter powers around 20kW, receivers not of the highest sensitivity, and with 1 mm of noise on the screen, it was possible to obtain a range of 135 miles for an aircraft whose echo height was 2mm; echoes of 4mm were seen from six aircraft flying at a distance of 100 miles. Larger echoes of 3cm were only achieved by aircraft between 7,000 to 10,000 feet at 60 miles with heightfinding errors of the order of ± 2,000ft. It was noticeable at Dover, where the transmitting array was six tier at a height of 380ft above sea level, that aircraft flying at 10,000ft gave echoes between 5 to 6cm, compared to the four tier array at Bawdsey that was only 50ft above sea level, which gave 3cm echoes.

The improvement in the ability to measure accurately with larger echoes is shown by the figures for direction finding accuracy, ± 2 degrees at 40 miles but ± 10 degrees at 80 miles. The MetroVick transmitter was expected to give at least ten times the power that would treble the echo height with the same aerial. The receiving aerial was now part of the direction and heightfinding array and remained 'all round looking'.

Contract clearance for the 20 sets of equipment hit a major snag, which threatened to introduce months of delay. On the 21 April the DCAS received advice from Mr A. H. Self, a Deputy Under Secretary at the Air Ministry, that it was not possible to give financial approval (£320,000) until the TISC had authorised the expenditure for the complete chain. He also thought that it was unlikely that sanction would be agreed until the results of the air exercise had been assessed, a recommendation obtained from the Tizard Committee and confirmed by the ADR sub-committee. Freeman did not accept this advice and informed Mr Self that two months had already been lost and to wait for the final approval would put the chain completion date back to the Spring of 1940. He urged that preliminary action should be taken now to obtain the receivers and the transmitters; the firms had already outlined their designs and were waiting approval to go ahead. Additional support came from the DCAS who wrote on 14 May to Mr Self:

"As I think you are aware, the Air Staff regard the development of R.D.F.1 as of the greatest operational importance. The results achieved are so promising that we are confident that an organised system of R.D.F.1 stations will give us early and accurate information on the approach of enemy aircraft, the lack of

which up to the present has been one of the most difficult problems facing the
A.O.C.-in-C. Fighter Command in the defence of this country...I think there is
not the slightest doubt that we shall require to erect at least 20 stations..." [1]

Leedham and the Director of Contracts conferred with Mr Self and a means
was found for finance to be made available for the initial designs. Freeman
was advised on 25 May that it was possible to use research and development
funds that were available for the 'redesign of the apparatus and its assembly
for manufacturing' which clearly applied to the manufacture of the two
prototypes. The expenditure was based on the assumption that the work
would in any event be necessary and for use even if the full scheme were
not proceeded with:

> "If a technical requisition is prepared for the 'redesign' [the prototypes] we
> will release it at once to Contracts for action." [1]

On 1 June Freeman advised Mr Self, through the DCAS, that a requisition
was being raised to cover the design and assembly of one transmitter costing
£15,000 and one receiver costing £5,000. He added:

> "It is important to get the design work started without further delay, but I see
> no reason to defer obtaining Treasury approval for the production and building
> entailed...the delay which has already occurred makes it practically impossible
> to complete a chain of 20 stations by March 39." [1]

MetroVick have recorded that they received a telephone call on 11 June to
proceed, which was followed by the contract on 2 July, the same date as the
contract to Cossor.

    The next step was for the DCAS to prepare a comprehensive document
to obtain the approval of the CAS. He wrote on 11 June:

> "The trials have shown that R.D.F. can give us useful reports at ranges up to
> 80 miles... equipment is sufficiently satisfactory to go into production...Such
> limitations as have been disclosed can...be remedied by....an increase in the
> number of stations... With two or more stations...bearing errors should be largely
> eliminated.... At heights of 8,000ft or more, reports are good...improvements
> in reporting the numbers of aircraft ...[are] expected from the improvement of
> technique and experience of the operator..." [1]

There was a minor bureaucratic hurdle to be overcome as the approval for
the chain of 20 stations depended on the results of the air exercise, not with
one but with five stations. The DCAS took the view that if they had to wait
until the five stations were in operation and another air exercise, then the
chain would not be ready, at the earliest, before March 1940, or even later.
He concluded:

> "The R.D.F. experiments so far as they go have shown such important results
> that I am certain we cannot afford to delay development of the chain...any longer,
> and we have ample grounds now on which to go to the Treasury for approval of

the scheme. The cost of a chain of 20 stations is estimated to be £1,250,000... If you agree it will be necessary to go to the Treasury as soon as possible." [1]

The CAS agreed the same day and instructed that the matter be attended to urgently. The next day, Finance were ordered by Mr Self:

"Please put in hand as a matter of urgency and pending C.A.S. approval, the preparation of a draft memo for submission to the T.I.S.C. The draft must be submitted to the Secretary before going forward." [1]

The Air Ministry were requesting financial approval to extend the chain by a further 15 stations at a cost of £52,000 each, made up of land £3,000, towers £28,000 (8 x £3,500), power £8,000, buildings £3,000, wardens' quarters £1,200, roads and fencing £5,000 with £3,800 for contingencies. Additional costs were transmitters £300,000, receivers £20,000, and the additional land, buildings and towers to extend the five estuary stations, a total cost of £1,237,000. There were a few more bridges to cross before Treasury sanction was obtained; the 20 station scheme had to be referred to the ADR sub-committee, and its recommendation submitted to two committees of the Committee of Imperial Defence for endorsement. Only then could the Air Ministry submit the detailed costs to the TISC and commence contract action.

The ADR sub-committee recommended the proposal for 20 stations on 5 July but Swinton thought that the detail given on their performance was much too secret for the next sub-committee, the Defence Plans (Requirements). He drafted a letter to the Chancellor of the Exchequer asking for his agreement to approve the recommendation or for an early reference direct and above to the Defence Plans (Policy) sub-committee. The document summarised the progress of RDF to date; detection at 10,000ft up to 80 miles, recently extended to 116 miles, range determined more accurately than bearing, the accuracy of height at 6,000ft and over was good but the exact number of aircraft counted was unreliable. As an exceptional measure authority was now sought for the erection of a full chain; an early decision was necessary, but if deferred until the trials with the five stations contemplated had been concluded, it would retard completion to the end of 1940. On 25 July the sub-committee gave the Air Ministry full authorisation to proceed as soon as possible with the proviso to submit detailed costs to the TISC, whose next meeting was 12 August.

Swinton's message to the (Permanent) Secretary, now Sir Donald Banks, was brief:

"The Secretary of State would be glad if the Secretary would take urgent action to obtain Treasury sanction." [4]

The memo was ready on 10 August and contained a most vital sentence:

"All estimates [are] provisional, [and the] authority of the committee is sought for immediate sanction to acquire sites and incur expenditure on Works and apparatus." [4]

(ie, to dispense with the time-consuming peace time practice of providing detailed costings.) Sanction was given on 12 August. The Chairman of the CID sub-committee thought that the word RDF was too revealing and ARDAP was suggested as a 'portmanteau' word for Air Raid Detection and Plotting, but the DCAS decided that a change of name at this stage might only draw attention to RDF.

On 30 June a meeting was held in the office of the DCAS to consider whether the chain of 20 stations to be erected along the east coasts of England and Scotland was an Interim or Final scheme. Watson Watt suggested that they should be sited between Portland Bill and Dundee, with others to fill the gaps where greater accuracy was required. But the DCAS said that the Secretary of State, in putting forward the scheme, would require to be free from any Treasury criticism that this chain was, in fact, not a full one, but might require more stations at a future date; their positioning should be to give full operational cover without subsequent additions.

Watson Watt explained that the siting of the stations was dependent on the minimum height of the approach of hostile aircraft and the range; it was fortunate for him that the specified altitude, which reflected the Air Staff criteria of the day, was just within the capability of the RDF system. The DCAS gave the requirement as 3,000ft and range 40 miles from the Isle of Wight to Lowestoft and from there to St Andrews (Firth of Tay) 5,000ft and 35 miles. There were four coastal areas that were exposed; the Forth, Tyne, Tees and Humber, which also required 3,000ft and range 40 miles. Watson Watt advised that the coast would be covered with stations every 20 miles from Ventnor to Lowestoft and then 40 miles from Lowestoft to Seaham Harbour, a total of 20 stations. A further five would be required for Whitley Bay, Coquet Island, St Abbs Head, Dunbar and St Andrews when CID approval for expansion was received.

One awkward technicality for BRS to solve was how three towers could carry eight aerials; they submitted that two receiver towers could support two aerials each and the remaining tower could carry four transmitting aerials weighing a total of ten tons. In a letter to Works, BRS stated that it was for consideration; it was certainly considered very promptly a few days later, the answer being in the negative. It was agreed that the tower loading would permit two sets of receiving dipoles on one tower, but the best that BRS could expect for the remaining tower was the support of one transmitting aerial. After much discussion, including the possibility of tower redesign, it was finally accepted that the policy to be adopted was one aerial per tower, a total of eight 240ft wooden towers per station.

The technical requirements at BRS could change rapidly, a fact noticed and commented upon by the Director of Works for, at the end of July, BRS decided that the 240ft wooden towers for the transmitting aerials would be changed to 350ft (107.5 m) steel towers. The change would permit larger transmitting arrays that gave a better 'illumination' at lower angles of elevation, greatly increase the certainty of the location of distant and low flying aircraft, and allow the transmitting and receiving arrays to be at the same effective height so as to avoid gaps in the vertical coverage through which echoes 'disappeared and reappeared' on the CRT screen. Works had agreed that the change to a steel tower was acceptable provided the cost did not exceed that of a wooden one and remained within the financial limits.

BRS were now able to complete the ideal design for the Final stage of what was to become known as the coastal Chain of stations for Home Defence (CH). There would be four in-line steel 350ft towers with a minimum spacing of 175ft or more if land was available, with the transmitting (T) block in front of the towers on the seaward side. At a minimum distance of 700 yards from the nearest steel tower a group of four 240ft wooden towers would be arranged where possible in a rhombus shape some 250ft apart with the receiver (R) block in the centre; a brick built standby generator house at a suitable distance, a total area covering about ten acres. Watson Watt had laid down the guide lines:

"An R.D.F. station will operate over an arc of about 100 degrees to a distance of 50 miles...Spacing between stations should be chosen so that if one station in a chain is put out of action, the resulting gap in the defences should not be of the highest importance. This means that on the average the adjacent stations will be about 18 to 20 miles apart...The best site is one not more than half a mile from the coastline and situated on cliffs overlooking the sea. Alternatively, the site may be on high ground near the coast. The station may be set back from the coastline without loss of working range at the rate of ten miles for every 100ft gain of height above the average level of the country in front of the station. No buildings, trees, or other obstructions within half a mile of the towers, with stations more than half a mile from potential sources of interference such as neon signs, electrical machinery, electric railways and roads carrying heavy traffic." [8]

From the very earliest days, Watson Watt was aware of the need for the plots to be what he called 'reconciled'; tracks from each group of three to four stations would be connected together so that a single master could be forwarded to an operations room as a positive and definite track. The first opportunity to provide such a service took place during the 1936 air exercise when information was sent from BRS to the Uxbridge Operations Room. Range was conveyed by telephone and plan position appeared as a spot on a cathode ray tube that moved to a new position as the information changed, but because the display did not show a continuous track it was thoroughly disliked by the operators and was never used again. There were discussions at BRS on the method to be adopted for the transmission of plotting information; subject to jamming, radio was eventually ruled out in favour of the telephone line. There was one trivial aspect that was not normally a handicap that of leakage of speech from one telephone line to another and although it was very, very small, it was considered by Watson Watt that as it could be amplified to an adequate listening level it was a security risk. He set up a small section at BRS to develop equipment that 'scrambled' the speech on the plotting lines of the estuary stations, but Dowding considered it unnecessary and cancelled it for the remaining stations.

The whole purpose of the chain was to ensure that an operations room received accurate plots on the table so it was one of the tasks of BRS to examine the overall system and suggest improvements. Plots in the form of a horizontal and vertical co-ordinate, were telephoned direct from the Observer Corps to the operations rooms of adjacent sectors and groups, and to Uxbridge, HQ of 11Group. The first indication of aircraft activity was five miles from the coast that was considerably reduced by cloud and bad weather.

On a large horizontal table a map was fixed on which one inch diameter (25mm) counters were placed to represent enemy aircraft and, to ensure that the information on the table remained updated, the counters were supplied in three different colours, orange, blue and red that matched the five minute segment of the operations room clock. Only two colours were allowed on the table so it was easy to see the latest information by reference to the clock. Looking down on the map were the sector and other controllers with direct access to operational telephones.

Two drawbacks were identified by BRS; the noise level produced by the operators speaking to distant members of the Observer Corps in the transfer of plots, and the partial covering of the table when the counters were moved. A vertical screen was proposed with the counters replaced by spots of lights from optical projectors on one side of the screen that was viewed on the other side by the controllers. As existing commercial projectors were found to be unsuitable due to overheating and optical distortions, a small group was set up at BRS to design, construct and operate a suitable replacement.

Additional Army scientific officers had arrived at BRS in February and in a letter to ADEE a Captain Young remarked:

"The house problem is an acute one. I can find nothing here fit to live in under £115 a year, Pollard has fixed on a new house but he had to choose a very poor type of house, [and] we both loathe Bawdsey, so far!" [9]

P.E.Pollard was the senior scientific officer in charge of developments for Gun and Light laying (GL), but progress was slow as a memo by Rowe as the Co-ordinator of Air Defence on 26 May to the Deputy DSR, showed:

"The main War Office interest at B.R.S. is the control of A.A. guns by radio and they regard this as of great importance, but it must be realised, however, that there is not a one per cent chance of the early solution of the problem, and one can reasonably doubt whether it will be solved in our time. There is much fundamental work on short wavelengths, and the measurement of ranges in yards and angles to within minutes of arc that need to be done." [10]

The AA gun predictor was a mechanical/optical device, whose function was to determine when and where the shells would arrive and explode. To provide the information it required range, bearing and elevation to be provided continuously. In operation, a high magnification telescope, which in good weather could see an aircraft at ten miles, was followed by two telescopes to give bearing and elevation. Success depended in the first instance on the preciseness of range yet this was the most inaccurate because there was only about 20 seconds available when the aircraft was first seen. This gave little time for the taking of a number of spot readings upon which the accuracy depended and in many cases it led to errors as high as half a mile in six miles. The ideal set to assist AA guns would need to have a range in thousands of yards correct to within ±25 yards, an elevation from 10 to 55 degrees and the observed bearing both within half a degree.

But on 18 November, Pollard submitted a memo that contained two major breakthroughs. The first proposal was to centre the echo in the middle of the CRT display by continuously altering the range, and the second was for azimuth; two aerials so designed that the forward lobes overlapped and, by mechanical or electrical switching before connection to the receiver, were turned until the amplitudes of the two echoes were identical in height. Field trials showed that the azimuth was not sufficiently precise to enable the GL set to replace the predictor, but the War Office was impressed with the range precision, ±14 yards, which was superior, and would allow guns and men to be on 'standby' rather than at 'action stations' for many hours; at least 600 sets would be required.

In wartime the Army would be responsible for the detection of ships approaching the coast that might be the prelude to an invasion plus the defence of major ports, what was known officially as Coast Defence (CD). Dr Paris had seen the results of the airborne 1.5 metre set, which had been set up on one of the 240ft tower platforms, 100ft above sea level, that had shown clear echoes from sea-going vessels some three to four miles out to sea. His request for more scientific effort to be diverted from GL to CD was refused on the grounds that the GL work was of higher significance.

The finding of suitable locations was now much more difficult to achieve because of the big increase in land required, some ten acres, for an eight tower station. The receiver site was surveyed first in order to satisfy the strict requirements for heightfinding – flat for half a mile then gently sloping towards the sea. The transmitter site only needed the ground to be reasonably even to maintain the tower levels and could be on either side of the receiver. To ensure economy of land purchase a few sites had to be split, some by a public road. During August, Wilkins and Works officers returned to the estuary stations to find land for the additional towers. The Dunkirk site was not suitable for a receiver because of the poor heightfinding quality and earlier in May, Watson Watt had proposed that a new location should be found further towards the coast at North Foreland, but the high cost of land, about £450 an acre, forced the idea to be rejected. The single T wooden tower at Dunkirk was too near the proposed siting of the steel towers to support receiver aerials so it was abandoned; along with Bawdsey, it would have the distinction of having five 240ft towers.

To complete the chain Watson Watt had decided that only a further ten stations, not 15, would be required along the south, southeast and east coasts of England. The first surveys were for three locations west of Dover and by an examination of Ordnance Survey maps, Wilkins had chosen Fairlight in Kent, Ditchling Beacon or Bird Brow in West Sussex and Dunnose or Stenbury Down on the Isle of Wight. At Fairlight two sites were investigated about three miles east of Ore, the first on the highest point of the area some 550ft and the second, 520ft, half a mile further east. But the whole locality was a well-known beauty spot that would invite unwelcome publicity.

The next area was virtually in the middle of the South Downs, Ditchling Beacon at 813ft, a well-known and popular viewing point with the remains of an old Roman encampment on top of the hill. There was no power within a mile or sufficient space for both sets of towers. The next possibility was at Bird Brow, Newmarket Hill, near Brighton, a height of 624ft but road access was poor with only bridle paths. The opportunity was taken to see the District Valuer, whose opinion was that great opposition was likely to be met locally to the construction of a station anywhere on the South Downs, but if imperative, there would be less opposition to Bird Brow than Ditchling. On the Isle of Wight, St Boniface being on the edge of the cliffs was ideal for range but not for height, and Stenbury Down and St Martin's Down were considered unsuitable. Wilkins wrote:

> "The Ventnor siting was something of a jest. At the period concerned it was considered unlikely that in the event of a war there would be much air activity as far as Ventnor and Watson Watt and I did not regard the siting there as a very serious matter. As the site was 760ft above sea level with an immediate drop to Ventnor and the sea, we could not resist the temptation to use it to see whether a station there was good for low flying aircraft. It was of course realised that height measurements were out of the question but standard height finding equipment was fitted." [11]

North of Bawdsey it was expected that the somewhat flat and uninteresting coastline might prove less irksome. In Suffolk two sites were found at Darsham and Westleton Heath, but at Corton, Lowestoft, the only two suitable places were all zoned for building. Near Cromer (Norfolk), Bodham Hill and West Beckham were found appropriate, while in Lincolnshire at Withcall near Louth only one was found at Stenigot; at 480ft it was found to be excellent from the technical and Works aspect and considered to be the best of all areas so far visited. In Yorkshire, Thwing, on top of Staxton Wold at 580ft, was preferred to the alternative at Sharp Howes, Flixton, that would have required an access road to be constructed. Fylindales Moor, 780ft and only a mile inland appeared suitable but was without water or electricity and required an access road but the second one at Ravenscar, 850ft, south of Whitby was found acceptable.

The Cheviots in Northumberland was well favoured by Wilkins as it had the advantage of great height, 2,700ft, which would give a longer range and so obviate one or two stations at a lower height with less range. However attractive it looked on paper it was a different matter when Wilkins and the Works officer tried to get to the top as hill fog prevented it from being reached. Reliance was placed on local enquiries that it was a bog with the land sloping very steeply in all directions from the top with poor access; a precipitous climb for about two and a half miles over moor and bog. With no electricity or water supplies the siting party certainly knew that it would be an impracticable operation to build except at enormous cost; no contractor would undertake the construction of the towers and a road except on a time and material basis and living conditions would be extremely bad requiring buildings of a special design.

With the chain expansion and research rapidly increasing the post of Deputy Superintendent was approved at BRS. There must have been intense speculation amongst the senior scientific officers as to whom would be selected as the secret nature of the work would appear to rule out an 'outside' promotion: many thought without question that either Wilkins or Bowen would be the best candidate, perhaps preference for Wilkins. The selection of A.P.Rowe was perhaps greeted with more than a measure of surprise especially when his own words are considered:

> "Although knowing nothing about radio, I was sent to B.R.S. because of the lack of anyone who had experience with Service affairs." [12]

Professional feathers at BRS were certainly ruffled. Treasury parsimony may have played a small part here as Rowe's headquarters post of the Co-ordinator of Air Defence was abolished. His scientific background understood the basic points of issue and his Civil Service training brought a much needed core of central administration by the circulation of files and frequent meetings with the heads of the various groups. Rowe set up a number of progress files that were to be the subject of a written report every two weeks and to the Group officers concerned he suggested that 'one typed page should normally suffice and that three typed pages should never be necessary.'

Cossor had developed the prototype receiver (the RF5) in total secrecy in their 'cabinet' works, a private house in Dalston Road, Hackney, north London, some distance from the main factory at Highbury. Their task was to make the BRS model suitable for quantity production and able to select one out of four pre-set wavelengths within 15 seconds. To meet the sensitivity specification Cossor added an extra RF stage over that used in the BRS design and, to ensure the highest signal to noise ratio, the first RF valve was the Mullard EF8, unique in its day as a low noise pentode. The 'front end' was indeed novel, the three RF and frequency changer stages in push-pull and balanced to reduce input damping and for connection to the gonio search coil: a stabilised grid bias supply prevented paralysis by the local transmitter pulse. Weighing 15cwt, over 7ft in height and 7ft in width it was too large to reach the front door when the time came for delivery to BRS; a demolition squad was called in to cut through the walls. Watson Watt reported to the Tizard Committee that the receiver exceeded the specification and was much beyond their expectations.

There were ongoing problems with the MetroVick prototype transmitter, which specified that the master oscillator and the driver stages worked continuously followed by the pulsed amplifiers. At a very late stage in development BRS considered that this arrangement, which allowed a leakage of 1 microwatt, would cause continuous interference to the nearby receiver, so the circuit arrangement was changed in that all sections were pulsed. Another part of the specification appears to have been abandoned, the requirement for the four incoming aerials to be switched between the two transmitters, both with a common power supply.

The precise reasons for the changes cannot be ascertained as the Air Ministry file titled '*The M.V. Papers*' was 'lost' during circulation among the official historians and, with the relevant contract files, it appears to have been destroyed. What is known is that both prototypes were intended for the CH chain, because the contract raised on 28 October to meet the 20 chain station requirement was for 19 receivers and transmitters. As the alterations to the specification rendered the original unusable, the contract was subsequently amended for the supply of 20 transmitters. It is probable that Watson Watt had to decide on the aerial switching system; either inside the two transmitters, which would have created a very large dimensional piece of equipment, or outside the building. The latter decision resulted in a self-contained transmitter known as a ½CH, which became very convenient, but even that was in three parts weighing three tons each. BRS were faced with the decision to provide either external high power switching between transmitters and aerials or a duplicate set of four aerials; the latter was chosen no doubt due to the shortage of time.

To provide main and standby transmitting arrays, BRS had proposed that they be rigged on each tower and between the steel towers but this arrangement was vetoed by Works, which had calculated that a suitable tower would weigh 180 tons, require concrete foundations of 140 cubic yards and cost £8,000 that was well outside the set financial limit. BRS had to compromise with two arrays comprising six tiers of dipoles with two reflector curtains stretched between the upper and centre and the centre and lower cantilevers; this arrangement gave two wavelengths per tower and provided main and standby arrays on separate towers. Works gave their approval as they had calculated the stress values in sufficient detail and that the arrangement was practicable within the agreed cost of £3,250 per tower. BRS agreed to design the aerials so that under conditions of maximum wind and ice they would fail, and so prevent the tower from collapsing; replacing a tower would be far more costly and time consuming than the restoration of aerials.

During October and November many additional surveys were made; along the south coast Ditchling and Bird Brow were considered problematical so another site was selected at High and Over near Alfriston. Along the east coast Corton was replaced by Stoke Holy Cross at 210ft, some 17 miles inland, and Ravenscar by Danby Beacon at 940ft. The Cheviots was replaced by Steng Cross at 1,088ft and found to be technically very suitable but, according to the locals, was blocked by snow in winter. By the end of the year Wilkins had considered that all the sites selected had represented all the best that could be obtained as there appeared to be no obstacles to overcome and land purchase was not expected to be troublesome; 'beauty spots' had not been looked at so as to avoid public clamour and possible questions in Parliament.

The training of RAF operators had continued throughout the year. After six weeks at Bawdsey they were posted to one of the estuary stations for three months' practice on the tube: their notebooks made under instruction were kept in the station safe for security. Progress was being made by the operators at Canewdon and Dover in assembling tracks but it was not easy as there was little flying in front of the stations. With the appearance of an echo the first check was to decide if the aircraft was in front or behind the station, ie, seaward or inland. An aircraft flying behind the station produced an echo that without being 'sensed' could be taken for an incoming aircraft and possibly labelled hostile. After sensing, the range was obtained by the tracking of a cursor, the receivers of the time having no range scales.

The next step was to establish the bearing, which had to be taken before heightfinding, and this was where the difficulties began. The gonio was turned until the echo was reduced to the smallest height but this was almost impossible to determine for distant aircraft. The instruction to 'swing' the gonio backwards and forwards over the echo to determine the minimum produced a wide variation in the bearing figure to such an extent that subsequent plots had widely different figures. Connected together they produced a zig-zag appearance on the plotting table that only gradually converged to form a recognisable track as the aircraft came nearer to the station. Because the gonio reduced the echo size, the station was then 'blind' at that setting, in fact at any setting, and that is why it was continuously rotated.

For heightfinding, the incoming echo was received on aerials at two different heights and the gonio then turned for the lowest amplitude. The angle indicated, plus the range and further arithmetical calculations, gave the height and for this operation a specially constructed and calibrated protractor had to be used. The last figure required was for counting; how many were there? Calculation was most difficult as it depended on the shape of the echo that for two and more aircraft was continually altering in the vertical axis, known as 'beating', and few operators had seen more than three aircraft in formation – it was sheer guesswork. Rowe held the opinion that:

"...it was generally agreed that there is no hope of producing within the year an optical and/or mechanical system which will automatically translate the tube readings into a continuously recorded track without the aid of speech. Nor to my knowledge are there any promising ideas on how this can be done within acceptable limits of complexity in any period of time." [13]

One little known experiment that took place in 1937 was a different way of obtaining the bearing, suggested by a Corporal Chapman when on training; the advantage was that there was no ambiguity compared to using range cuts. The operator looked at two tube displays, and when turning the goniometer watched for two echoes that reduced to the minimum at the same time ; there was no need to find the minimum as the gonio played no further part in position finding, only identification. As the echoes were produced by transmitters at two different sites the position could be obtained by the operator measuring the ranges on a special map (hyperbolic patterned). The idea was adopted to the extent that Canewdon and Dover were fitted with a dual display receiver and the operators trained to use both methods of position fixing. But complications arose in developing a phase control for the common wavelength and, due to improvements in the accuracy of the original method, the idea was abandoned by Watson Watt.

The Biggin Hill interception trials had continued throughout 1936 and by April, 1937, it was reported that 85% of 20 experiments had advanced to a stage at which the fighters had been navigated to within three miles of a bomber even though it was changing height, speed and course. Tizard expressed his satisfaction and proposed that further experiments should be made using RDF and, specifically, the 'interception' of Dutch (KLM) airliners and others from Bawdsey plots that were regularly recorded; he conjectured that the approach to London by German bombers in the event of a war would be very similar to those taken by civil airliners. A view was expressed that these actions might invoke political clamour but Tizard explained that it was not the intention to bring about a 'dead' interception; all that was required was for the intercepting aircraft to fly above the height of the KLM aircraft with the time and place of interception recorded. Because of delays in providing a mobile at Dunkirk to cover the inland area and the provision of additional HF D/F stations, the first flights to use RDF information from the Bawdsey Filter Room did not commence until December.

REFERENCES

1	AIR2/2618	2	AIR2/2669	3	AIR2/2684	4	AIR2/4488
5	AIR2/2612	6	AIR2/2615	7	AVIA7/333	8	AIR2/4484
9	AIR2/2802	10	AIR2/4486	11	AFW PAPERS	12	AVIA10/348
13	AVIA7/156						

Chapter 5   1938

AT the beginning of the year land acquisition was still in progress and Works were meeting opposition to the purchase of some of the selected sites. At Fairlight, which comprised an estate of 800 acres, the owner's land agents had written that they would strongly oppose the proposition, expressing the opinion that construction of the station would have an injurious effect on 400 acres; very serious claims would arise, costs would be high and negotiations long and drawn out. Rowe was annoyed at their attitude and wrote on 16 March to Wilkins:

> "Sooner or later we shall be forced to make a stand in the national interest ..[and] we cannot be driven from pillar to post in this fashion. We must, however, make sure that there is no reasonable alternative before we make our stand, and I would be glad if you would comment with this in mind." [1]

Wilkins replied that it was impossible to find another one that would give much hope of heightfinding, as an alternative proposed at The Mountain had already been rejected on those grounds:

> "Immediately west is Pevensey, [but] higher land north west of Hastings would be unsuitable due to the screening action of Fairlight. Further west is Beachy Head unsuitable for height. If we cannot obtain Fairlight then the requirements are for a station east and west, one on the Pevensey levels and one on the Rye marshes." [1]

Rowe wrote the next day to Watson Watt:

> "If we give in whenever any difficulty arises we shall encourage opposition. The reference to long drawn out negotiations is more serious than the high cost. I say we must have Fairlight, and quickly." [1]

As parts of the South Downs were National Trust property it was suggested to Works that they be consulted and the Trust Secretary advised that the only sites involving publicity and any great opposition would be those at Ventnor and Alfriston and, for the latter, a national protest might be expected. He recommended approaches to the 'county clerk' of the area on proposals to buy the land. The Chief Clerk of the East Sussex County Council was on sick leave so the letter was handled by his deputy, who disliked the plan and leaked it to a local member of the aristocracy, Lord Gage. He visited

Swinton to complain that the erection of a station south of Alfriston would cause serious damage to the amenities of the district; Swinton requested Works to investigate the matter with preference for another site on the Downs above Peacehaven. During February visits were made along the Sussex coast from Hastings to Littlehampton by Watson Watt and Wilkins with Works to investigate the possibilities of finding acceptable alternatives.

The places visited were Newmarket Hill and Truleigh Hill but both suffered from unsuitable land contours giving poor access or uneven levels for the towers. The area behind Worthing was also explored but was found to be already zoned for building and expensive to purchase as was all the land near the coast between Worthing and Brighton. Between Seaford and Eastbourne any suitable land had the same restrictions that applied to Alfriston but east of Eastbourne there were appropriate areas to be found at Pevensey although the ground was low lying.

The most apt location was found at Poling, near Littlehampton, as the land was arable, not on the Downs and was thought easy to acquire. But the Works officers arranging for the purchase of the land were advised by the Commissioners of the Duke of Norfolk's estate that the Duke would oppose the acquisition of Poling if the towers could be seen from Arundel Castle, the ducal residence, some three miles away. Watson Watt complained that;

> "...the site [had been] selected after numerous visits, surveys and discussions....
> I recommend very strongly the case for the acquisition of Poling on the grounds
> that we have already gone to the limit of concessions to amenity and its conflict
> with security." [2]

On the Isle of Wight, none of the county councillors liked the idea of a station right behind Ventnor, but were ultimately convinced of its national importance and the need for secrecy. They were possibly influenced by this letter dated 17 February from Works:

> "The wireless station will form an integral part of a system of active defence
> against air attack on this country. It is required for the guidance by wireless of
> defence aircraft and must be situated in a position which is very closely defined
> by technical requirements and topographical limitations. Exhaustive surveys
> on the mainland and on the island have established the fact that no completely
> satisfactory site can be found and that the site on Boniface Down...is so much
> superior to any other site in the district....it is essential in the national interest
> and in the interest of the Isle of Wight that the proposed site be situated there.
> Since this station is only a link in a passive chain of defences, it is very unlikely
> that it would be the special object of an attack and therefore its presence would
> not increase the possibility of enemy attacks on the Isle of Wight." [3]

(What the councillors said when Ventnor CH station was dive-bombed and put out of action on 12 August 1940 was doubtless expressed in a few eloquent and very explicit words.)

There was a minor setback to the purchase of Danby Beacon in Yorkshire; an objection was raised by the owner's agent that the site chosen was a prime grouse shooting moor and an alternative was offered a few miles away. Watson Watt's view was that the chosen site was the best in the area and must not be changed. The site was 'seized' under special powers but the Air Ministry had to agree that no overhead wires would be erected on the property. It is likely that this particular case was responsible for the most repeated myth of all radar statements that 'sites must not gravely interfere with grouse shooting'. Embellishments have been added by enthusiastic writers that (1) A.F.Wilkins was firmly instructed by the Air Ministry not to build stations where they might interfere with grouse shooting, and (2) site drawings were returned to Wilkins with one change that the choice of site should not gravely interfere with grouse shooting. Both statements are, of course, completely untrue and show a total ignorance of the selection procedure laid down by the Air Ministry and BRS.

Yet this myth, which has reached the level of folk-lore, has appeared in almost every book and even in a few learned papers that have covered the early history of radar, and accepted without comment. (The 'grouse' statement appears in an Official Document titled *Material Basis for Information of the Public on Radiolocation* edited by an Air Ministry radar 'expert', whose doubtful interpretations of a number of events are accepted as fact.) All the pre-war surveys were by Wilkins, sometimes with Watson Watt, with usually more than one site in the area to be visited. The Works officer was mainly concerned with the suitability of the ground to support buildings and towers, the latter confirmed or otherwise by bore hole tests a few days after the survey. Any reasons for objections to the purchase of the land would have arisen from the owners when Works were making enquiries some weeks later.

On 1 February a 'D' notice had been placed on the Press Association that forbade in national and local newspapers the mention of the erection of towers, which were part of stations being erected as part of the air defence of Great Britain. The eagle-eyed would have noticed in *The Times* issue of 29 June a reference to a wireless station at Stengcross. A resolution had been passed by the Northumberland and Newcastle Society for the Preservation of Amenities asking that consideration should be given to other sites in the neighbourhood 'that have not the beauty of landscape or historic associations of Stengcross.' The Lord Lieutenant of Northumberland thought that there could be another site on the neighbouring hills with equal height but less beauty. By May the decision was taken to abandon Fairlight in favour of Rye and Pevensey and at Stengcross the negotiations with the landowner had broken down so another site was selected at Ottercops Moss near Otterburn. During the same month Watson Watt and Wilkins carried out surveys at Haud Yauds, north of Berwick-on-Tweed, later changed to Drone Hill a few miles south at the request of Works, and Monikie, Angus, at Gallow Hill, whose name was altered to Douglas Wood to avoid confusion with a similar name nearby. The last two stations were in Scotland and concluded the siting of the CH chain, a total of 18 stations. There was no Air Staff policy to proceed further.

In a memo written by Watson Watt he gave the two compromising factors in site selection, [1] the height of the station above sea level and [2] the land in front of the station:

"The greater the station height the greater the range at which approaching aircraft can be detected and roughly located. The smoother the fall of the land over the radius of a few miles in front of, and to the flanks of the site, the more accurate the heightfinding and direction finding...When the first selections of sites were made, equipment made it necessary to give special weight to long range and to sacrifice the heightfinding accuracy [but the] apparatus has improved so that the range from a site has improved. On the other hand the need for accurate heightfinding is becoming more obvious and pressing as the technique for interception develops... [and is] desirable to reverse the earlier balance between range and heightfinding. No change on the East coast suggested even if practicable but the change made from Alfriston to Poling and the abandonment of Fairlight are both changes in the right direction technically forced on us by factors that were not radio-tech. The survey and choice of the two Scottish sites has been made with special reference to the new emphasis, but we are fortunate in finding sites there which do not sacrifice range very seriously for heightfinding and direction finding." [2]

In February arrangements were made for Dover and Canewdon to be transferred from the administrative control of BRS to the RAF. Each station was secret and was known as an Air Ministry Experimental Station [AMES]; for pay, rations and all non-technical matters, the RAF were posted to the nearest Fighter Command station. An RAF warrant officer or flight sergeant was in charge with a corporal operator/mechanic, corporal wireless operator and four operators, who all lived in the nearest village. Motor transport had been grudgingly approved by the Treasury, which required a written assurance that there were no local buses going past the station.

The following personnel were posted on 8 February to RAF Hornchurch for special duties at Canewdon; 291279 Warrant Officer Scarff T.A., 560047 Cpl Colquhoun J., 565505 LAC Evans J., 550188 LAC Jeffries E., 564401 LAC Townson R. and 514872 LAC Pearson A. The lists of barrack, domestic utensils, tools and stationery required were forwarded to the officer in charge of the stations for action. A minor matter to be settled was the cutting of grass, of which there were many acres; in the first instance a scythe was provided! There was a small library to be provided of technical books, a few the best of their day; *The Admiralty Handbook of Wireless Telegraphy* (remembered to this day by many thousands of ex-trainees), *Short Wave Communication* by Ladner and Stoner, *Radio Engineering* by Terman, *Electrical Engineering Data*–3 Volumes, *Alternating Current* by Moorcraft, *Modern Radio Communication* by Rayner, *Reports of the Radio Research Board* and *Cathode Ray Oscillography*.

Among the many items of barrack stores was one that will never be forgotten, this time by all those so unlucky to be given 'fatigues' (a word almost impossible to describe to anyone who has not served in the armed forces but does appear in one dictionary as a soldier's non-combatant duty), and in particular the fatigue of 'shining' lino floors, with 33D/221 Polish, Floor, of which two tins a month were allowed.

No. 10 Department of RAE was responsible for the specifications of receiver and transmitter buildings but it was not until April that BRS were able to supply the equipment dimensions. Works began to press for detail on the internal layout and advised RAE that there was usually a nine months' duration from the receipt of drawings to their completion. Another factor was the late approval by the Air Staff of the protective measures to be adopted: buildings were to be gas proofed, with an eight inch thick concrete roof and six feet of shingle above and a concrete traverse around the walls. Freeman and the DSR perceived that the impact of RDF would completely change the existing air defence organisation, which depended on a complex chain of communications. In practical terms CH stations to locate and provide plots, transmission to the filter, command, group and sectors operations rooms, and by radio-telephone to the pilot of the intercepting aircraft. Watson Watt had, of course, outlined this policy nearly two years ago, with himself as the undisputed director, when he moved from the NPL to BRS. Because of the need for secrecy the new department would also control research, development and production, the building and maintenance of the chain and the provision of spares and documentation.

Freeman did not like Watson Watt's suggestion, a Directorate of Investigations of Communications, and put forward the Directorate of Communications Development (DCD). The DSR's view was that the title should not contain a reference to the word 'research' as it was important that the DSR should remain the recognised official channel of communication in research with outside organisations. Donald Banks, the Permanent Secretary, wrote to Swinton, through the CAS (now ACM Sir C.L. Newall), that the proposed creation of a Directorate of Communications and the appointment of Watson Watt seemed to be well justified:

"So far as we can judge from Mr.Watson Watt's interests, this should not conflict with the Directorate of Signals, but it may be well to ensure at the outset that the dividing line is clearly defined." [4]

The CAS added his consent: 'I see many advantages in the creation of this new directorate...' and Swinton concurred: but could the Treasury be convinced?

A letter on 8 April conveyed the Air Council's opinion that as special research and development was of an unusual difficulty and, as the operational efficiency of the RAF both on defence and offence was being more dependent on communications, it was proposed to set up a Directorate of Communications Development. Their Lordships were requested to endorse the appointment of Mr. R.A.Watson Watt;

"..[and] it is the opinion of the Air Council that the salary should be £1,600." [4]

Their first reply was that it would be contrary to the general practice of government service to have more than one Director of Research, as the proper place for research was under the DSR and development under a deputy director. They proposed the post for a deputy director but with a special and personal rate of remuneration for Watson Watt giving him a similar one as a director. After further correspondence the Treasury eventually accepted that they recognised the departure from existing arrangements, which in their opinion was justified by the highly specialised problems that awaited solution.

They held on to the view that the proper course would have been to appoint Watson Watt as Deputy Director of Scientific Research but, in deference to the strong opinions expressed by the Air Council, and upon the basis that the post and title was personal to Watson Watt, they were prepared to sanction the appointment. The sting is always in the last sentence:

"..My Lords are of the opinion that £1,500 is a proper salary for the post." [4]

Watson Watt took up his appointment as Director in May and immediately complained that the word 'research' was missing from the Directorate's title and those for his officers, but he was advised by Freeman that the word would appear in the official list of duties but not in the title to avoid confusion with the DSR. Three months later he requested that his salary be reviewed as he had expected £1,700, the same as the DSR, but he was informed that £1,600 was a more likely figure: Watson Watt was not the type of person to accept such a final reply; he would raise the question again.

His promotion and move from BRS raised the question of his successor:

in ordinary circumstances Rowe would have been held to be too junior for the post as he had only recently been promoted to a Principal Scientific Officer. The Air Ministry Finance Branch had put forward the view that Rowe should take the post of Superintendent and retain his existing pay, with the addition of the rent free flat at BRS, but Freeman disagreed strongly with that proposal. His opinion was that Rowe should get Superintendent's pay, as there was much work of the utmost importance to be done at BRS during the next two or three years, and he did not think it would be commensurate with the dignity and the significance of the station that the Superintendent should be paid as a Principal Scientific Officer. (Wimperis was to write after the war that he appointed Rowe, a post graduate at the Imperial College, as his personal scientific assistant, and who gave such brilliant service that he had no hesitation in transferring him to work with the Tizard Committee and later as the Deputy Superintendent of BRS.)

The proposal for Rowe's accelerated promotion did not go unnoticed at the Treasury. An official wrote:

"The creation now imminent of a Directorate of Communications Development under the A.M.R.D. with the present Superintendent of B.R.S. in charge, leads me to ask whether the activities of the scientists will not in future be a facet of the field which that Directorate will cover, and whether in the circumstances the position of a Superintendent and a P.S.O will be essential. But we would like to know more of the oversight that Mr.Watson Watt will keep over B.R.S. if his transfer–this I think a bishop's move–be approved." [5]

A further communication followed in which the Treasury queried the scale of the Superintendent's post, claiming it was not comparable to that of either of the Superintendents at RAE Farnborough. This evoked the reply, which appeared to terminate the correspondence, that the activities of BRS were probably of far greater importance to the defence of the country than any work undertaken at Farnborough:

"...and is not too much to say that the successful working of the R.D.F. chain is entirely dependent upon the work at Bawdsey, and would double or treble the effective value of the Home Defence Air Force." [5]

The experiments of the interception of civil airliners had continued but results were disappointing at first because of the low rate of interception, just three in ten days, and were temporarily discontinued to discover the reasons. They were an accumulation of RDF equipment and telephone line failures, aircraft losing height as they approached the coast going below RDF cover or suddenly changing course with consequent loss of plot. In April it was reported to the Tizard Committee that interference was being caused by military aircraft flying from Manston and Eastchurch; Tizard insisted that the problem must be solved. Watson Watt mentioned the poor quality of RAF observers and raised the question of the employment of women. In May and June the interception exercises re-started with the RAF observers supervised by the BRS scientific staff and the flying around Eastchurch and Manston restricted for certain periods of the day to reduce the number of echoes on the screen.

The number of interceptions began to increase and proceeded with growing success; over the last four months fighters had sighted the target aircraft on three out of four occasions usually at a range of one mile or less; civil airliners were being intercepted with ease. The words to become most familiar in 1940 on the fighter aircraft radio telephone such as 'Angels', 'Tally Ho', 'Pancake' and others, were devised during this period. The rules were that essential R/T traffic had to be kept to a minimum so a simple code was introduced which had to be memorised and NOT carried in the aircraft.

These 'interceptions' and other civil and military flying highlighted the slowness of hand operations in extracting information from the tube and conversion into plots. One of the original Orfordness scientists, L. Bainbridge-Bell, was given the task of producing a machine, the first of which was mechanical and very noisy and was soon replaced by the Optical Converter. This was an ingenious device in which a high intensity spot light was directed onto a mirror that could be tilted along its axis in the horizontal and vertical planes by strings attached to the range and gonio knobs of the receiver; a spot of light shone on to a ground glass screen under a map that indicated directly the two co-ordinates. It was accepted that it would only be an interim device as it could not measure height and was only suitable for one wavelength as the bearing indications were tied to calibration amendments. The prototype was completed by April and was in use at Bawdsey by the end of July.

The RAF operators were able to find the bearing of large echoes with ease but for small echoes the gonio had to be swung over an arc to ascertain the minimum. Compared with the scientific officers the operators used a wider one that introduced errors; it was also apparent that they were taking insufficient plots to allow a decisive track to be assembled and the plotters were influenced by preceding ones. Rowe wrote on 8 June to Hart that;

"..the existing uncertainty as to whether Service personnel can be trained to use R.D.F. equipment cannot be allowed to continue longer than necessary. The performance of R.D.F. equipment in war is that of Service personnel trained over a long period. Mr. Wilkins has suggested that poor results have been obtained from Service personnel-scientific personnel can obtain good results with the same equipment, when Service personnel are tried again the results are as bad as ever." [6]

Hart replied that he was completely confident that Service personnel were now being trained to operate the apparatus satisfactorily for operational purposes. Squadron Leader Hart was, in modern parlance, the key interface man between the RAF and the civilian scientific staff at BRS; the ability of scientific officers to integrate themselves with high ranking RAF officers was of prime importance and took precedence over their scientific knowledge.

The belief that women would make better plotters and operators than men was claimed by Watson Watt and he gave his reasons in a letter to the DSR on 15 June:

"Some considerable time ago I made a verbal suggestion to A.M.R.D. that the recruitment of women for R.D.F. would be advantageous, and should be explored. A.M.R.D. agreed in principle.... the matter has not been advanced recently because we were studying the performance of service operators...but I now feel that the problem of women observers should be examined now. The main grounds on which we believe women would be specially suitable for the work are: (1) Higher power of sustained concentration on a limited field of observation devoid of 'entertainment value' (as in the R.D.F. indicator in the absence of targets) and lower liability to boredom in an unchanging routine. (2) Higher average finesse in relatively delicately setting of the light moving parts involved in making and communicating the observation. (3) Higher scale of general conscientiousness. (4) Lower average tendency to magnify individual importance by part disclosure of secrets specifically confided. (5) Longer period of individual availability for specialised duty in comparison with the normal posting of service personnel. (6) Release of manpower for duties for which women are not yet regarded as available. At least 600 would have to be trained..." [7]

Watson Watt proposed that three secretaries at BRS with knowledge of RDF secrets should be trained as observers at Bawdsey, then have a five day trial run at one of the estuary stations. Dowding, who thought that the original idea was Tizard's, was quite sympathetic to the experiment, Freeman had supported the idea from the beginning and the CAS was in favour of the proposal to enrol women in time of peace for training, as was the Secretary of State.

The existence of the BBC London television service may have jeopardised the secret of RDF. An article from the *New York Herald Tribune* dated 21 April was published in London two days later:

"Since television broadcasts have been in progress over London, it has been noted that when aircraft are flying in the vicinity there are ghost images in the television receivers caused by the reflection of the television waves from the metal aircraft surface. The reflected wave arrives at a slightly different time at the television receiver than the ordinary wave and the result is a dual image of the scene transmitted. The image of the plane is not received. Accordingly to

British reports the displacement of the ghost image has been correlated with the distance of the plane from the television set. A system has been worked out whereby television sets in England's eastern coast could serve as spotters for approaching enemy aircraft in time of war. Recently the British Air Ministry have ordered a number of television receivers for installation at strategic points along England's eastern coastline, and by operating them in unison and co-ordinating the shadow image caused in them by approaching aircraft, it is said to be possible not only to receive warning of enemy raids long before even the most sensitive listening devices could detect such a peril, but by triangulation to ascertain the direction and approximate speed of their approach. Experiments already conducted are said to have established that it is possible to detect the approach of a plane when it is still several hundred miles away." [8]

A letter dated 18 August on the detection of aircraft by using the television station had been sent to BRS from the War Office, which it had received from a Mr A. Scroggie:

"My experiments were carried out near Croydon and used... the London Television transmitter....By using a receiver that can be adjusted to balance out the direct reflection...it can be made extremely sensitive to stray reflected waves." [9]

To Watson Watt, Rowe commented:

"Mr. Scroggie appears to have been more intelligent than we like members of the public to be, and it is thought that he may be satisfied with the intimation that the possibilities of applying his observations have not been overlooked." [9]

The television transmissions had caused some unwelcome attention for BRS as there were sets being operated nearby by enterprising dealers, who were determined to show that the service was not confined to the London area. Mr R.J.Dippy, a young scientific officer, had written to Watson Watt on 11 October 1937:

"When looking for a radiogram cabinet in Ipswich on Saturday, I called in at 'West's' to see if they could supply me with one. Seeing cathode ray tubes in his shop, I remarked about them and asked him if he was the Mr West who had recently been receiving good signals of television, saying that I had found the reception of even the Medium Wave [radio] transmissions so bad at Bawdsey, that I wondered about the reception of television. He said immediately 'Oh, you are from Bawdsey are you ? What are you doing there?' and going on to say that he had picked us up [as we should expect] as a thin horizontal line on his 'frame'. He seemed quite definite about it being us who caused the interference- I neither denied it nor confirmed it, but hedged in the best manner. He asked if I could tell him the exact frequency on which we were working, as he wished to design a 'straight' set for his television reception, and saw no point in increasing the bandwidth if it meant merely picking up a good fat signal from us." [10]

Another dealer had a shop in Wickham Market, five miles north of Bawdsey, and he had written to the Post Office in February to complain of interference in the form of dots and dashes across the tube and he was blaming Bawdsey. The letter eventually arrived on Rowe's desk and a scientist was sent to see the owner and look at the interference. He saw two distinct types, one slight, just a couple of horizontal dots but the second one was more severe as the entire picture was almost blotted out. The scientist, unable to admit that BRS was the culprit, said that the interference might be due to harmonics from a nearby Post Office transmitter or due to an amateur Morse signal operator as the owner, a Mr. Cutting, had admitted that he had only blamed Bawdsey when he saw the towers. The scientist said that Bawdsey was an unlikely source of interference and, hopefully keeping a straight face, thought that they might be able to assist in tracing it. On returning to BRS he checked the times of the interference with the times of test transmissions and found that they coincided exactly, the TV light interference from a 12 metre transmitter and the severe interference from a 7 metre transmitter.

In 1937 there had been correspondence with the Post Office, which had been receiving numerous complaints of interference on the short wave bands with modulation frequencies of 40 to 60 cycles (Hertz), and it had been suggested that therapeutical apparatus was responsible. Watson Watt wrote a memo to his group leaders:

> "You will remember the story of a variable frequency emission of unusual modulation which jammed everybody approximately everywhere. It was explained away as due to elecro-therapy in the U.S.A., the frequencies changing due to the patient wriggling in his cage. It had been suggested that this explanation is a blind to cover something like R.D.F." [10]

There had been other forms of 'leakages'; an AOC was known to have stated in the open air at BRS and within audible range of a tower erecting crew of his demand for a range of 30 miles or more. A contractor employed in erecting the wooden towers was known to have said in Canada in 1937 that the timber for which he was negotiating was for radio towers that would enable German aircraft to be detected long before they arrived. An assistant on the BRS staff, while in a convalescent home, was told by a fellow patient that when working on a crane at RAF Felixstowe an airman had told him that the Bawdsey towers were for the detection of aircraft up to 100 miles.

Calibration of each station was necessary so that errors in direction and heightfinding arising from land contours and electrical mismatches were identified and used for corrections. It was the most frustrating part of the installation of each station but the most essential as plots were otherwise suspect and unreliable and could not be passed to the filter room. Before calibration the receiver array was checked to ensure that the signals from any pair of dipoles were in phase. This action was not favoured by BRS staff as the first interface box was outside at the 160ft tower level, but the remaining five were inside the building. Any work on the aerial system required another exercise of phasing and re-calibration to restore the station's accuracy; this took 50 hours to complete and during that time the station was non-operational. To calibrate the goniometer the aircraft had to be plotted circling as tightly as possible about 1,000ft above eight selected positions in a semi-circle in front of the station at a 20 mile range. For heightfinding the aircraft flew at particular heights and distances and returned on two or more specified bearings. The final overall check was for aircraft to fly and return for 50 miles at 5,000ft, 90 miles at 10,000ft and 120 miles at 15,000ft, on the Line of Shoot repeated at 30 degrees on either side. The tediousness of obtaining observations by aircraft is easily imagined: irritation often arose when in the middle of calibration the aircraft would report a fault and return immediately to base, bad weather intervened or sometimes the exercise was cancelled without warning.

The increase in the number of calibration and test flights was exhausting the capacity of Coastal Command to supply crews and aircraft; Watson Watt had wanted a special squadron to provide all the test and calibration aircraft but he was told that the RAF did not favour elitism. (There was Air Staff resistance to what was being referred to as Watson Watt's private air force.) The alternative of using a balloon had been submitted and during the summer of 1937 one fitted with a half wave dipole had given satisfactory echoes at a distance of 50 miles from the station at 5,000ft.

But there were limitations to using balloons in that Dowding would not allow their use if operated in cloud, and the Civil Aviation side of the Air Ministry wanted four days notice to prepare a NOTAM (Notice To Airmen). Concern was also expressed over what would be a widely distributed warning of balloon activity to all airliners approaching the coast, but it was understood that a NOTAM was not required if they were to be flown outside territorial waters. Rowe had advised Watson Watt in May of the painfully slow progress in calibration. So far only Bawdsey, out of the original five, had been calibrated on just one wavelength and he considered that the completion of 18 stations on four wavelengths would be an exacting and prodigious task. His only possible solution in terms of time and money would be to purchase a boat of about 4,000 tons with a speed of 12 knots and a crew of 18.

On 12 May, Swinton was called away from an Air Defence sub-committee meeting and with little formality dismissed by Prime Minister Chamberlain, who felt compelled to change the arrangement that he had to answer for the Air Minister in the House of Commons as Swinton was in the House of

Lords. A number of high government officials expressed their shock and dismay to him at the Prime Minister's action and the way it was done. There was deep regret that Swinton was leaving the Air Ministry having achieved almost the impossible in re-arming the Royal Air Force and defence against air attack. Freeman expressed his sorrow at the news and averred that success in the next war would be wholly and solely due to Swinton's foresight and driving power. Tizard wrote to Lord Swinton to convey his sadness at the news saying it was all due to him that the strength of the RAF was growing stronger every day and that he had been a real source of inspiration to all. Lord Weir, the architect of air power from 1914 and a trusted adviser to Swinton, resigned from the Air Council; Sir Kingsley Wood was appointed as the Secretary of State for Air on 17 May.

Works reported progress; the additional wooden towers were being erected at the estuary stations, four at Dunkirk, three at Great Bromley, two at Bawdsey and one at Dover and Canewdon. Further north the erection of four wooden towers was continuing at High Street, Staxton, Stoke Holy Cross and Stenigot and, on its own in the west, Ventnor. It was Dowding's task to organise the chain into operational control by Fighter Command with the main decision to be made on filtering; where was it to take place, should it be at sectors, or groups or at Stanmore, Fighter Command HQ? On that answer depended where the plotting lines from the CH stations would be terminated. In March the Post Office had advised Signals that failure to act quickly to place line orders might hold up commissioning of the whole chain.

In reply to the Air Staff's query about the delay, Dowding explained that he wanted to build up the telephone network from experience gained from the stations already in existence, to submit a complete plan rather than one built up piecemeal, which he thought would be uneconomic. To gain a little time he told the Air Staff that there was no reason why lines from the CH stations to the nearest telephone exchange, known as the 'local ends', could not be ordered immediately but by May this had been done and the Air Staff were writing again to urge Dowding into action. At a meeting that month he pointed out that, as there were only two stations at his disposal, it would not be easy to lay down the whole of future policy but, in view of the necessity for work to go ahead, he had come to the conclusion that all plots would have to be reported to the Filter Room at Stanmore.

The specified plot would then be 'told' to the Operations Room and repeated to the three groups and sectors. The Biggin Hill experiments had shown that sectors required information at the rate of one plot per minute. Dowding, who always considered the cost of telephone lines, was of the opinion that as plots would eventually be passed by teleprinters, further expense would be avoided if the main and standby plotting lines were routed to Stanmore via the nearest sector and group, which would also supply flexibility if lines to Stanmore were damaged by enemy action. The Post Office advised that standby lines could not be provided in peacetime as only when the war commenced would public telephone circuits be drastically reduced to allow Service needs to be met.

By July the equipment at Dover and Canewdon had been changed to 13 metres with new feeders and aerials providing bearing and height. Great Bromley and Dunkirk were in the process of installation. All this work had been carried out by the scientific and technical staffs at BRS that had resulted in a serious loss of research time. Like his predecessor, Rowe had repeatedly made requests for additional staff, especially scientific, but he had not been any more successful than Watson Watt, as the salaries offered were still low in comparison with commercial posts.

It was evident that the installation of another 13 stations could not be undertaken by BRS to the same extent as the five estuary stations, so in June the Air Ministry set up a unit on the same lines as was already in existence for the installation of major wireless stations, to be known as No 2 Installation Unit (2.IU) and at the same place, RAF Kidbrooke, London, SE3. This decision had the advantage that as a well organised workshop it was fully equipped with machines, stores and men to provide emergency repairs both mechanical and electrical. There can be no question that the rapidity of the early installation work was wholly dependent on the skill and expertise of those working at Kidbrooke where a blind eye to the rules was the rule rather than the exception.

On 9 August Squadron Leader W. Rose, the officer in charge of 2.IU, opened his office that had been 'found' by moving vehicles out of Shed 18. He had the mammoth responsibility of organising the manufacture of all the receiving, transmitting aerials and feeders for which there were no stores available or even ordered: equally acute was the recruitment of RAF and civilians for the installation work. The most immediate undertaking was the making of screened copper wire feeders for the receiving arrays that required 400 copper pipes in 22ft lengths, 400 straight, 100 elbow and 250 Tee couplings, 20 gross of assorted hardware and 1000ft of assorted lengths of creosoted red deal; dipoles were to be cut from 1¼ inch diameter 14 gauge brass tube. Subsequent installations required the raising of a major contract that included thousands of copper pipes, couplings and two million ceramic triangular insulating beads.

The Director of Contracts ruled that the RF5 receivers were not to be sent to the RAF equipment depots, as this would have widened the field of those who needed to know about RDF, but direct to Kidbrooke; strict instructions were issued that neither equipment nor documentation was to be seen or handled by any person other than those directly concerned with operations or installations. The ever growing volume of work that was placed on 2.IU from day one ensured that the unit would be permanently overworked and understaffed for the next seven years.

The Air Staff were expecting the whole chain to be in operation by the end of 1939 and to ensure that some form of operational service would be ready in the shortest possible time, they agreed that the aim should be for one steel and one wooden tower to be erected at each site by the end of November, with either a brick built receiver or transmitter building a month later. All the remaining towers and buildings were expected to be completed by August 1939 yet Works had advised that although a contract had been placed for 44 timber towers, there was only sufficient timber in the country for the completion of two, the remainder having to be imported from Canada (British Columbia).

The air to ground communication system between fighter aircraft and the sector controller had been gradually built up over the inter-war years. The requirements were planned at an annual conference where equipment and development were decided by RAE and the Directorate of Signals. The standard procedure was for a small trial to be made using hand-wired models followed by large scale re-equipping using production sets. The present radio was the single channel High Frequency (HF) band TR9, but RAE were developing, somewhat slowly, a set in the Very High Frequency (VHF) band; the Director of Signals was concerned at the delay.

During the summer of 1938 he was made aware of the existence of VHF in the Dutch Air Force that had been in use for over 18 months and obtained CAS approval for two Signals officers to make a 'semi-official' visit to their headquarters. They were surprised at the high quality of reception and the simplicity of the sets both on the ground and in the aircraft. But the formation of the DCD had removed the influence of the Director of Signals at RAE to supervision by Watson Watt, who made the comment that the Dutch set could not provide the number of channels, selectivity or stability required by the RAF. Moreover, he was aware that not only was the speech quality far superior to that of the HF band but also had the advantage that the transmission was virtually line of sight so it was not possible for the enemy to 'listen in', which was particularly important when speech information would be derived from RDF, and it was not possible for the transmissions to be jammed from distant transmitters, especially at night.

Jamming was an ugly word at BRS; it would defeat RDF if it was proved that it could be successfully applied by the enemy with very little effort. The 10 metre wavelength had ensured that jamming from distant ground based transmitters would be almost impossible (only correct, of course, if the enemy were not occupying the French coastline, a possibility that would not have been ever thought likely at that time), and 5 metres would ensure complete freedom leaving only the possibility of airborne transmissions.

Narrow band jamming would not be effective but nothing was known about the effect of a spark transmitter that emitted a very wide band of frequencies. To test the theory that the chain was immune to deliberate jamming from the ground, a spark transmitter was installed at Orfordness and connected to a simple dipole stretched across the top of the 250ft guyed masts. On 14 January two test runs were made with a London flying boat with the transmitter switched on for the second one. The receivers at Great Bromley and Canewdon were able to operate through the jamming, but the Bawdsey receiver just ten miles away suffered severely. Operationally this was not too prohibitive as the echo was visible through the interference and could be reduced considerably by turning the gonio to the direction of Orfordness. In May another test flight was arranged; this time a London flying boat was carrying a transmitter set to emit interrupted continuous wave transmissions. Flying at a height of 3,000ft at a distance of 50 miles from the coast the receiver was jammed at all three stations, but this was not quite as serious as it appeared to be, as turning the gonio to the bearing of the aircraft the effect was considerably curtailed.

Another factor that decreased the effectiveness was that continuous wave emission was not phase locked to the echo seen on the screen. The display continued to show the slow moving echo but with the jamming clearly identified as a constantly moving pattern. BRS were convinced that the answer to the reduction in the effect of interference, natural or deliberate, lay within the cathode ray tube screen material, which would respond strongly to a succession of indications that appeared in the same place, the echo, but to a much reduced extent if the trace varied randomly, the interference.

When Watson Watt was at the NPL he was very interested in the operation of cathode ray tubes and had tested the effect of various screen powders under electron bombardment. Apart from the different colours that were produced such as blue and green, the duration of the colour when the electron bombardment ceased varied tremendously. The afterglow, as it is termed, was very short for blue, of medium duration for green and very long for red. One of the many possibilities being discussed and tried at BRS was the use of a cathode ray tube with a very long afterglow, when the wanted echo would appear as a black patch against a coloured background. On 2 September Rowe wrote to Tizard:

"...[it is] extremely important to obtain a C.R.T. with afterglow. Cossors have a research contract but their whole approach to the matter is extremely disappointing. A real brainwave is needed and you promised to raise the matter in hopeful quarters." [11]

Within a very short time Tizard replied that he had written to Thomas Merton, who was Professor of Spectroscopy at Oxford University, and he had made the following remarks:

"I very much doubt whether your problem with an afterglow with electron excitement can be solved in one step – but is there any objection in doing it in two stages? I did some experiments with this a good many years ago and my belief is that most of the afterglow due to electronic excitement is a secondary effect, that is a photo-phosphorescence caused by the light emitted when the electronic excitation is on. If this is correct then it would be almost a miracle if a single substance did all you required of it. Is there any objection to a sandwich? Both materials, that is electron fluorescence and photo-phosphorescence have been brought to a high degree of efficiency, the former of course used in television tubes... Could you not have on your screen a very thin sheet of mica coated on one side with electron fluorescent powder and the other side with photo-phosphorescent powder or better still embed the photo-phosphorescent powder in a varnish of sodium silicate and then coat the varnish with the electron fluorescent powder. Would you let me know if I can be of any use, it is the kind of problem that I rather like." [11]

Rowe replied to Tizard:

"I am having a detailed investigation made of Merton's suggestion but what ever happens I have got quite a kick out of this line of thought. I do not know whether any small snag will arise, but at the moment it all looks very simple." [11]

The idea was communicated to the General Electric Company (GEC) and a sample was quickly produced; it became known as the anti-jamming (AJ) tube and in use was supplemented with coloured glass filters. The jamming signal that was fast moving only activated the first layer, a quick delay phosphor producing a blue colour whereas the wanted signal, the echo, very slow moving, activated both layers producing a yellow colour. Viewing the tube through a yellow filter blocked the blue colour of the interference allowing the colour of the echo to be clearly seen. In practice the double layer tube proved to be supreme over all other methods to reduce interference to a level that allowed the operators to work through although at reduced efficiency. It was the first tube, one of many, that was specifically designed for RDF. (A claim was made by Cossor after the war that they had invented the anti-jamming tube and were eligible for financial payment, but their work had been based on the use of mixtures, not layers. Professor Thomas Merton (later Sir Thomas) was the acknowledged inventor.)

The Air Ministry had already selected MetroVick and Cossor for the manufacture of 20 sets for the CH chain but the War Office were intending to order nearly 600 GL sets. The Tizard Committee was uncertain about the capacity of the radio industry to manufacture such large quantities of high class professional equipment and, at its request, an investigation was made by the DSIR, which found that the components industry as such was made up of a large number of small firms with virtually no research facilities. The bulk of electrolytic capacitors came from Holland and France, silver mica capacitors from Germany, paper capacitors and resistors from Austria. All high stability cracked carbon resistors were imported from Germany and Italy; the German imports ceased in September 1939 but those from Italy continued until its declaration of war against the United Kingdom and France in June 1940. By that time, however, English firms had copied the Italian technique and were able to maintain supplies.

The inquiry had also ascertained that radio receiving valves, which would be the limiting factor in quantity manufacture of equipment, were produced by only a few firms with no research departments and almost exclusively for the domestic radio receiver market at the rate of 12 million a year plus half a million for government contracts. It was safe to assume that in the event of a war the total capacity would be more than adequate for the Services. But the supply of transmitting valves from the Admiralty was barely sufficient for the Air Ministry and the radio valve industry would have to be involved to meet the demand. The conclusion of the investigation was that there appeared to be no reason why industry could not provide high grade electronic equipment for RDF purposes.

The supply of cathode ray tubes is of interest because of a questionable post-war story that the British television service was hastened into the public domain by the government, not for entertainment, but for British manufacturers to become familiar with large scale cathode ray tube production. Without that experience they would not have been able to keep the radar sets coming for the Battle of Britain. The London TV service was opened in November 1936 and by October 1937 only the equipment for 20 CH stations had been ordered that would have required no more than 100 tubes including spares. The point must be made that the Air Staff then considered the chain to be complete and without the need for further expansion. But what was of great benefit was the wide bandwidth video section of the TV receiver for which a new type of valve had been developed. A commercial chassis was found ideal for the experimental AI set for amplification after frequency conversion and was subsequently known as the '45 Meg (MHz) I.F. strip'. Without this technical bonus from the TV service, the development of AI and ASV sets would have been seriously delayed.

From 5-7 August a Home Defence exercise involving over 900 aircraft was held to defend a line of defence against attack from the east, stretching from Lincoln to the Thames Estuary. To introduce a feeling of realism a number of 'firsts' were introduced by Dowding; the Observer Corps posts and centres were fully manned as well as the operations rooms, with the air raid warning system tested to certain RAF aerodromes and the five estuary stations working into the BRS Filter Room. Not only was the exercise for the development of the art of interception but also to test the feasibility of identifying the friendly from the enemy bomber. After a number of ideas had been put forward, tried and discarded, there was final acceptance that the only workable way of identifying returning bombers was for the aircraft to transmit a half minute signal to Fighter Command direction finding stations. The exercise opened under very adverse wireless conditions, with continuous thunderstorms producing excessive atmospherics and the D/F stations experiencing great difficulty in receiving signals.

During the whole of the first 24 hours only one aircraft was heard, but many bomber radios were off-tune, the half minute transmission was found to be too short and was extended to three minutes with a perceptible improvement. Despite the electrical storms, which played so much havoc with radio communications, they did not seriously affect the range and accuracy of the RDF plots and it was very evident that RDF was essential for the identification of friendly aircraft. Dowding agreed that RDF had worked remarkably well although there were the known difficulties in the interception of low flying aircraft; he was of the opinion that the full scale of the problem would not be apparent until stations were stretched from Dover to Fife (Scotland). He also commented on the fact (but without expanding) that certain deficiencies in personnel had been perceived particularly in the senior ranks. During the exercise the BRS Filter Room was manned by the RAF and supervised by scientific officers, who reported:

> "Filtering apparently [is] still an art rather than a science, many filtered plots giving the impression of being inspired, but in the main were confirmed by subsequent plots. In a few cases a plot was obviously wrong...[and] only slowly corrected...[but] should improve when larger echoes are available...." [12]

During August, a discussion had arisen at the Air Ministry on whether the secret of RDF should be revealed to the Americans. Watson Watt was against disclosure but thought that a statement should be made in Parliament. It would convey that experiments on the detection of aircraft approaching our shores had been remarkably successful, that science had achieved something which science could not yet counter, that a chain of detecting stations was now in course of erection around our coasts and that the vulnerable parts were being quadrupled to make them safe from being put out of action by enemy bombing. Added Watson Watt:

"The deterrent effect on a potential enemy of such an open announcement would, I believe, be great." [8]

There was a short answer from the CAS:

"The release of information to the U.S.A. or the British public as proposed is quite unacceptable." [8]

The need for a mobile set had arisen from the early days at Orfordness to provide a second line of chain stations or to plug gaps in the RDF cover caused by enemy damage, and the likely replacement for the Observer Corps.

The basic Orfordness transmitter was the starting point; Dr Bowen had reduced the pulse width and improved stability, with further development undertaken by the Army group for a 30 mile maximum range and all-round looking. As pulse output power is basically dependent on valve emission, the Admiralty had been asked to provide a triode with an increased filament diameter, and although their DSR was aware of the use of the valves by BRS, he was not allowed to communicate that fact to the valve designer. The valve was the NT57 with a filament rating of 15.2 volts, 48 amps, that gave, in a pair, a maximum pulse output power of 50kW at 13 metres. Transmitter research had continued towards lower wavelengths which required the use of tetrode valves; the Admiralty produced the NT60X with a bright emitter tungsten filament rating of 130 amps at 18 volts and, for a pair, 80kW of pulse power at 5 metres. The lowest wavelength was 3 metres set by the mechanical design; a more practical aspect was that silica envelopes were not suitable for mass production.

On 18 August BRS sent to MetroVick a TM1 transmitter for prototype production as a single channel mobile, the MB1, and five months later BRS reported that it was superior in all respects to their model; 12 were ordered before the approval date to cover the possible late arrival of the CH transmitter. MetroVick used the same basic frameworks and power supplies for all types that would follow, only the output power, wavelength and pulse aspects being different. The finished product was instantly recognisable and dubbed by RAF and Army mechanics as 'fish and chip fryers' or 'upright pianos' that they closely resembled.

In early August it became clear to Works that the money allocated for the building of the chain was insufficient mainly due to the increased cost of the 350ft steel towers and the extra protection for the operational buildings.

Treasury approval was required and although it was plain that it was a mere formality, it required a well thought out 'case' in order to escape criticism that the original application (for which no doubt the Treasury would have passed whatever the cost), was inadequately prepared. On 16 August Watson Watt wrote to the Head of the Finance Branch a major memo of which the following is a précis: The cost of each steel tower had exceeded the original estimate of £3,250 by an additional £3,000 to ensure that the steel transmitting towers would be of sufficient strength to resist bombing attacks and, if struck, not easily demolished. The 350ft height would support much more complex aerial arrays than at first envisaged and these would increase the accuracy and working range of the stations. The other substantial cost was for the transmitter building, which was to be of a greater size, because when the first estimate was made the dimensions of the transmitter were unknown. There was also provision to be made for the possibility of the addition of bulky apparatus as a safeguard against deliberate enemy interference and the standby power building was to be separated from the transmitter block on the grounds of vulnerability. It was essential that there was no extensive rebuilding that would be expensive and compromise secrecy.

The Air Staff had recently ordered that all permanent buildings were to be protected and gas proofed, all of which had added substantially to the cost. Watson Watt pointed out that the wartime effectiveness of the chain would be greater as the 18 stations now proposed would give better cover from Portsmouth to the Tay than the 20 station estimate covering Portsmouth to the Tees. He argued that if the original estimate was adhered to then there would be a serious risk of restricting further improvements in operational efficiency that were bound to flow from continued research. If the Air Staff requirements on dates were to be met then an immediate decision on the revised estimate was required.

The Head of Finance wrote to the DCAS on 22 August commenting on the immense increase of £381,750 for a revised design layout and measures for rendering the stations less liable to be put out of action by enemy aircraft which, rightly or wrongly, were not embraced in the original scheme. It was expected that before agreeing to the heavy increase in costs submitted, the Treasury:

> "is bound to ask for an assurance that there is no doubt as to the value of the scheme and that the additional increases are not only desirable but essential." [13]

Finance received a reply the following day from the DCAS:

> "R.D.F. is a vital component of Fighter Defence of this country... I am prepared to say that the additional measures are essential." [13]

By 12 September an Air Ministry memo had been prepared, submitted to the Treasury and approved without comment on the 20th.

When Works received replies for the supply and erection of 24 steel towers from each of three tendering firms, the Radio Communications Company (RCC), Blaw Knox and J.L. Eve Construction, the Air Ministry design was priced at around £9,500, some £3,250 higher than their own. The three sets of towers were of a slight, but noticeably different construction to one another with weights of 94, 100 and 86 tons each.

Germany had re-occupied the Rhineland in March 1936 and two years later had marched into Austria. Her aggressive intentions were made clear in September when she began to make threatening noises to annexe the Sudetenland, the German speaking province of western Czechoslovakia. Known as the Munich Appeasement Crisis, the nation was brought to the brink of war, which was only averted after a number of visits by the then Prime Minister, Neville Chamberlain, to the German Chancellor, Adolf Hitler, and solved by the agreement that Germany could take the province. With Hitler saying 'I have no more territorial demands to make in Europe' and with Chamberlain returning to Heston aerodrome, waving a piece of paper in his hands to the assembled news cameramen, and his 'I believe that it is peace in our time' speech, there was tremendous relief by the British public that war had been permanently avoided. There were many people who believed him, but there were murmurs of a 'sell-out', and those who had read the signs correctly knew that it was only a short breathing space before the outbreak of another war with Germany, the second within 20 years.

The Treasury were aware of all the heavy expenditure that would be needed for war but there was no question of an open cheque book; a nod from the Treasury Secretary at a meeting was only an agreement in principle, a formal application being necessary. On 17 September, the day after the first visit of Chamberlain to Hitler, the Air Ministry acted:

> "I am commanded by the Air Council to request that you will lay before the Lords Commissioners...the following proposal to provide a permanent operations block for the Headquarters of Fighter Command...at Bentley Priory [Stanmore]....A suitable site has been selected...and the works services...are estimated to cost £45,000. The Council are desirous of proceeding with this essential and urgent provision at an early date and I am to request that you will be good enough to move Their Lordships to accord their sanction as soon as possible...." [14]

A reply followed six days later:

> "In reply I am to ask you to inform the Council that ...My Lords sanction the execution of the work involved at a cost not exceeding £45,000..." [14]

One fear of the government was the possibility of an unannounced air attack on London by Germany and one of the many urgent measures adopted was the placing of the five estuary stations on a 24 hour watch, which remained in force until May 1945. Instructions were also issued for the installation of 'Advance' CH (ACH) stations at Ventnor, High Street, Stenigot, Stoke Holy Cross and Pevensey. These stations consisted of a transmitter and receiver, each in a wooden hut behind 90ft guyed wooden masts to support the aerials, with power supplied by a mobile generator. Dowding, upon whom rested the responsibility for ensuring that enemy aircraft approaching the coast would be attacked, asked for three extra ACH stations to be installed immediately to cover the Firth of Forth, Tyne Tees and the Humber areas. There were suitable CH sites already purchased nearby at Drone Hill and West Beckham in addition to the site already acquired at Ravenscar but discarded in favour of Danby Beacon. At the Air Ministry the files containing instructions for telephone lines, Works services and RAF personnel to operate and guard the sites, were marked VERY URGENT TO BE PASSED BY HAND.

On 17 September, the order was given for BRS to proceed with three 'Advance' installations and, due to the gravity of the political situation, to requisition the Mobile Base (MB) equipment that was being prepared for Aden and Malta. As there was not sufficient time for Works to complete competitive contract action for the 90ft tower footings, standard RAF 70ft steel guyed masts were supplied for the transmitter aerials, and a single 75ft 'Merryweather' wooden tower, which was part of the Mobile Base station, for the receiving aerials. 2.IU obtained special authority to order six 20ft by 20ft wooden huts from the Lewisham Timber Company for the receivers and transmitters.

On Thursday 22 September the first scientific officer from BRS arrived at Drone Hill to discuss with the local Works officer on how a four ton truck with a five ton load was expected to reach the site without an access road; he was promised that plenty of stones would be available for Saturday. The next day was spent with the assistance of seven riggers, who had arrived from 2.IU, in siting and digging the mast footings so that the aerials faced a specific direction, Borkum in the German Heligoland, from which, it was expected, would be the direction of an attack. On Saturday morning the trailer from 2.IU with the 70ft guyed masts had arrived, but the BRS diesel truck could only manage the steep slope when half the load had been removed. It was not until 2330 that all the equipment was on site.

Sunday was spent on erecting the huts, masts and aerials plus the 'Merryweather' receiver tower that had arrived with nine riggers from BRS.

The tower was no easy item to erect as it weighed over two tons, and was supported by eight bottle-jack feet on a 16ft square base. By Tuesday all the heavy work had been completed and the Kidbrooke riggers left the site to proceed to Ravenscar, where by Thursday the station was ready to be handed over to a small RAF detachment, who found themselves living in tents and surrounded by barbed wire. From Ravenscar the riggers travelled south to West Beckham where all went well until the weekend, when it rained all day on Sunday, which delayed the erection of the aerials until Monday, and then that evening a gale blew up that lifted the roof of the transmitter hut. The scientific staff had a desperate time to rouse the riggers from their lodgings, find a farmer with spare tarpaulins and make the transmitter hut wind and waterproof. The next day the wind increased to such force that guy ropes had to be anchored across both huts.

When the installations were completed Drone Hill reported a single aircraft 30 miles at 7,000ft but it was thought that the range would be substantially greater over the sea, possibly 60 miles. Before Ravenscar could be air tested a gale on the night of 4/5 October so badly damaged the receiver tower that it had to be lowered to the ground, as were the transmitter masts, to repair the aerials. The tower was found to be unrepairable on site but when 90ft guyed wooden masts were installed, a range of 80 miles at 10,000ft could be expected. At West Beckham only a 30 miles range at 10,000ft was possible due to the low level of the site.

The 'Merryweather' tower, designed by a firm making fire brigade extension ladders, was one of Watson Watt's ill-fated attempts to hasten the progress of mobile RDF: it was never used again and its early failure perhaps showed that the conservative approach of Works to tower stability was the correct one. Of technical interest is that for Advance CH stations the action of 'sense' was moved from the receiver to the transmitter aerial. The reflector was normally 'open circuit' so that power was radiated equally front and back but for 'sense' the reflector was made active so reducing the back and increasing the forward radiation; the effect on the echo was identical to that with receiver aerial switching.

Telephone plotting lines from the three sites went direct to an emergency room at Stanmore, which acted in advance of the move of the filter room from BRS and with it the closing of the episcope experiments using a vertical screen. There had been progress; the Secretary of State had seen a demonstration, which looked promising to such a degree, that Dowding had suggested that a large scale experiment be attempted. The RAF filterers perhaps had ideas of their own as the scientific officer conducting the experiments reported 'that some difficulty was being experienced in obtaining enthusiastic co-operation.'

A report in November on Drone Hill noted that there was no great progress in road making and no sign of the electricity supply:

"Both will prove difficult to complete with the bad weather coming on. It will be impossible to get to the site in winter if the road is not available soon [as] there are not enough men on it and they stop when it rains. The existing road is so bad that it has been necessary to trespass over sown ground and the Crossley lorry has seriously offended in this respect and the farmer has reported the damage to the Air Ministry. The present huts have steel hawsers fitted over the roofs to prevent gales from lifting the roofs. Scientific staff have to use gumboots, Mackintoshes, blue overalls or s'westers." [15]

Following the installation of these three stations, instructions were given to Works to accelerate the Advance CH stations at Ventnor, Pevensey, High Street, Stoke Holy Cross and Stenigot and to ensure that at least one wooden 240ft tower was completed so as to take both receive and transmit arrays, or that 90ft guyed masts could be erected.

The government took the opportunity offered by the Munich Crisis to order all civil and Service departments to report on the effectiveness of their war preparations and, like all the others, the Air Ministry was far from complete, a tribute to years of political ineptitude. The summary of shortcomings could only emphasise the point that in September 1938, it would have been very unlikely for hostilities to have commenced anywhere with any chance of success.

There were only nine satellite airfields ready from a total of 63 required, only 17 direction finding stations completed from 48 approved, of 11 operations rooms under construction none was complete, bomber squadrons down by 38%, reserve bombers down by 89%, reserve fighters down by 98% and the Observer Corps down by 32%.

Only 140 barrage balloons were available from 450 required for London, many sites had not been selected, with hydrogen supplies and men down by 65%. There was a pressing need to enlarge aerodromes too small for modern fighters, there were no Vickers light anti-aircraft guns, searchlights down by 65% and long range anti-aircraft guns down by 85%. The CH chain of which 18 stations were approved had five that were incomplete, five Advance stations under construction plus three Mobiles. There was no Post Office 'ring' cabling around London.

One of many decisions taken by the Air Staff to increase war readiness was to bring forward the chain completion date from 31 December 1939 to 1 April 1939, just seven months away. Watson Watt chaired a meeting on 5 October to discuss the emergency measures required to meet the new timetable. He was of the opinion that the stations could be completed, but uncalibrated, by that time, provided compulsory powers for taking up the sites were applied without any further delay, and that the manufacturers of the steel towers should work on a 24 hours basis in workshops and in erection, with the same for the technical and electrical equipment makers. Financial approval had to be sought immediately for the various works required:

"In particular the Director of Works must be granted the absolute freedom of action to organise and complete the necessary works services involved. It must be accepted as a principle that the needs of security outweigh financial considerations in so far as the R.D.F. chain is concerned." [16]

It was not now possible to adhere to the original arrangement for one wooden tower, one steel tower and one brick building at each site; the only way to meet the new deadline would be for all stations to be taken to the Intermediate stage, ie, two wooden towers with a hut at the base for the equipment. The Director of Works, upon whom the greatest burden was falling, wrote on 18 October to his superior, the Air Member for Supplies and Organisation (AMSO):

"Immediate permission is required for approval to instruct all contractors...to proceed by continuous day and night work until completion. Naturally, increased costs will require Permanent-Under-Secretary [P.U.S.] approval. Authority to dispense with normal contract procedure requires Secretary of State approval. Authority to arrange during course of work by what ever method appears suitable and quick, despite cost any further work that may be necessary also requires P.U.S. approval." [17]

On 1 November the PUS intimated that he was ready to render what assistance he could and on 9 November when the papers were ready, he sent them to the First Deputy Secretary with a note – 'Will you kindly give this a hearty shove.'

The new schedule also brought the question of calibration once more to the forefront and the Air Ministry approved in principle the chartering of two diesel engine vessels. The search began for suitable ships but it was not until November that the SS '*Ialine*' was chartered and modifications made to the vessel to take balloon and technical equipment followed by the SS '*Recovery of Leith*'. Exception was taken to the word 'dipole' appearing in non- secret papers; officials were told the word was dangerous for security and must not be used. In December it was considered that the purchase of boats would be cheaper than chartering so an application for the sum of £30,000 was made to the Treasury, which was advised that because it had been assumed that the RAF were supplying aircraft for calibration, there was no previous application for finance. The Treasury official, in giving his approval, added in his letter that the Estimates Committee in the past had always shown itself vigilant and critical on the subject of the ownership of fleets by Service departments other than the Admiralty:

"The War Office fleet has received a lot of attention on this account and we would
prefer, if possible, not to add to our troubles in this respect by giving the committee
an R.A.F. fleet as well as the War Office to shoot at !" [18]

The SS '*Ialine*' was found inadequate for the task and was returned to her
owners and another vessel, the MV '*Miss Elaine*' together with the '*Recovery
of Leith*' were purchased and arrangements made for calibration work to start
in January 1939.

One of Watson Watt's own ideas in his memorandum of the 12 February 1935
was that there would be provision for distinguishing on the tube face between
friend and foe, but no immediate action could be taken due to the shortage of
staff. It was not until December 1937 that Wilkins was approached by the Army
group to assist them in identifying test aircraft when GL trials were under way.
His first attempt was to fit a 6.8 metre wavelength dipole underneath the
undercarriage of an Anson aircraft that would increase the echo and, to ensure
that it would be noticed, the dipole was electrically 'broken' by a motor driven
cam that caused it to flash; at five miles the height was doubled. The experiment
was repeated on a flying boat and was so successful that Dowding wanted it
adopted immediately, regarding it as one of the most important developments
of its kind at that moment and, if successful, would obviate the cumbersome
system of identification by direction finding and letters of the day.

But Wilkins was able to convince Dowding that the use of external dipoles
was too restrictive in that only a narrow band of frequencies could be used, and
resolving the aerodynamic problems would impose an unacceptable waiting
time – it would be better to wait for a more efficient apparatus. He advised
Rowe that the beating of echoes from a formation of aircraft would mask the
changes of signal strength produced by simple dipole keying. Wilkins put
forward two outstanding innovations for improvement; the first was power
amplification of the retransmitted pulse that would increase the range of the
received echo, and the second that there was the possibility that the aircraft
structure could be 'tapped' to act as an aerial.

The subject of Identification Friend or Foe (IFF) had been discussed by a
Tizard Committee meeting held at BRS, the minutes showing that the meeting
had continued subsequently in a First Class carriage on the train back to London.
Tizard had reminded the committee of the dangers inherent in the fitting of
special aerials to bombers since if they were shot down over enemy territory
the method of identification would probably be divulged and copied.

Again it was Tizard who had seen into the future. As early as 1936 he had urged
the development of a rotating beam, but he had to agree with Watson Watt that
'floodlighting' had to take precedence. But some theoretical work was done at

BRS and using a wavelength of 4 metres as recommended by Tizard, calculations showed that a 6 degree beam width needed 500 elements covering 120 square feet. That was certainly impracticable, but not at 1.5 metres the wavelength in use by Dr Bowen for his airborne set. One such set had been assembled on the platform of one of the 240ft towers at BRS and another had been constructed, at a later date, as a mobile using Yagi transmit and receive aerials with a telescope as a visual aid for direction finding. Tizard had recorded in his diary on 30 May:

"Beam technology developing rapidly, the detection of ships up to five miles away with a 1 metre wavelength quite satisfactory. It seemed to me that the system could be developed for shorter waves and therefore detecting aircraft at a greater distance. Watson Watt agreed that more effort should be put into this." [19]

A further entry on 1 September was prophetic:

"On CH, the possibility of jamming and the exposed nature of the stations renders them liable to concerted attack. For these reasons I am still very much in favour of developing the very short wave beam system as a standby. It may replace the broadcasting system in the end." [19]

The possibility that the Army's need for Coast Defence could be met by using RDF had already occurred to Dr Paris when he saw the report of ships being detected by Dr Bowen's 1.5 metre AI set in 1937, but the War Office declined to provide the additional research staff then as GL work was more important. In the meantime pulse power had increased from 5 watts to 1 kilowatt with destroyers' echoes seen at four miles and those from aircraft seen at 16 miles over the sea and 12 miles over land. But the echo was liable to fading and the bearing accuracy of ±5 degrees was not reliable so a contract was raised on MetroVick for a higher power transmitter. Dr Paris again urged the War Office for the CD research work to be accelerated and after the usual bureaucratic delay, a small team arrived at BRS in October from ADEE headed by the scientific officer in charge, Mr W.A.S. Butement, with a brief to design a CD set with radio direction finding of accuracy sufficient to enable a searchlight to be directed on the target. Two to three degrees was adequate as there was no need for the high accuracy required for fire control of coastal guns.

Hart had obtained the approval of Dowding to organise another series of interception trials using a single fighter and bomber, not from a sector operations table as were the Biggin Hill experiments, but direct from the Bawdsey CH station. Known as the 'Lamb' experiments because the hostile aircraft was known as 'Mary' and the nursery rhyme said that 'everywhere that Mary went the lamb was sure to go'. They were conducted by Squadron Leader J.A.Tester during October/November with the interceptions taking place some 25 to 30 miles out to sea. He sat at the tube face and had the demanding and fatiguing task of tracking both aircraft by taking separate readings of range, bearing and height and operating the R/T to the fighter.

The experiments were not successful because of the inherent failings of the early equipment to provide coherent plots, the limitations in range and quality of the aircraft HF radio and the lack of fighter identification on the tube. Dowding insisted that they be repeated at a later date for, with Hart, he saw the great advantage of interception from the tube face – the plotting of tracks was eliminated and was a pointer to what would be needed in the future for night interception.

Rowe received notification of two 'leaks' in newspapers that required official action. At Ventnor, on the Isle of Wight, the progress of the station became public knowledge with the issue on 3 November of the local newspaper *The Isle of Wight Chronicle* under the heading of 'Pylons on Wroxall Downs':

"Public speculation as to the reason behind the erection of a steel pylon on Wroxall Downs, immediately above Ventnor station has increased since a second pylon has arisen by its side. Such government activities are not always an open secret, and consequently public opinion on the use to which these pylons will be put have varied considerably. We are given to understand, however, that they are aeroplane sound detectors for locating aircraft. Their advent is not a result of the recent crisis because the concrete foundations, which are sunk many feet into the ground, were commenced about a year ago... the site will become a conspicuous landmark for we understand that two more pylons are to be erected. The height is said to be about 150-200ft." [20]

A second breach of the 'D' notice was incurred by *The Times*, which received an official warning for its issue on 15 November, when it reported a speech headlined 'Britain Prepared for Raiders' that made reference to the RDF chain.

To meet complaints that RAF operators had not seen more than nine aircraft echoes, Watson Watt had arranged in November for 24 aircraft to fly from Orfordness to the North Hinder Light Vessel and back again in squadron line astern and repeated in flight line astern. The responses were distinctive with good direction finding. A second run of 18 Blenheims gave different echoes from the 24 aircraft as they were flying in close formation – three echoes were resolved with rapid beating; both displays were filmed. The exercises confirmed what was already known that counting was more an art than a science and depended entirely on the estimation of the operator and solely on his experience.

Squadron Leader Hart reported on training that had taken place with civil aircraft; at Dover, Dunkirk, Great Bromley and Canewdon a considerable density of air traffic permitted airmen to be under instruction almost continuously from 0900 until sometimes late at night. This watch was the chief asset since it was impossible to fulfil the operator course at Bawdsey. For stations in the north, substitute Service aircraft were provided and two Blenheim aircraft were on loan, a temporary arrangement to be replaced by a permanent establishment of four Blenheim 1Es and two 1Rs at Martlesham. At least two runs a day were required. Hart had earlier appealed for apparatus that could produce simulated echoes as no operational equipment could be spared; it reveals the difficulties in preparing Service personnel for war.

Asked in November to prepare notes on the history of BRS, Rowe added a number of unusual factors:

> "The discovery of R.D.F. was at least five years too late for its ordered development, thus every single member of the scientific and technical staff is engaged on emergency work....Several millions of pounds are being spent on it and the change of policy to the production of fighters rather than bombers (so mysterious to Aeronautical Press correspondents) is largely associated with the discovery of R.D.F....In the midst of almost panic measures to develop and produce R.D.F. equipment, research must be kept alive, not only for the next war but for the one after and the one after that..." [21]

There were eventually a number of RDF Committees dealing with small or large aspects, the first of which was on the recommendation of Watson Watt, who was concerned that the War Office and the Admiralty should not act independently. It was known as the InterServices RDF Committee to co-ordinate research and development, examine progress, recommend relative priorities for research and development, applications and production. The first meeting in November identified the various types:

(a) CH   – range 130 miles at 10,000ft better than ½ mile, bearing within 1 degree, height dependent on range. Blind angles of elevation to be filled in by aerials (gap fillers), provision against jamming from aircraft only, mitigated by several wavelengths. Detection of raids, formations of 10-12 aircraft plotted.

(b) IFF   – mechanical/ electronic devices.

(c) MB   – 70ft towers, range 30 miles at 10,000ft, 50kW peak pulse output.

(d) CD   – ships 1,000 tons+ detected 8 miles, suitable for production.

(e) GL   – frequency range 40.5 – 58 Mc/s (MHz). In war would require closure of the London TV service.

Although the committee failed to prevent the War Office and the Admiralty from organising their own research establishments in the following year, the meetings continued and were instrumental in implementing common operational requirements that ensured great economy in the use and supply of airborne and ground equipment. Watson Watt held the view that the Army CD and GL sets should be manned by the RAF on the grounds of security. He was concerned that the secrecy of RDF would be compromised if Army personnel were allowed to operate the equipment but the ACAS did not agree. In a memo to the DCAS he added:

> "The argument adduced by Mr. Watson Watt is the old one of security. He is afraid that the secrecy of R.D.F. would be compromised if we allowed Army

personnel to handle the apparatus. This strikes me as a very weak argument...
there is no fundamental reason why an Army signaller in a khaki uniform should
be less secretive than a R.A.F. W/T operator in a blue uniform." [22]

A letter from Works on 17 November to BRS hinted at hold-ups to come:

"At Ottercops Moss....the weather and ground conditions on the exposed site
are already so adverse that it is doubtful how much longer the workmen can be
induced to continue." [23]

At the beginning of December it began to appear at BRS that the April
deadline would not be met and their letter to DCD on 2 December
emphasised that;

"...one major defection on part of the Contractors, No. 2.I.U., of Works, of this
establishment, or Signals will lead to failure to conform to the schedule. There
is no margin and there is no time in which to recruit and train additional
personnel to make good the loss of time involved in any major departure from
the enclosed schedule. Moreover... no margin for exceptionally bad weather,
for more than the average sick list or for other acts of God...unless towers and
huts are erected on the dates specified...completion date is impossible." [24]

Works, which had also received a copy of the letter, replied a few days later
that all possible acceleration regarding the construction of the towers had
already been done and remarked that huts had not been requested. Rowe
too, added his doubts to DCD in a letter of 15 December 'that all acceleration
had been done' and suggested;

"[that] there must be many methods of dealing with the situation short of the
heroic one of erection by the Royal Engineers throughout 24 hours using
floodlighting at night....Important researches have been stopped and intensive
effort has been demanded on the staff." [24]

On 9 December a concerned Director of Works wrote to RAE:

"The delay in receiving final drawings [for the T and R blocks] is causing
considerable anxiety in view of the fact that the building contracts at 14 of
these sites have now been let out, and the contractors have started work on the
foundations." [17]

REFERENCES

1	AVIA7/267	2	AIR2/2685	3	AVIA7/231	4	AIR2/2709
5	AIR2/2663	6	AVAI7/437	7	AIR2/3323	8	AIR2/4487
9	AVIA7/1	10	AVIA7/418	11	AVIA7/428	12	AVIA7/183
13	AIR2/2665	14	AIR2/1841	15	AVIA7/299	16	AIR2/4488
17	AIR2/2145	18	AIR2/2593	19	AVIA46/49	20	AVIA7/533
21	AIR20/195	22	AIR2/4488	23	AVIA7/298	24	AVIA7/256

Chapter 6   1 January to 2 September 1939

THE very bad weather at the beginning of the year had brought all the outside building work to a standstill for at least a month. The two wooden towers on each site, necessary for the completion date of 1 April, had, by the beginning of February, still not been completed at Rye, Pevensey, Ottercops, Drone Hill, Danby Beacon, Staxton Wold and Douglas Wood. BRS had written again on 10 January to DCD:

> "The 240ft tower situation is one which in its present state absolutely precludes completion...by April 1st. There is no evidence that the contractors have been informed that every effort should be made to have two towers on each site by the end of January [a BRS request]. As far as is known, the instruction to contractors to complete two towers per site by the end of February still stands. In some cases it is doubtful whether this date can be met, even approximately. On several northern sites, no work we are informed has been put in hand for six weeks due to weather conditions..." [1]

The Director of Signals wrote on 13 January to the Director of Works:

> "I should be greatly relieved to know that the... works will be completed to the specified time. Any delay will prevent completion of the Intermediate Coastal R.D.F. chain by April 1st, which could be a matter for grave concern." [1]

Works replied on 25 January:

> "All our contractors have been impressed with the urgency of the work and doing their utmost. It should be noted that we are in the hands of the weather and if it is unduly bad, there may be a delay in these dates. Since the beginning of December it has only been possible to erect towers on 15% of the daylight time." [2]

The Works progress report for 17 January made anxious reading:

> "From December 17 '38 to 1 January 1939 all work at each site [was] at a standstill, by reason of snow and frost, [and] on 11 January further falls of snow on some Northern sites...caused further cessation of work. At Ventnor...little progress with building as the approach road across the Downs is impassable due to thaw. At Poling the first 240ft wooden tower [was] completed in October but [is] now partially dismantled following a lightning strike. Pevensey [is] the worst site in the southern group as the whole area [is] flooded and buildings sited on silt subsoil...[with] continuous pumping required to keep the trenches clear of water and silt. At Rye the site is on a marsh extremely exposed to high winds and the general subsoil over the water is

only a foot below the surface level. Continuous pumping required...At Danby the 2½ mile approach to the site from a public road is a moorland track and it became impassable immediately lorries started to deliver ballast and other materials. [At] Ottercops, the highest and most exposed of all the chain, since taking over the site in October, severe weather renders any constructional work impossible. The greater part of the site is a useless bog, [with] no satisfactory foundations to a depth of 25ft." [3]

BRS had organised three groups of three teams for equipment and aerial commissioning, ordering nine vans and advertising locally for drivers. Outside weather clothing was being organised for the nine parties; an admin officer's objection on the grounds that it was only supplied to those working continually in the open was firmly quashed. He was told to get Air Ministry authority and advised:

> "You will appreciate that although these parties will be working in huts they are faced in many cases with the difficult task of getting to them first! Hence the gum boots!" [1]

An important administrative rule required immediate attention. It is Civil Service policy that it is the responsibility of the employee to make his own way to and from his place of duty, thus, if the rule was to be observed, the vans could not be used to transport the staff between their lodgings and the station. A letter to the DCD conveyed the point that if the rule was strictly adhered to, then the target date would not be met. In not so plain English:

> "The restriction of this transport to within the limits laid down by instructions in the appropriate paragraphs of Kings Regulations and Air Council Instructions would be definitely inimical to the successful adherence to the schedule." [1]

A reply followed:

> "While the Department has no power to waive the general principle...it is recognised that the circumstances in the present instance are exceptional, and it is agreed as an emergency measure that the Singer vans may be employed to convey the installing officers between lodgings and stations. The minimum amount of running must be insisted upon, [and] no more than two return journeys each day may be authorised." [1]

At Drone Hill and West Beckham the equipment that had been hastily installed in September 1938 during the Munich Crisis was re-sited when the first two 240ft towers were completed, that involved a tedious switching exercise with special precautions taken to ensure that when the transmitter and receiver were moved some 100 yards away, they were not seen by the outside contractors' workmen. The equipment huts had been completed at most of the ten stations with the MB1 transmitters and RF5 receivers being installed by 2.IU as fast as they were being produced. Kidbrooke were assembling the aerials; for the receiver a single pair of crossed dipoles with sense reflector at 240ft and a single height dipole at 80ft, and for the transmitter a three tier array with a single reflector.

The Optical Converter had been fitted to the five estuary stations where it was expected that the majority of plotting would take place at the beginning of a war. At the other stations the operators were receiving instruction from scientific officers on converting range and direction into plan position and obtaining the height by manual methods; a specially constructed ruler and protractor. At Dover a machine was under test that was able to compute the height directly from the gonio and range settings plus additional information. The switching operations needed were performed by motor-driven high speed selectors made by Siemens. The BRS scientific officer in charge of all aspects of plotting in Fighter Command, Geoffrey Roberts, had obtained four from a reluctant ADEE who were using them for an alternative location scheme using the sound mirrors.

The success of the prototype, apart from the high noise level, led to the conviction that with a display the human element could be removed from plotting calculations. The proposed development confirmed Rowe's view that the Post Office should be contacted at an early stage to ensure conformity with established switching practices. In February they undertook to manufacture what became known as the Electric Calculator to be ready at Poling in early 1940 with the installation of one system at all the 20 stations by December 1940 followed by the second one at a later date.

At RAE, Fighter Command's HF set, the TR9D, was waiting for the Air Staff to approve full scale production but they were persuaded by Watson Watt that the VHF set currently under development was a better proposition and to endorse the 'handmade set', which he considered had every chance of being successful. ACAS (AVM W. Sholto Douglas) wrote to the CAS on 12 January outlining the advantages of the VHF set over the HF set; it could not be jammed or overheard, had complete freedom from atmospheric interference and more specific channels would be available with a superior sound quality. There were disadvantages in that VHF ground transmitters, receivers and direction finding equipment would have to be designed; it was a gamble. The CAS replied on 16 January:

> "I am satisfied that this proposal is sound and in view of the international situation, urgent. I therefore approve and therefore proceed as a matter of first importance. If you are held up by the 'machine' [Air Ministry bureaucracy] please let me know." [4]

Two aircraft were to be fitted with VHF as soon as possible for air trials in October. RAE were advised by phone on 16 January that the CAS had given his decision to proceed at once with all possible haste on matters relating to the installation of VHF equipment in Fighter Command. Watson Watt on 11 February told RAE to take all steps to ensure that the whole of the VHF organisation was in operation by September 1939.

The Cabinet had lifted the embargo on the expansion of the chain by extending the area to where enemy aircraft would be expected to appear. A conference had been held at the beginning of the year, chaired by the DCAS, to discuss the various proposals that had been circulated for increasing the number of stations. Dowding had asked for three extra stations west of Ventnor as early as July 1938 but the Air Staff had restricted action to one of surveys and these had been carried out by Wilkins in September 1938.

He had recommended sites at Portland (Dorset), Prawle Point (Devon) and the Lizard (Cornwall) and had made a general observation on the difficulty of obtaining good heightfinding anywhere due to the hilly nature of the West Country. In November 1938 there was a proposal for an extra 13 stations to provide cover for the southwest and west of England, which might be the targets of enemy aircraft overflying at a great height, and then attacking from the west where there was no Observer Corps. The DCAS ruled that the only extensions justified was a station at Kirkwall and Stonehaven to give early warning of attack on the fleet based at Scapa Flow in the Orkney Islands, and to extend the western cover by two additional stations at Plymouth (West Prawle) and Exmoor (Simonsbath).

In view of their remote positions it was agreed by the Air Staff that all stations west of Ventnor, to be known as the West Chain, would be on a reduced scale with two wavelengths only, unprotected buildings and no standby power plant. The disadvantages of a reduced defensive capacity in terms of jamming and resistance to hostile air attacks was acceptable as it was expected that the main thrust of enemy action would be on the East Chain. The question of raids from German occupied airfields in France would not, of course, have even been considered.

Approval had been obtained from the Air Council in February to reveal the secret of pulse operation to GEC for the manufacture of transmitting valves, a step taken none too soon and of the greatest importance in the substantial increase in pulse power that was to follow. The immediate task was the replacement of the silica glass envelope, which was a very labour intensive operation needing an oxy-acetylene torch, by an external copper anode and a glass-to-metal seal capable of quantity manufacture. Again, the London television service had provided an unexpected bonus as the technique had been applied to the ACT10 air-cooled valve as used by the BBC in mobile television relay vehicles. With a mechanical and electrical redesign it was subsequently known as the VT58 and eventually replaced the silica envelope valves in the MB2 and GL transmitters and, at 1.5 metres, 25kW for the CD transmitter. The second was to investigate the replacement of the bright emitter tungsten filament with a thoriated one, which gave four times the emission at a much lower filament current. The unfinished experiments at GEC had shown an upper limit of 5kV and it was not known how coated valve filaments would react to pulsing. Tests undertaken at BRS confirmed that long life and higher powers were attainable; the work was of the highest importance.

On 16 February, postponed from last November, the three secretaries at BRS, Miss N. Boyce, Miss M.Girdlestone and Miss H. Brooker (who was Watson Watt's personal secretary at the NPL but had remained at BRS when he departed for London as the DCD), went to the Dover station for a week of instruction as trainee plotters. The BRS memo, full of praise, was based on the report from the Warrant Officer at Dover:

"In general, the women operators performed excellently, they seemed to be superior to equally experienced [RAF] Service personnel of the type employed on this work. They certainly 'picked up' the job more rapidly. The only criticism is that, in general, they appeared more easily flustered under difficult conditions...it is felt that this peculiarity would disappear with more training. When a member of the scientific staff visited Dover on the fourth day of the experimental period, they were handling the apparatus with great confidence, and the plots given were equal in accuracy to those given by other outstations on the same tracks. The impression gained at Headquarters, Fighter Command, on the following day was that it was hardly possible to discriminate in accuracy between the Dover plots and those given by the other outstations, all of which were, on this occasion, using quite experienced Service observers." [5]

Air Commodore K.R.Park, Dowding's deputy, wrote to BRS to confirm the belief of Squadron Leader Hart that women could be trained to operate receivers and to obtain reasonably good results...the criticism could almost certainly be justifiably launched against an observer of limited experience of either sex. He concluded:

"It is agreed that women operators would be employed at R.D.F. stations, but that women alone could not staff a station, [as] this situation would introduce certain administrative complications. It is also for consideration whether women are to be intentionally placed in stations in war which are likely to be the object of direct enemy attack." [5]

Squadron Leader J.A.Tester who had more experience than most on the operating work at CH stations wrote to Rowe:

"...the ladies have proved to be capable plotters and shown every indication that they may become satisfactory operators." [5]

It is odd that in all the books that tell the story it is always mentioned that they were 'flustered', ie, that the capacity for collective thought or decisive action was impaired or destroyed. One official publication summarised the women's visit as:

> "Mr. Watson Watt (D.C.D.) had expressed the opinion in February 1937 that they might make better operators than men, but at the Air Ministry it was considered that it was not known how women would react if flustered by heavy air activity." [6]

Fighter Command were of the opinion that the employment of women in plotting and telling might be the solution to a difficult situation. In a memo to Signals on 3 January it was explained:

> "Experience has shown that only a small percentage of aircraftmen posted for duty as plotters are suitable for retention. Those retained by virtue of keenness and intelligence are particularly suitable for remustering to trades with the result that they are posted away very shortly after they became experienced in plotting duties. The number of R.D.F. stations is increasing rapidly, yet the total number employed for Filterers is two N.C.O. filterers and nine airmen plotters and tellers. Of those, four awaited a balloon operators course and one is awaiting an armament course, total number shortly reduced to six.[It is] now urgent to consider alternative methods for obtaining a permanent crew." [7]

Alternatives were proposed such as clerks, approved on the grounds of extreme urgency but admitted to be a mis-employment, or to establish a new grade of plotter or clerk (ops room). This was opposed as it was considered that promotion prospects were minimal and the general undesirability of adding to an already large number of grades, or to employ men in the new trade of teleprinter operator as recommended by Signals.

On 23 February Rowe wrote to Watson Watt that last minute changes at the chain stations had involved 60% of the scientific and technical officers at BRS plus 80% of the workshop and the Drawing Office staff. There remained only 30 officers for 14 research tasks mainly on airborne devices, anti-jamming techniques and training equipment. One of the casualties was the development of the mobile transmitter, which was being redesigned to take two NT60 tetrode valves in the output stage. He was asking for an order of priority and added that:

> "... the only expression of personal opinion I would like to contribute is the hope that the aiding of bomber aircraft, for which I am convinced there is a great future, should not be put on the pending list." [8]

It had been noted that an aircraft fitted with an experimental Air to Surface Vessel (ASV) set could be navigated solely by observations on the coast line and a meeting with Bomber Command was being arranged. (The meeting took place on 28 March with Rowe reporting in June that the conference which promised so much should have led to so little.)

On 10 March, added emphasis was given to accelerating the completion of the chain when German military forces invaded the remainder of the state of Czechoslovakia, an act that finally convinced many peace-loving British of the real aggressive intentions of Hitler and the growing certainty of war, not if, but when. The fear that Germany would carry out a sudden air attack on Great Britain without any warning, even before there was an official declaration of war, became more likely; the Air Ministry was charged to ensure that it did not happen. Dowding received his directions, issued for his guidance during the continuance of the present period of tension on 25 March from the Air Staff:

> "When any potentially hostile formation, however loose, six or more in number is ascertained to be approaching this country, aircraft are to be dispatched on your orders so as to gain early contact with them. By day, if the formation is identified as German, the aircraft are to be engaged, by night if identification impracticable it is assumed to be hostile and to be engaged. The aircraft however, are not to be engaged either by day or night until they have crossed the coast with the intentions of proceeding inland... thereafter aircraft are to be so dispatched as to engage subsequent formations to the best advantage without restriction to the limits of territorial waters. Air Raid warnings are to be issued as the aircraft cross the limit of territorial waters...." [9]

To ensure that this order could be complied with, Dowding ordered the CH stations to be placed on a 24 hour watch as soon as they became operational thus causing a training crisis as overnight three times the number of personnel would be required. The proposed RDF school at Tangmere was now too small and not even ready so No. 2 Wireless and Electrical School at RAF Yatesbury (near Calne in Wiltshire) was chosen for its permanent home.

All plotting lines to the Stanmore Filter Room were routed separately for security; at Drone Hill the main line was routed via Berwick, Alnwick, Newcastle to London and the standby via Berwick, Dunbar, Edinburgh and Glasgow to London. But that was where separation ceased as all the incoming and outgoing lines, including those for the whole of the air raid warning system, passed through the London Central Telephone Exchange and would remain that way until the Post Office had completed the London 'ring' cabling circuits. The Air Staff considered the existing situation was too vulnerable with the only way to ensuring adequate security by a second filter room and access to the lines without going through London.

Hendon was put forward to the Post Office as a standby but this did not meet with approval; they explained that there was inadequate cable capacity in that area, plus the exposure of the Colindale Exchange in north London to possible enemy action. An alternative was proposed at Leighton Buzzard with a temporary building near the existing Air Ministry telephone exchange and a permanent one at Lipscombe Park, two miles west. Dowding did not agree on the duplication; he thought it an unnecessary expense and offered as an alternative that the Stanmore Operations Room being constructed should have its defences increased, either by additional concrete or surplus battleship armour plate. Works informed him that to increase the protection from a direct hit by a 1,000lb bomb the structural alterations necessary would introduce an unacceptable delay to the completion of the building that was already overdue.

He received a letter from the CAS explaining the vulnerability of Post Office lines and that the scheme for duplication had received CID approval, but he would hold a meeting on 1 April to discuss the need for additional security. Although there was agreement to proceed with the temporary Operations Room at Leighton Buzzard, which Fighter Command put to good use at a later date, the need for an alternative permanent site was made the subject of a review at a later date; it never took place.

On 3 April the CAS was advised that 17 stations out of the 19 (18 permanent stations plus the temporary one at Ravenscar) had been handed over to the RAF and were functioning except for Ottercops and Rye, which were waiting for completion of the 240ft towers. At all stations there were very few spares and no standby power supplies with building priority for the permanent T and R blocks followed by the standby power plant, wardens' quarters and police huts. The excavating and concreting of the footings for the 350ft steel towers was in progress with the five estuary stations receiving precedence in men and materials.

Work on the chain by 2.IU and BRS continued at fever pitch, as the worsening political situation had caused an order to be issued in May by Watson Watt that not only all outstanding commissioning and installation points were to be cleared up (known as a 'clean up'), but that gap filling and heightfinding aerials were to be fitted as soon as possible followed by calibration. This order stopped all research at BRS as the majority of the scientific and technical staff were away at the chain stations, and all the Drawing Office staff on maximum overtime to produce the aerial drawings.

In April, at the request of Watson Watt, the Air Ministry made another application to the Treasury for an increase in his salary, which was rejected. Freeman, now the Air Member for Development and Production, had suggested a 'return to the charge' with an approach based on Watson Watts' exceptional personal qualifications. He wrote:

"Communications research and development are now of such importance that a separate Director would be required for their investigation, quite apart from the fact that, in Mr. Watson Watt, we have an officer not only qualified for the work, but pre-eminently suited, by virtue of the work to which he has devoted so much time under the N.P.L. and at Bawdsey on special aspects of radio work, for the highly important and secret work upon which the directorate is at present engaged. These qualifications are to be found in Mr. Watson Watt only; I doubt if it would be practicable to find anyone else so qualified as he is in his particular sphere. I feel, therefore, that it would be only equitable that his special qualifications should be recognised by the salary which we give him, and I should be disposed, therefore, to regard £1,600 per annum, if approved, as a salary personal to him." [10]

Archibald Rowlands, then an Under-Secretary, had a different perspective; he wrote on 4 July to Freeman:

"From the viewpoint both of our general relations with the Treasury and the interests of Mr. Watson Watt himself, I very much doubt the expediency of returning to the charge once again on the subject of Mr. Watson Watt's salary. From private enquiries I have made, I have reason to think that the matter was considered at a high level before their letter was written. I am satisfied that if we return to the charge again, we shall merely antagonise the Treasury and receive another refusal. I think the wiser course would be to wait until there has been a further development in the Directorate which would justify our re-opening the question." [10]

With only three research workers IFF was beginning to show its promise with the powered version suggested by Wilkins. Dowding was present at the first air demonstration on 4 April at BRS, which was very impressive as the aircraft echo was visible for 100 miles at 4,000ft; he recommended to the Director of Signals that development and production be given the highest preference. Rowe reported to the DCD on 12 May;

"...that the I.F.F. Equipment was redesigned to provide amplification of the received pulse and its re-transmission using the aircraft structure as an aerial. The equipment had been successfully flown in Wellington, Hampden and Whitley bombers and the tapping position for the aerial on the tail plane on each aircraft had been found with ease, which had come as a pleasant surprise." [11]

(IFF remains in use to this day but is now known as secondary radar and transmits height and other information from the aircraft on demand – the provisional patent, 25133/36, was assigned to Watson Watt on 16 September 1936.)

Another RDF conference took place on 5 May to discuss in detail the extensions to the chain. Proposals were made by Dowding for the defence of Belfast and Glasgow in order to track raids that would outflank the Forth-Clyde defences either south or north. He also said that there were the possibilities of attacks on Birmingham and Liverpool from the west by bombers that would outmanoeuvre our defences, or pass through them, for instance between Newcastle and Edinburgh. He drew attention to the sparse population and lack of communication facilities in the areas covered by the Lancaster and Carlisle Observer Corps. If it were to be established at full strength in these districts the observers might have to live permanently at their posts, but he considered that better results might be obtained by the use of RDF. Watson Watt produced a map that showed the extent of the existing cover and suggested at least two sites that would be suitable, a station on the Isle of Man and one at Stranraer. He also raised the question of RDF for the southwest of England as there were gaps in the RDF screen between Ventnor and Prawle Point and the approaches to the Bristol Channel. Dowding's opinion was that these were unimportant particularly towards the western end of the English Channel, since enemy aircraft intending to attack vital points would be located during their flight along the Channel, and would be intercepted long before they reached their objectives. He also agreed that enemy aircraft would be unlikely to fly over Devonshire; the possibility of raids from the Spanish mainland were also considered very remote since an enemy based in Spain would be more likely to devote his attentions to shipping than to hazardous flights over the Bay of Biscay.

Watson Watt's proposal for the two stations was agreed but, on his advice that Exmoor would not give appreciable cover in the English Channel, it was abandoned in favour of 'strengthening' Prawle Point with two switchable Lines of Shoot of 107 and 130 degrees, to be known as a twin beam station. This idea was no doubt thought to be an advantage in extending the cover from a single station in a chain that was considered to be in areas where enemy activity would be noticeably less than in the east. Initially, west coast CH stations were sited for twin beams by arranging for the two transmitting towers to be angled by the difference in the Lines of Shoot.

The additional areas agreed at the beginning of the year had already been surveyed and sites selected at Schoolhill, ten miles south of Aberdeen, at Netherbutton four miles from Kirkwall, capital of the Orkney Islands and West Prawle, near Prawle Point in Devon. The Post Office were now represented on the survey teams because lines were sometimes more favourable to one site than another, even in moorland country, and considerable expense could be saved in providing ducting to existing cable junctions.

The ever vigilant Finance Branch had noticed that Treasury sanction for 20 stations had been exceeded and that it might be necessary to go back to the ADR sub-committee for additional authority. The Treasury view was that the CID had given endorsement for the chain in principle but applications for financial approval were required for all extensions. The cost to date for the CH chain now exceeded £2 million.

A householder at Sandown, about four miles southeast of Ventnor, had written to Murphy Radio in May that a recently purchased wireless set suffered from severe interference over part of the medium wave broadcast band. The company had written to the Air Ministry (the letter eventually found its way to BRS) stating that it did not know the fundamental frequency, but it could also be heard very strongly at 22.5 metres (13.3 MHz) and that the transmissions appeared to be beamed across the mainland as it was very much stronger on the Sandown side than the other. The letter continued:

"We are told that these installations are to be erected at 50 mile intervals around the coast so that if the interference is to be general then some action must be taken quickly." [13]

It was, and investigations showed that the long transmitter feeders were acting as quarter wave radiators and suitable measures were taken that considerably reduced the interference. At a later date, to the surprise of the BRS investigators, it was reduced to almost negligible levels when the transmitter was electrically 'locked' to the receiver, instead of the incoming mains supply. The Post Office had also received similar complaints as a van fitted with radio measuring equipment appeared outside the entrance to Ventnor station, the engineer demanding access, which was refused. He threatened to close down the station, which he suspected of producing severe over modulation and causing widespread interference.

During May, Watson Watt and Wilkins went to France to inspect the system for detecting aircraft in use by the French Navy and Air Force called Détection Electromagnetique (DEM). Using continuous wave transmissions, detection was shown by the rapid movement of a meter needle, known as 'beating', which was produced by the interaction of the re-radiated wave and the direct ray from the ground transmitter. A soldier in the receiver hut noted the meter observations on a blackboard while another one telephoned them to the control station.

What Watson Watt and Wilkins had seen, however, did not compare to what was happening back across the Channel; no high power pulse transmitters, receivers of only average sensitivity without a cathode ray tube display, no extensive aerial systems, no IFF, no filter room and a 30 mile range limit; the only common factor was the wavelength which was between 8 and 10 metres. The opportunity was also taken to inspect the single channel R/T set fitted in the new 'Morane' fighter that provided for transmit and receive duplex operation on 5.2 and 5.6 metres.

The secret of RDF had been disclosed to the French the previous month and plans were being considered for four chains stretching across all the French frontiers. One in active preparation was for a 12 station CH chain to be erected from Dover to Troyes, effectively just behind the border with Belgium, with filter rooms at Arras and Rheims.

Earlier in the year the Admiralty had obtained Cabinet approval for immediate RDF cover over Scapa Flow and a site at nearby Netherbutton Farm had been chosen. Works had advised that it could not be purchased until the end of May, the completion date, but that was quickly overcome by the land agents agreeing to the payment of rent until the land was purchased. The 'Advance' CH station at Ravenscar was to be dismantled and taken direct to Netherbutton but Fighter Command wanted to retain it as a standby to Danby Beacon. A compromise was adopted in that only the TM1 transmitter and, equally ancient, the RF2 receiver, with the generator would be removed, new huts would be ordered and redundant 90ft guyed masts taken from Drone Hill, all to arrive at Rosyth dockyard by the beginning of May. To ensure that there were no delays, Squadron Leader W. Rose, the Commanding Officer of 2.IU, took personal charge of the operation and arrived at Kirkwall on 1 May.

He sorted out the site map errors with the land agents, who gave permission for work to begin, and made arrangements to meet a local builder the next day for the assembly of the two huts and footings for the masts and met Post Office officials to discuss ducting and line terminations. He arranged for a mobile crane to be available at Stromness, the island sea terminal, to lift the cases off the ship and for their transit to Netherbutton. At Rosyth Docks he inspected the crates and boxes that had arrived and obtained confirmation that all the items would be loaded into the S.S.*Barrahead* that would leave on 8 May and arrive at Stromness at midday the next day.

A telegram arrived at Kidbrooke on 6 May to confirm that all the Works services had been completed; the 2.IU installation team left on 13 May followed by the BRS commissioning teams on 23 May and on 2 June the station was handed over to the RAF. On the test flight, a Blenheim aircraft was followed for 60 miles at 8,000ft on a Line of Shoot of 130 degrees, chosen as the expected approach of German aircraft from their bases in northwest Germany. Plotting lines had been ordered, one to Stanmore and the other to the Senior Naval Officer, Kirkwall. The electricity supply at Kirkwall was DC with only a small AC conversion supply; Works would have to arrange a permanent main and standby generator supply for the Final installation.

The proposed station in the Stranraer (Dumfriesshire) area conformed to the layout of two wavelengths with two Lines of Shoot, which were 247 and 337 degrees, unprotected buildings and no standby supply. Surveys during May and June had selected two sites, the first was at Mid Moile, ten miles from Stranraer at 800ft, overlooking Cairnryan, that needed an access road to be built. The alternative, Balker Moor, five miles from Stranraer at 600ft with immediate access but with consequent loss of range, was the one preferred by BRS.

Watson Watt disagreed as he preferred the first one, writing:

"We cannot sacrifice performance at Stranraer to economise on roads." [14]

There had also been a number of visits to the Isle of Man with at least six sites being surveyed to use 90ft towers but none was acceptable. Another visit was made to West Prawle where the farmer had complained that the preferred site would take all his best fields with the rest of the farm being of little value, so the location was changed.

The question of the move of BRS from Bawdsey was a continuing headache for Rowe. As early as September 1938 he had asked the Group Leaders to estimate the cubic capacity and weight of their equipment. On 16 January they were told to arrange for their apparatus and office furniture to be distinctly marked, Yellow, Light Blue, Green, White, the Test Room Red and Accounts Dark Blue. Packing lists were to be prepared. There had been some discussion at the Air Ministry before the purchase of Bawdsey Manor as it was thought that its position in time of war would be too near the Continent and liable to frequent enemy attention. In 1936 these considerations were completely outweighed by the many benefits; the isolation conducive to security, the nearness of the RAF stations at Felixstowe and Martlesham Heath, which would provide experimental air installations and all round the year test flying. It was not in a congested flying area that generated interference from ground or air radio transmissions.

The primary advantage at the time was that buildings could be occupied immediately, and the 150 acres of land was sufficient to allow a number of field researches to take place without mutual interference. The CAS had ruled that the research station would stay at Bawdsey during peacetime but would be evacuated in time of war. Rowe was of the opinion that he had a say as to where the station would be relocated; he favoured Poling as it was not far from London, accommodation was a simple matter, and plenty of land and flying facilities should be available, but he was told by Watson Watt that it would be an Air Staff decision.

By February it appeared that Newquay, in Cornwall, had been approved to the point where official arrangements were being made for the transit of personnel between Newquay and St. Eval and the names of local estate agents distributed at BRS. Rowe made his feelings known:

> "I cannot concede that a decision will be reached until the Superintendent has had an opportunity of talking to those with whom a decision finally rests. The problem of locating aircraft has been largely solved, but the more important problem of interception has not..." [14]

In April, Rowe heard that the move would be to Dundee in Scotland. There was a CH station at Douglas Wood, just a few miles north, there were RAF aerodromes at Leuchars, Montrose and Edzell, a civil airport not too far away at Perth, flying boat anchorages in the River Tay, easy access to the Rosyth Naval Dockyard and a gunnery range at Barry. There were ample stocks of engineering equipment and materials, supplies of skilled and unskilled labour, vacant convertible buildings and a plentiful amount of housing in the area. Wilkins suggested that the University might have spare accommodation and a visit there by Watson Watt secured an assurance that this would become available in the event of a war.

Rowe would retain overall maintenance of the chain when the move to Dundee took place and a new organisation to be known as the Base Maintenance Headquarters (BMHQ) would have to be ready. For economy in the demand for telephone lines, a site was found near the central Air Ministry Telephone Exchange at Leighton Buzzard where all the CH station standby plotting lines were to be terminated. He wrote to all members of the group responsible:

> "In the event of a war, we must consider the maintenance of the chain in continuous operation as our sole duty. We must place ourselves voluntarily and unreservedly on the same basis as Service personnel, the job must come first, 24 hours a day if necessary." [14]

In advance of BMHQ, maintenance was the responsibility of three small groups, each with a car, being set up at Bawdsey, Staxton and Pevensey. For the last two stations a temporary hut was to be erected in the technical compound. Every member of BRS received a copy of the evacuation order, which specified their wartime role, with instructions to memorise, then destroy and sign a certificate of the action taken. By July it had been arranged that a special goods train would be ready in 12 hours and nearby lorry and van owners contracted to go to Bawdsey at two hours' notice.

On 22 May Dowding wrote to the Air Staff requesting cancellation of the directive to engage enemy aircraft approaching the coast, and asked for it to be held in abeyance until the next period of political tension arose, with an amendment to exclude the movement of German aircraft, which were carrying out exercises across the North Sea to our coast. The Air Staff sent a ciphered signal. The instructions were to remain in force until further orders but amended to read:

"[aircraft] to be dispatched on your order so as to be in a position to make contact if the aircraft cross the coast." [9]

Dowding's observations had been noted:

"The orders are intended to apply only to potentially hostile aircraft. You must use your own discretion from the information available to distinguish such aircraft from those carrying out training exercises." [9]

Dowding's deputy, Air Commodore Keith Park, was of the opinion that the orders were impractical; the Group Captain in charge of Operations thought the Air Staff were living in a fool's paradise and he suggested that if the Germans were going to make war on this country they would send over several hundred aircraft in a dozen or more formations. The time for air raid warnings was when this intention was 50 to 100 miles away and appearing on the RDF screens. As for other action to wait until the enemy was over the coast, that would be negligence and Dowding agreed.

But the Air Staff stood firm; Dowding received a communication on 29 July stating that there was to be no relaxation of the present state of readiness. He raised observations that as it was impossible to identify friend from foe at 50 to 60 miles from the coast, it was of the utmost importance that IFF was provided and essential that the existing fighter R/T stations be installed at the coastal CH stations if interceptions were to be effective.

In a major report to Watson Watt on 19 June Rowe reported on research progress and how projects were being deferred by the demands of the CH chain. He added:

"It is of the utmost importance that Headquarters should be aware ...of what it will do and what it will not do...Any implied assumption by the Air Staff that the Intermediate chain is fully available for controlled interceptions might well lead to a dangerous sense of security...The R.D.F. Chain now provides for early warning to an extent which perhaps alone justifies its existence. It is clear that the chain can be made to fulfil all, and more than all, the promises made for it. Only staff and time are needed. Except in the Estuary, the Intermediate Chain is not suitable for controlled interceptions; even in the Estuary much remains to be done...It is important to stress that there is no mystery in the situation. The five estuary stations took 18 months to install. Twelve additional stations were installed during four months of the past Winter. Admitting that the figures are not strictly comparable, and that the staff worked during the last winter at an intensity which could not have been continued indefinitely (a fact of which Headquarters may be unaware), it is clear that no one can expect the stations to be all that could be desired. The aim was to provide something by April 1, and we are now paying a penalty for an incorrect assessment of the all important date." [8]

He again urged that an organisation should be set up to relieve BRS of the chain installation and maintenance, which dominated its activities at the expense of research.

The beginning of June saw the acceptance of a small number of ½CH transmitters, a second one to Bawdsey where 2.IU were erecting an experimental 13.22 metre array on the first completed 350ft tower, and to other stations where the T block was completed. As the installation was considered to be beyond the resources of the RAF, MetroVick were contracted and they took a total of five weeks; three to assemble and interwire three separate units, a week for valve sealing and clearing high vacuum leaks and a further week for the initial commissioning using strip lamps as a dummy load. Final commissioning by BRS into the aerial array would take another week.

Research by the Army group on Coast Defence (CD) was showing results for in the short space of time from late 1938 to the summer of 1939, a major change was under test. With a 25kW 1.5 metre transmitter from MetroVick, the single hut was replaced by two spaced 50 to 75 yards and each fitted with a multi-dipole aerial array, the familiar 'mattress' type. A single beam has the inherent defect in that the following of a craft is initially uncertain and location cannot be given to a greater accuracy than five degrees. Butement solved these two problems with the invention of 'beam switching'; the aerial was shifted, electrically, a few degrees horizontally, 20 times a second. A single ship appeared as two echoes of different heights that showed the direction immediately and when the aerial was turned to make the echoes equal and adjacent, that was the Line of Shoot and the bearing.

Called 'split' by Butement, it was a major step forward as it opened the way for the future development of high precision equipment. The attainable bearing accuracy was of the order of a ¼ degree, which was at least ten times better than the CH chain and far in excess for CD that was 2 to 3 degrees. But because of the primitive mechanical method of turning the array and the height of the echoes that became smaller as the bearing was approached, the accuracy obtained was never greater than one degree.

The Air Ministry workers at BRS were also engaged on the problem of the detection of low flying aircraft, understood from the earliest days at Orfordness, but their line of research was on 10 metres using balloons. At 1,000ft, two balloons, one with a three tier full wave dipole connected by an open transmission line to a transmitter on the ground and the second balloon carrying an array with a receiver which had been modified to take the I.F. output down to the ground. Ranges of 35 miles were obtained but without bearing or height information; further proposals were to fly balloons at 3,000ft and obtain bearings by the standard triangulation method. Watson Watt gave his approval but he was overruled by Tizard whose view was that 1.5 metre CD being developed by the Army was the only solution to the location of low flying aircraft.

Cossor had made a small number of ASV and AI sets that did not meet favour with BRS because of their excessive weight for aircraft use. BRS had reported to the DCD on 18 April that there was a 'serious difficulty' in the use of Cossor valves;

"...[as the] performance in their standard range [is] so poor compared with what can be obtained elsewhere, that roughly twice as many valves have to be used by Cossor to obtain the same result..." [15]

BRS added that the video part of the Pye TV chassis was of small size and weight with the rated gain and bandwidth suitable if it met the specification to follow a 200 Mc/s (MHz)) mixer. In conclusion:

"As a result of investigations we feel confident that there are firms more competent to build A.I. and A.S.V. equipment than Cossor." [15]

A week later BRS wrote again to DCD that tests on a Pye production chassis were completely successful, the improvement in performance due to the bandwidth being three to four times greater than the Cossor CD set.

On 20 June, Park wrote to Rowe that he had been told by Squadron Leader Hart that the Army CD equipment was giving excellent results and that it should prove interesting to see how one of the sets could be linked up to supplement long range reporting; a trial at Dover to check aircraft flying below 2,000ft was proposed. The set produced impressive results as aircraft were detected 32 miles at 1,000ft, 25 miles at 500ft and 15 miles at 50ft. Watson Watt wrote to the Director of Signals on 29 July of the CD's performance, its modest cost of less than £3,000 and, as the situation in respect of the lack of the detection of low flying aircraft was so serious, he was recommending that the Air Staff approve immediately the purchase of 24 copies without waiting for trials or improvements. One set was to be placed at each CH station midway between the T and R permanent buildings with the remaining four for spares and development.

Within five days the authority to raise contracts was received, the transmitters from MetroVick who were already making GL1s for the War Office and the receivers from Pye Radio of Cambridge who no doubt welcomed the unexpected opportunity to be given a government contract that would enable factory production to continue if war broke out. It is pertinent to mention here that without the development of the CD 1.5 metre equipment by the Army at BRS, there would have been nothing available for the Air Ministry at the very critical time when it was needed. The equipment was titled CHL (CH equipment against Low flying aircraft) and was expected to be available by the end of the year. The only deficiency was the lack of heightfinding as the CD set had been designed for the detection of ships.

The radio part of the CHL receiver was also identical to that used for ASV and AI, the prototype using 'Acorn' valves at the 'front end' for RF amplification and frequency conversion followed by a television video chassis for further amplification. The first Pye CHL chassis used Marconi/ Osram KTZ41 radio valves but for the Mark 2 a change was made to the EF50, the first of a new series which radically changed circuit and layout design that led to more efficient production techniques. To ensure that the manufacture of CHL receivers was not delayed by valve shortages, the complete stocks of American made 'Acorn' valves in the country were purchased by Pye, and all the EF50 production taken from the Mullard radio valve factory at Mitcham, Surrey. (Now demolished, an eventual victim of the semiconductor; the famous name, however, lives on as the area is a housing estate with the main road 'Mullards Close'.)

From the 1920s onwards, with the advent of broadcasting, the radio valve had reigned supreme as an amplifying/ power device and during the years were made by the million, but by the late 1930s it was beginning to reach the limit, in its present physical form, of amplification at wavelengths lower than 5 metres. In America and Europe 1 metre had been achieved by the development of 'Acorn' valves that used miniature components requiring very great care in assembly and manufacture, which resulted in a very low rate of production.

In Holland, at its Eindhoven headquarters, the Philips Company, which owned Mullard, was developing a new group of valves known as the all-glass type that would remove all the extensive labour involved with capping, function efficiently at lower wavelengths and with vast savings on production. One of these types was the EF50. In these days of semiconductors with type numbers running into thousands it is only possible to remember the numbers of the types currently in use, that change almost year by year, but this was not the case with radio valves.

In the Services it was a poor mechanic who merely knew the types of valves used at his station. There were many who could name not only the type numbers of all the Service valves in use, but also all the civilian ones including the American Octal plus their main characteristics and alternatives. All CHL mechanics will remember the Mazda Octal base valve, which was completely incompatible both electrically and mechanically with the

American Octal types. The Mazda valve PEN46, which was used in the CHL transmitter, was one of a number of British types manufactured in the USA ; hundreds arrived in the UK fitted with an American Octal base that had to be removed and changed to the Mazda type. In contrast to semiconductor type numbers that in the main are meaningless, valves and type numbers had an aura of their own; who could forget the 807 transmitting valve, the PX4 output triode, the KT66 and 6L6G output tetrodes, the 5U4G rectifier and many others. Old stagers will remember the unique 9 pin base Mazda valve AC/TH.

In June, Watson Watt became aware that the Admiralty was proposing to expand the HM Signal School at Portsmouth for RDF research, and he put forward to Freeman the dangers of duplication and the shortage of skilled workers. He urged that the War Office staff at BRS should be retained as there was an agreement that the Air Ministry would control contracts and production for the War Office and this view was accepted in principle by Freeman and the Secretary of State. Meanwhile, the Ministry of Supply (MOS) had been formed in July to take over from the War Office all the production and research functions. In August, without informing Rowe or anyone in the Air Ministry, the Army group at BRS, together with all its equipment, including the GL and CD, was ordered to Christchurch where purpose-built accommodation was being provided to replace the ADEE at Biggin Hill. This peremptory order produced immediate reverberations. Freeman wrote to the CAS:

> "It is important to avoid anything approaching a departmental wrangle, but the matter is now brought to a head by the War Office, without reference to us, giving direct orders that the whole of the War Office research team is to move to Christchurch on MONDAY. This means that the GL and CD and the low flying set will be removed to Christchurch where any further developments of these sets will take place. This implies two things, that research on these sets will cease and contact with the contractors on the production line will be done by the War Office, although the contracts are Air Ministry....confusion is inevitable." [16]

At an Under-Secretary of State meeting, it was finally agreed by the Ministry of Supply that the group could remain at BRS until it was evacuated. They would not have long to wait.

There had been an agreement by the Committee of Imperial Defence that in the event of a war the RDF stations would have first claim in their defence with men and equipment to be provided by the Army. There was correspondence from the CAS to his counterpart in the War Office, the Chief of the Imperial General Staff, as he was anxious that the Army should be seen to be on the stations. He wrote:

"As you are aware, the Germans are known to have a parachute force of 3,500 men, the aircraft used are Ju52s and we have information that on August 21st, 124 aircraft were seen at Berlin airport being camouflaged. There is a likelihood of an attack on our R.D.F. stations which should not be ignored on account of their vital role and they are very exposed. The C.A.S. would be glad if arrangements could be made for military detachments to be prepared to take on an attack of this kind, and be provided with the additional equipment and personnel necessary." [17]

Defence against the air would be by Bofors LAA guns supported by Lewis machine-guns for very low flying aircraft, and on the ground there would be sentries and lookouts for anti-sabotage and landings by parachutists. By day there would be men aloft in the towers and by night there would be two patrols for the steel and wooden towers, with a third to visit the others. The Army presence was to be elaborate; for the ground defences, 60 soldiers with two lieutenants and one captain, and for air defence another 40 soldiers of the Royal Artillery with two lieutenants. Works received urgent calls for the provision of living quarters, trenches and bomb proof shelters inside the compound, and the building of ammunition stores. Because of the large numbers of Army personnel and the expected addition of CHL the Air Staff had decided that a commissioned officer should be in charge of the stations. Joubert's opinion was that the RAF officer should be of equal status with the Army, but the CAS did not agree; the majority were Flight Lieutenants of the RAF Volunteer Reserve (RAFVR) with high academic qualifications.

The report on the three women trainees at Dover was under consideration at the Air Ministry and the authority to recruit women was given approval on 15 May by the Air Member for Personnel. On 7 June an application was made for Treasury permission to employ local women, who would be restricted to six CH stations and for one watch only; it was thought desirable to employ civilian females from the locality of the stations so as to avoid billeting problems. A suitable pay scale was requested. The Treasury replied:

"As a solution we see no harm in their being engaged at 55/- flat [£2.75p] a week....It occurs to us that this would be a very useful form of service for the Women's Auxiliary Air Force. Has this possibility been explored? " [7]

Signals, which was organising the direct recruitment of women, thought that the pay offered was not nearly enough to attract the right type, an ordinary local typist found in a seaside town being unlikely to be what was wanted. It was felt very strongly, however, that:

"the W.A.A.F. would be of the greatest assistance to us and have no doubt that if we place the recruitment of these women in their hands, we would stand the best chance of getting what we want." [7]

There was little delay for on 25 August the Air Ministry issued instructions that a plotting school for training WAAF personnel was to be opened at Leighton Buzzard. Hart received instructions to pick his own instructors from Bawdsey and find his own trainees up to a maximum of 65 women from companies that were within 100 miles of London. The introduction of the WAAF was not without dissent. One view was their considered reaction under fire; it was claimed that mixed watches were essential as the panic factor was two to one in favour of men, but some thought that such watches were undesirable because it implied that the WAAF could not be depended upon to carry out their duties reliably. Dowding had added his concern that they could successfully ask for a discharge whenever required, which led to a turnover in personnel and if this occurred in operation and filter rooms, then much information of a secret nature would be spread abroad. His views were not accepted by the Air Staff, who thought that the main advantage of using the WAAF was that they could be retained at any one station for an indefinite period whereas airmen were always liable to be posted out of a station at any time. Dowding did, however, insist that the WAAF were not to be posted to the more remote CH stations, only those near centres of civilisation such as Poling, Dover, Rye, Ventnor and Bawdsey. He was at first reluctant to use the WAAF as he thought that they would not be able to stand up to the stress of long watches as well as men, and also that they should not be employed in unprotected or exposed locations. The Director of Operations said that he would be prepared to reconsider the ruling that women should not be employed in operational units.

There was concern by the Air Staff on the continuing lateness in completion of the underground Operations and Filter Rooms at Bentley Priory; the Director of Works had explained the reasons for the delay on 21 July. He was satisfied that the contractor was doing his best:

> "...since 10 January working 24 hour a day, 7 days a week, 70 men on the day shift, 25 on the night shift. This particular job is not the happiest which we have been called upon to carry out – dogged by bad weather, a landslide of serious dimensions and stop and start orders from the C. in C.... Sir Robert McAlpine, at the request of the A.M.R.D., did his best to demonstrate on this particular job how it could be speeded up. We have paid for this, and will continue to do so, as the water leakages inside the building are attributable entirely to speeding up operations during the worst possible weather conditions." [18]

It was not until 9 March 1940 that the changeover was made to the underground rooms.

A possible major air raid alarm was averted on 31 July when at 1649 tracks of more than six aircraft flying westwards were reported by the CH chain at a distance of 35 miles north east of North Foreland making a landfall for Foreness Point. The senior officer in charge of the operations room decided, however, that from the look of the track movements that they were not German. The origin of the mysterious tracks was only solved when a telephone message was received by Air Ministry Signals at 1730 from the Admiralty, advising that 'salvoes of aircraft' would be released from HMS *Ark Royal* during daylight hours in the North Sea on 31 July / 1 August. To emphasise the blunder the Admiralty sent a confirming cypher message at 2015. Another scare occurred on 13 August at 1300 when a track of five aircraft was reported at 5,000ft approaching Flamborough Head, following the coast northwards, crossing between Whitby and Hartlepool then finally disappearing. As no RAF aircraft was involved it was considered that the Fleet Air Arm was responsible but this time the Admiralty denied all knowledge of the aircraft. During August the Air Staff were made aware of aircraft operating in the North Sea; none came near the three mile limit, but the undisciplined use by pilots of their radiotelephones clearly identified the activity as the German Air Force on training exercises.

On 4 August it was reported in the English and Scottish national newspapers that an airship, identified as the German *Graf Zeppelin LZ130*, had been sighted off the Aberdeen and Kincardineshire coasts the previous afternoon. It was identified by two aircraft of 612 Squadron from RAF Dyce, near Aberdeen, which carried out 'an inspection' and, for the Air Ministry, there was no cause for alarm as there was no definite infringement of the three mile limit.

There were two airships named *'Graf Zeppelin'*, *LZ127* and *LZ130*; the former had made passenger flights that were discontinued after the *Hindenburg* caught fire when landing in America in May 1937 and where the only supplies of non-inflammable helium gas were withheld because of the right wing nature of the German government. Unable to carry passengers the *LZ130* was fitted out with military radio equipment and German records show that it made a total of 30 flights in the North Sea and along their adjacent continental coastlines on wireless and other trials, but without specifying when and where the flights took place.

There was official suspicion that photographs were being taken from German civil airliners on their way to and from Croydon, then London's major airport. The existence of the easily identifiable 240ft wooden towers was, therefore, expected to be known to German military intelligence; the 'visit' of the *LZ130* to the eastern coasts of England in May, and Scotland in August, can be considered as an attempt to evaluate their purpose.

But, like the British, the Germans were of the view that only they had location systems, which was, no doubt, confirmed when fixed 240ft wooden towers were first seen that conveyed nothing to indicate locating equipment: the Germans were using moving aerials on 125MHz. (The author's opinion is that the Germans had misconstrued their purpose and were listening for military radio traffic in the HF band and that is why the RDF stations remained undiscovered. It was very unlikely that the *LZ130* was fitted with receivers with a cathode ray tube – essential in searching for pulse waveforms – or the operators trained to listen for pulse transmissions.) The huge metallic structure just outside the three mile limit must have produced a very large echo on the station tubes, but there is no mention of this unique occasion as all log books have since been destroyed.

The last pre-war major home defence exercise was held from 8-11 August covering the Humber to the English Channel. The Observer Corps posts and centres were manned and, for the first time, the CH stations from Stoke Holy Cross to Dover were connected to the Filter Room at Stanmore, which had been transferred from Bawdsey and IFF fitted to 'friendly bombers'. To make certain that there were no breakdowns, BRS had arranged for the maintenance centre at RAF Driffield to be additionally supplied with a 30cwt truck full of spares plus five technical officers, who could be summoned to the telephone at any hour of the day or night: a Magister aircraft was also made available so that spares could be flown if required. On the first day of the exercise there was too much information coming into Stanmore, so Dowding ordered immediately that no Observer Corps tracks were to be 'told' unless they clearly referred to raids that had been identified and numbered by RDF. The result was extremely promising as the mass of confusing information disappeared completely from the sector and group tables. Dowding commented:

> "The skill of plotters still leaves something to be desired, [that is] inevitable so long as plotters are drawn from the grade of Aircrafthand General Duties, and liable to re-posting directly they have been trained...but the R.A.F.(V.R.) plotters were, however, extremely satisfactory....The R.D.F. stations worked extremely well although the counting of aircraft was not consistent, and could only be relied on to give a very rough indication of the strength of the raids...I feel that a very great advance has been made during the last year in the mechanism of intercepting raids in daylight." [19]

Dowding added that the eventual solution of night fighting would be found in air to air RDF and that a specialised type of night fighter would be required for that purpose:

> "I have a flight of 25 Squadron standing by to initiate experiments on these lines in the very, near future when the apparatus is provided." [19]

He concluded that in his last year's report he stressed the necessity for the provision of mains broadcasting apparatus and:

".. it is distressing to be informed that at the end of a critical year that matters have got no further than an invitation to tender. In view of this lamentable delay and the present critical political situation, it would perhaps be preferable to purchase some existing pattern of broadcasting apparatus which I understand was recently tried at Uxbridge with promising results." [19]

The success of this exercise, which was the first major test of RDF in the hands of the RAF, was due to the presence of scientific officers from BRS in the filter and operations rooms; their services did not go unnoticed by Dowding and he asked for their retention on a permanent basis. An agreement was reached by Rowe, Watson Watt, Hart and Dowding that in the event of a war a small number of senior scientific staff would go to Stanmore. The impact of IFF was also unmistakable; the 30 sets were handmade by Ferranti without drawings from a single breadboard model, but there was a high mortality rate in the air, mainly due to their connection to an unregulated power supply that had caused some to catch fire. Orders were placed for 500 sets that was quickly amended to 1,000.

The upgrading of the chain continued unabated for by 7 August it had to be war-effective with gap filler aerials fitted and calibration completed. The defence against jamming also needed to be improved because it was not known when the second wavelength would be installed. The RF5 was modified with a rejector circuit and a demonstration on aircraft echoes had proved it to be very successful. Subsidence had occurred at the Rye T building, the roof shingle had been unloaded and the walls supported; there would be months of delay so a temporary wooden hut was being built for the ½CH transmitter.

At the five estuary stations, where the biggest burden on plotting was expected to fall, 2.IU were installing the double layer anti-jamming tube. The chain was summarised as being ready with the following reservations: (a) good all round performance at Rye, Dover, Bawdsey, Stoke Holy Cross, Stenigot, Staxton, Drone Hill and Douglas Wood. As (a) but not calibrated completely were Ventnor, Poling, Pevensey, Canewdon, High Street and West Beckham, with the remainder Dunkirk and Great Bromley with height errors, Danby with calibration inaccuracies and Ottercops with range and cover insufficient. Schoolhill and Netherbutton were not included as the 240ft towers were incomplete. On 18 August Dowding sent a letter of appreciation to Watson Watt on the 'clean up', which had produced a general improvement on the operational value of the chain.

The prototype VHF R/T equipment for the air trials was nearing completion at RAE. In August a decision was made that the model, a four channel VHF set should go to industry as a sample with single tender action that in itself represented a major departure from standard Air Ministry pre-war procedures. But that was not the view of the Director of Signals, who reported to the CAS that the French had a superior VHF set and he suggested that a similar policy should be adopted of allowing commercial firms to have a specification. Watson Watt disagreed with the opinion of the Director, who was informed by him that the technical investigation of the French set was properly the task of DCD, not Signals, adding that he had already examined the equipment, had listened to the flight trials and had been unfavourably impressed with the results and the technical specification.

"As I have frequently informed the Director of Signals,"

wrote Watson Watt:

"he could have had a V.H.F. set as bad as the Dutch and the French several years ago, but his own requirement and on technical standards alike, very properly excluded it from proposals for introduction." [20]

(A year later Watson Watt wrote a postscript, in which he pointed out that the shortcomings of the French equipment, in actual operation with their Air Force, had been such to compel them to buy our VHF set for re-equipping.)

A decision was made to go ahead with the fitting of VHF sets in Hurricanes and Spitfires only, in eight complete sectors in 11 and 12 Groups with two squadrons in each, a total of 320 sets: action would be taken to ensure interchangeability with the TR9D. The contractor would make 16 ground transmitters and receivers, 24 D/F sets and 16 relay stations from models and sketches, with RAE designing the aerials and supports and providing drawings for the buildings and interwiring.

On 24 August Fighter Command Headquarters received the code word 'Afidock', the signal to place all units on a war footing and for Rowe to begin the evacuation of the research station. In the early hours of Friday 1 September the German army crossed the borders of Poland and the German Air Force began bombing Polish cities in defiance of guarantees that had been given by the British and French governments. At BRS a member of the non-technical staff, who had heard an early BBC radio news broadcast, was the first to know and give the alarm.

Watson Watt has written that he was at BRS on that day and as soon as the German attack had been officially confirmed he gave the evacuation order, which had been well-prepared. Harold Larnder went to Stanmore to form what was later called the Stanmore Research Section (SRS) with scientific officers acting as observers in the Filter and Operations Rooms.

Dewhurst moved to Carlton Lodge near Leighton Buzzard to set-up the Base Maintenance Headquarters (BMHQ) with 12 tons of stores on the way by rail. The airborne section under Dr Bowen had instructions to go to Perth aerodrome and the remainder of the staff began to prepare to make their way north to Dundee or to the CH stations as arranged. The Army Group went south to ADEE at Somerford, near Christchurch, Bournemouth, leaving the GL and CD equipment for collection at a later date.

The eminent American historian H.T.Guerlac has written an account of the BRS evacuation that is somewhat over-dramatic for it stated 'that the outbreak of war took everybody by surprise, that indescribable confusion reigned and at lunch that day the Superintendent announced that Bawdsey was sure to be bombed to the ground and that everyone had to leave before nightfall. When they arrived at Dundee no space was available until an emergency session of the Senate was convened'. Some doubt must be placed on the accuracy of this statement, which must be second-hand and likely to have been received some years after the event.

The BRS staff were certainly aware that war was not far away for the evidence was in front of them, 180 cases that were being packed; in fact all must have been ready by 1 September as they were on the train by the next day. 74 tons of stores, equipment and furniture were taken to Melton (Goods) railway station for transit to Dundee at a cost of £508.19s.6d (£508.97½p). An invoice in the file from the railway company to the Air Ministry for the cost of the move gives the date as 2 September. (The author has a letter from a senior member of the BRS staff that includes the statement that the move on 1–2 September was quite orderly and enough notice was given for those with houses and families to make domestic arrangements.) Rowe has written that he heard the declaration of war in a cottage in Northumberland while on his way to Dundee, which must mean that he had left Bawdsey on Saturday 2 September. The following day only a small nucleus of BRS staff remained, mainly the AI group, who were involved with the recovery of AI equipment from aircraft at Martlesham Heath.

At midday on 1 September the London television transmission from Alexandra Palace was suddenly closed down at the end of a Mickey Mouse cartoon, without any announcement to the viewers gathered around the estimated 25,000 sets. In the studio a drama production due for transmission the next day was stopped in mid-rehearsal to the annoyance of the cast, one of whom was the future film actor James Mason. It did not register at first that there would be blank screens for the duration of the war, to the dismay of the set manufacturers, who now had useless stockpiles.

By nightfall the 'blackout' was permanently enforced and the BBC had reduced the various national and regional programmes to one, which was radiated on two wavelengths, 391 and 499 metres. The transmitters of each group were synchronised so that they could not be used for navigational purposes by enemy aircraft and this was the excuse that was given a few weeks later for the closure of the television service.

For the British public the waiting was nearly over; for the past year they had watched the digging by night and day of air raid shelters in public parks and the issuing of identity cards and gas masks. Government policy for the protection of the public was based on two major considerations; there would be an immediate 'knock-out blow' delivered on London by the German Air Force as soon as war was declared, possibly sooner, and the number of casualties to be expected. These figures had been supplied to the Home Office by the Air Ministry, and were based on statistics collected from the 1914-1918 war when for one ton of bombs dropped there were 16 casualties. The intervening years had amended the figure due to the increase in the size and numbers of bombers. The advice to the Home Office, which based on it all the Air Raid Precautions and other matters, was that for the first two weeks of the war there would be intensive bombing causing some 5,000 casualties a day.

The 19 stations, 18 in England and Scotland plus Netherbutton in the Orkney Islands, were at the 'Intermediate' level – equipment in wooden huts with aerials on 240ft towers. Range was 60 to 100 miles at 15,000ft that dropped to 20 to 30 miles at 3,000ft. Height measurements were unreliable below 3,000ft and there was no plotting above 20,000ft; all plotting lines were connected to the Stanmore Filter Room. The Lines of Shoot were specific for Netherbutton to watch for German aircraft approaching Scapa Flow from northwest Germany, Douglas Wood and Drone Hill to cover the approaches to central Scotland, Ottercops, Danby Beacon and Staxton Wold to cover the north of England, Stenigot, West Beckham and Stoke Holy Cross the Midlands, and High Street and the five estuary stations to cover London from aircraft overflying Holland and Belgium.

The English Channel stations at Rye, Pevensey, Poling and Ventnor were originally positioned for attacks on Portsmouth and Southampton from aircraft overflying France, not for aircraft flying along the English Channel from east to west. No one could have imagined that within nine months these stations would be ideally placed for watching the activities above German occupied airfields in northern France; without them the Battle of Britain story may have had a different ending. The tension on the chain can be imagined, with more than one pair of eyes watching the tube, the mechanics constantly watching meter readings and the filter room operators listening intently on their plotting line; no one knew for sure where the first enemy plot would come from or when, but all eyes and ears were, no doubt, 'tuned' to the five estuary stations.

There must have been some measure of satisfaction for Watson Watt, Tizard, Wilkins, Rowe and Wimperis who, within just four and a half years, had seen the Daventry Experiment grow into a new and massive technological achievement. Dowding had also played a major role, first as the AMRD and then as the AOC-in-C, in welding the scientific to the operational needs of Fighter Command. Sitting in his office in Bentley Priory he was able to relax, safe in the knowledge that he would be made immediately aware of any enemy activity at least 100 miles away from the defended coastline; his pilots were safely on the ground with time to prepare for battle.

REFERENCES

1	AVIA7/256	2	AIR2/3487	3	AIR2/2665	4	AIR2/2946
5	AVIA7/411	6	AIR10/5485	7	AIR2/3323	8	AIR2/3404
9	AIR2/4109	10	AIR2/2709	11	AIR2/2985	12	AVIA7/418
13	AIR2/2685	14	AVIA7/600	15	AVIA7/582	16	AIR2/2942
17	AIR20/222	18	AIR20/2095	19	AIR2/2918	20	CAB102/641

Chapter 7   3 September to December 1939

ON Sunday 3 September at 11.15am Prime Minister Neville Chamberlain announced in a nationwide BBC radio broadcast that Great Britain was at war with Germany. His declaration was followed by an announcement that all cinemas and theatres were to close immediately and football matches and other events where large crowds could be expected to gather were forbidden; gas masks were to be carried at all times.

At 11.21am the air raid sirens were sounded in the Canterbury district, quickly followed by warnings in Maidstone, Tunbridge Wells, Brighton, Horsham and south London. Due to a mistake by the Post Office, a Yellow (preliminary warning) alert had been converted to a Red (action warning, sound sirens) and sent to central London. All road traffic was stopped and pedestrians herded into the nearest shelter but within 30 minutes the 'all-clear' was sounded, which led many to believe that the warning was simply an official test. High officials in London government offices thought differently; they were apprehensive indeed that the German Air Force was on its way.

This very first air raid warning of the war was caused by the CH chain detecting an aeroplane flying towards the south coast of England from France in one of the specified bomber lanes, with no positive identification; it was subsequently found to be a military aircraft that had hurriedly left France without notification. A second unidentified alert occurred off the Scottish coast causing sirens to be sounded in Newcastle, Berwick, Galashiels and Edinburgh at 11.33am, but by 11.57am the 'raiders' had been identified as friendly and the 'all clear' sounded.

Rowe was somewhat dismayed shortly after his arrival at Dundee. He wrote to Watson Watt on 5 September with the address not from the University as was expected, but the St. Andrews and Dundee Training Centre for Teachers, which was nearby:

"My first five minutes at University College were not at all reassuring; Professor Fulton told me that Professor Peddie was particularly kind-hearted by nature and had given away more than the Council was prepared to agree to. The accommodation which we had expected was in any case very scattered and inadequate. During the afternoon I was called to a meeting of the Council and

Fulton in the Chair opened his statement to me by saying that although the Council could not welcome us, they would tolerate us and that we could have the first floor of the Physics Department. This was clearly perfectly useless, and an examination of alternatives has led us to this place. We have all the accommodation we could possibly want at the moment....This acquisition has cheered us up tremendously. The Head of this College is as helpful as Fulton was unhelpful, and I think in writing to him his attitude should receive acknowledgement... [we] are now unpacking 180 cases... [and] absolutely dependent on the Works people arriving here as soon as possible.....If you agree, I propose to call this place 'Air Ministry Research Establishment'.....and, in a talk to the whole of the staff and employees, I have told them that no reference whatever must be made to radio or to our connection with Douglas Wood. As far as Dundee is concerned, we might simply be making aeroplanes fly faster."

A handwritten P.S. followed:

"Perth not so good. Squadron Leader Rowe in charge says that we and his present show cannot co-exist... Other than the absence of Works people we are very happy. We will all be working as labourers this week. " [1]

Rowe's attention was drawn to an unauthorised leakage of RDF information, almost on his own doorstep, published by a local newspaper, *The Kirriemuir Free Press and Angus Advertiser*, on 7 September:

"Military activity over the weekend was a chief source of public interest and crowds assembled at the Masonic Hall to watch the departure on Saturday of twenty members of the Kirriemuir Company of the 4/5th Black Watch under 2nd Lieutenant M.R.H.Allan, Brechin, to guard the aircraft detectors at Monikie [the Douglas Wood CH station]." [2]

Another letter from Rowe to Watson Watt followed on 15 September:

"Nothing done yet, at the beginning of our second week, [with] no Works Services. Mr.Wilkins, Works reps. and I have tentatively selected land covering about 20 acres about half a mile away from the towers at Douglas Wood [for the proposed research station]. There are 52 staff at Dundee, none at Douglas Wood, 20 at Perth and 45 at Leighton Buzzard, section HQ or Chain stations: maintenance should be taken over by the Air Ministry." [1]

To add to Rowe's discomfiture was the impending arrival of a number of highly qualified physicists from the Cavendish Laboratory, Cambridge, who, under an agreement with Tizard and Watson Watt, had agreed to join them for the duration of the war. No administrative arrangements had been made for their accommodation or pay; many were sent as assistants to the scientific officers now at all the CH stations.

(Rowe caused much ill feeling to the pre-war senior scientific staff when, at a later date, he promoted one of the 'new entrants' to act as Deputy Superintendent. After the war he wrote that AMRE Dundee was 'dead' but was revitalised by the incoming PhDs.)

Rowe sent a letter to BMHQ:

> "Now that we are scattered over two countries, weekly reports are requested. I do not want a whole list of jobs to be given with remarks such as proceeding, or in hand. I imagine that the reports should never exceed one page of typing." [1]

Within a month there was a growing feeling amongst the senior staff, who had been in favour of the move north, that Dundee was unsuitable. There had been no contact with the CHL group at Christchurch or with the HM Signal School at Portsmouth. Telephone calls were subject to long delays because of the severe shortage of cable capacity to Leighton Buzzard through the east side of Scotland and northern England. There was a high level of electrical interference in the city.

The reaction to the move by the workshops and other employees had also been disappointing with resignations occurring, with more to come when it was announced that their furniture would not be moved at public expense. The dissatisfaction with Dundee was discussed there with Watson Watt on 15 October, when an area near Swanage, Dorset, was proposed. A site at Renscombe Farm near the sea at Worth Matravers was examined and agreed by Rowe and Wilkins on 21 October and confirmed by Watson Watt the next day.

Rowe advised his senior staff of the impending change but insisted that other workers should not be told about the possibility of moving south until a later date. By November there was still no news and by the end of the month Rowe was getting increasingly anxious that the hutting, steel and timber earmarked for the research centre near Douglas Wood would be 'lost' when they left Dundee; he had remarked that conditions there were so appalling that:

> "I cannot think that there will be any difficulty in our moving to Swanage, meanwhile we are marking time in the middle of a war." [3]

The move of the AI section to Perth aerodrome had fared no better; it remained in use as a civil airport and was not a prohibited zone, there was no separately isolated and guarded area set aside for them and their arrival had not been welcomed by the officer in charge. In a very short time, as a result no doubt of very vigorous action by Dr Bowen, they moved to the RAF station at St Athan, a few miles south of Barry in South Wales.

The start of the war caught a number of university men, who had been 'borrowed' and were on their second week of initiation into the secrets of RDF, at some CH stations. The visits were the eventual result of repeated efforts by Watson Watt and Tizard to persuade the Air Ministry to recruit top scientific personnel to Bawdsey from universities but without success. The low salaries offered, the lack of further research facilities, and their not wishing to be involved in military or government employment were given as the main reasons. The observers sent in their reports to AMRE a few weeks later. Characteristic was the one from Dover, which had been visited by a Cambridge group of five undergraduates with three non-wireless and two wireless research workers. The group split into three parties, which studied the subject of aerials, height finding, time bases and pulse systems and at the end of the week reported together with unsolved technical detail and important theory discussed. One member of the group commented on the expertise of the RAF and civilian operators:

"...as very capable, very expert; they could see echoes and take bearings when I could not see anything." [4]

At Rye the observers had noted that when a valve was obviously going to burn out, they were often unable, even in quiet times, to receive permission from Stanmore to go off the air; this seemed to hold at all stations and was probably responsible for a general deterioration of equipment. The quality of observers varied, some were good, others ought not to be allowed on the tube. At Pevensey the group commented on the MB1 transmitter, which was overheating, with wax melting in the condensers (capacitors) during the hot weather, the covers having to be removed to prevent excessive heat rise, and the temperature in the hut appalling especially at night when it was 'blacked out'.

At High Street the group reported that they had arrived during the week before the war, with mornings that were spent in small groups studying the transmitter and receiver manuals, which they found considerable difficulty in following. The various descriptions did not tally in the three books and in some instances did not agree with the actual equipment, there were no up-to- date diagrams of the actual circuits or occasions for allowing members to get familiar with the transmitter and receiver adjustments; the station had to be kept on the air unless a breakdown occurred.

At Ventnor a team from Birmingham University, including Professor M. Oliphant, Dr J.T. Randall and Mr H.A.H. Boot had visited the station for several weeks, virtually the first contact that the Physics Department had with RDF. They took turns at operating and plotting, studying the circuit diagrams, evaluating the heightfinding and direction finding techniques and the general operation of the station. The maximum range for incoming aircraft was 94 miles, for outgoing aircraft 107 miles, the minimum range for outgoing aircraft being 10 miles and for incoming aircraft 7 miles.

The lack of IFF sets was the reason for a number of false air raid alarms and the cause of a most serious incident. At 0615 on the morning of 6 September a telephone message was received at the RAF fighter aerodrome at North Weald, from an AA gun and searchlight post on Mersea Island, west of Clacton, that an enemy aircraft had been seen flying very high. The sector controller at North Weald, without reference to Group Headquarters, ordered up both flights of 151 Squadron (Hurricanes) which were airborne at 0628 and 0634. At 0632 plot 'Raid 1' appeared on the Stanmore Filter Room table as hostile aircraft in the Thames Estuary. More aircraft were sent up and more tracks appeared on the table.

With indications in the Operations Room that a large German raid was in progress Group ordered additional formations mainly from Hornchurch (Spitfires) but some from Biggin Hill and Northolt which, as they left the ground, also appeared as new raids in the Estuary. The Senior Air Staff Officer, Air Commodore Keith Park, was in the Operations Room by 0646 and saw five or six tracks 15/20 miles from the coast. Within minutes the number of raids reported had increased from 5 to 12, of strength 6 plus to 12 plus and at heights from 2,000ft to 6,000ft. As the tracks were heading up the Thames towards London, Park ordered air raid warnings. The sector controller at North Weald had, by that time, sent up all his aircraft including reserves. Certain flights had been given incorrect information and found themselves over 30 miles out to sea, had lost radio contact and on returning to base had appeared as new raids on the table.

11 Group phoned at 0655 that they had a report from Southend that there were 50 German aircraft in the area and the naval liaison officer had reported that the Chatham guns had engaged them. At 0705 Park telephoned 11 Group to point out there were no hostile tracks reported by the Observer Corps and the raids appeared to be disappearing shortly after crossing the eastern boundary of London. Dowding had been alerted because of the appearance on the table of some 14 raids all appearing to converge on London through the Thames Estuary and he arrived in the Operations Room at 0715. At one time there were 27 raids numbered on the table but only one track had crossed the coast. By 0900 the raids had been cleared off the plotting table and the air raid warnings cancelled.

In what became known as the 'Battle of Barking Creek,' named after the main sewer outfall from Greater London, and close to where the offending Spitfire squadron was based, two Hurricanes had been shot down by friendly fighters with one pilot killed and the other injured. In the enquiry that followed it was discovered that the majority of the plots had come from the CH station at Canewdon, south of Mersea Island. Further, that the previous night a message had been received by the Filter Room from BMHQ that Canewdon had reported that 'sense' was unreliable as the relays behind the receiving dipoles were permanently energised.

Shortly after the fault had been phoned through to BMHQ the RAF at Canewdon reported back that it had been cleared but, as they were unaware that an error had been made in their handling of the test equipment, the fault remained. There was, in addition, no entry in the Filter Room log that would have ensured that the controller and the assistant controller on watch, and those who followed, were aware of the fault until it had been rectified.

Disciplinary action followed swiftly for the offender who had failed to record the message, and the sector controller and the two pilots were placed on open arrest. BMHQ sent a scientific officer from Bawdsey to Canewdon to investigate. On climbing out to the reflectors on the R array at the top of the 240ft tower, he found that the relays were energised irrespective of the position of the 'sense' switch due to a wiring defect.

Watson Watt received a letter from Dowding of the events of the day and in replying, he did not accept that the CH station was to blame, because he was aware that although there had been a 'sense' fault it been corrected by the RAF. However, he did not know that the RAF were in error or that BMHQ had evidence that there had been a defect that had been cleared later in the day. He had visited Canewdon and was completely satisfied that those on duty that day had made no mistake in their first reports, that there was an aircraft seaward of them at 0635, and there was no doubt about the 'sense'. He accepted the fact that all his conclusions were based on semi-official reports of the position of aircraft. He concluded:

> "In my opinion the whole of the events of the morning of 6.9.39 flowed from the correct operation of the R.D.F. observing, reporting and filtering system in application to an unidentified and unreported flight by friendly fighters across the front of the R.D.F. screen, which should be protected organisationally against such intrusions until identification processes are assured." [5]

In his reply to Watson Watt on 15 September Dowding apologised for the very condensed form that his report was worded and that he wanted him to realise that in his opinion:

> "the R.D.F. system is the greatest single contribution to the defence of this country which has ever been made. It more than counters the advance in the speed of bombers which has been made since the end of the last war...." [5]

However, Dowding also added that there were some inconsistencies from individual stations and he instanced an occasion when sitting in the Filter Room that a Blenheim sent out for a special test flew past the front of West Beckham without being detected. Enclosing a copy of the report from

BMHQ, he singled out Watson Watt's concluding paragraph as being in error:

"[as] there were no friendly fighters in front of the R.D.F. line at the time when the first plots were given by Canewdon. The first plots corresponded exactly with the time when the first Flight left the ground at North Weald." [5]

Dowding concluded his letter:

"I should be most distressed if you thought that I was unduly critical, or that I failed to realise in any way the tremendous benefits that the R.D.F. system has conferred on the Defence." [5]

A conciliatory reply from Watson Watt followed in which he agreed that it was now clear that his own conclusions, in so far as they were based on hearsay about fighter movements, could not be sustained.

In a tersely worded memo to the AOCs of 11,12 and 13 Groups on 8 September, Dowding advised that the sector controller, who had sent up patrols on a rumour from a searchlight detachment without orders from, or reference to, Group Headquarters, had been placed on open arrest and a Summary of Evidence taken; that information was to be confidentially communicated to all sector controllers. Two Spitfire pilots had opened fire on two Hurricanes and similar action had been taken with them; that information was also to be confidentially communicated to all fighter pilots.

The two pilots, both flying officers, were court-martialled at Hendon on 17 October and were acquitted, returning to flying duties within a few days. At a later date when Dowding was in correspondence with the CAS on the procedure to be adopted when friendly aircraft were fired on by friendly pilots, he gave his opinion that had the two officers been defended by a less famous 'prisoner's friend' the result may have been different.

It is highly likely that as the North Weald and Hornchurch aerodromes were only nine to ten miles west of Canewdon, the back echoes produced by fighter operations in a relatively small area behind the station had obscured the malfunction of the 'sense' system from the RAF operators, who were, no doubt, at the start of the war, over anxious to detect incoming enemy aircraft. There have been a number of accounts published of the 'Battle' with the majority told from the airborne angle. A few adventurous writers have attempted to enrich the story by introducing the presence of King George VI, who was at Fighter Command HQ that day, in conversation with Dowding in the Operations Room. The King, in one report, had recognised that there was a crisis around him and was endeavouring to remain calm, but Dowding was beginning to look distinctly worried as the controllers became overworked and the telephones lines overloaded.

In all these narratives the important factor of time is missing; it is vaguely 'in the morning', but the records show that it was all over by 0900. Would the King have been there at 0730? An extract from the Air Staff diary at Stanmore is given without comment:

"September 6. The 'raiders passed' signal was given at nine o'clock. Three hours later His Majesty the King, in the uniform of Marshal of the R.A.F., paid a visit to the Headquarters of Fighter Command." [6]

At Stanmore, Larnder and his team were conducting a special test that was laid on for Dowding, who had thought that the events of 6 September had shown up the possibility of high flying enemy aircraft escaping the RDF screen. Even at this early stage of the war the wisdom of having trained scientific observers in the Operations and Filter Rooms at Stanmore could not have been made more apparent. Larnder called for a single Blenheim aircraft to fly at 20,000ft on 7 September unannounced and watched the plotting of it on the tables. He reported a few days later that it was safe to say that no enemy aircraft had so far approached without detection although it might be wrongly identified when operating in a flight of one. No single aircraft operating from the general direction east, and proceeding westwards at 20,000ft, would have escaped detection if it ultimately made a landfall at Mersea Island.

Another trial run was made on 9 September, the one that Dowding mentioned in his letter to Watson Watt; a Blenheim bomber was arranged to fly from Dover to the Wash at 10,000ft at a distance of 60 miles from the coast. Canewdon gave the least information, losing the aircraft at 70 miles, Great Bromley lost it at 75 miles, Dunkirk followed it for 147 miles and Bawdsey for 115 miles. Nothing was seen at High Street although the aircraft was only 70 miles away or at West Beckham although at one point the aircraft flew 40 miles across the Line of Shoot. Counting was poor, the single aircraft reading as +3, +6. Larnder reported a few days later that a single aircraft was observed to be approaching the east coast; according to Bawdsey the height was 7,000ft, Dunkirk and Great Bromley said 18,000ft and the coastal liaison officer in the filter room said his aircraft was not over 5,000ft. The aircraft was judged to be at 10,000ft so it was called an enemy and ordered to be intercepted. It turned out to be a friendly Anson that was lucky it was not fired on; perhaps at night time the story might not have had a happy ending. Larnder urged the fitting of IFF, the lack of which 'is of a greater loss than our inability to detect really low flying aircraft.'

Dowding was certainly worried over the events of 6 September as a weekly intelligence summary dated that day stated that a force of 850 bombers, which had not been engaged in French or Polish fighting, lay waiting in northwest Germany to attack at any moment. In a letter to the

CAS and the Secretary of State on the strength of fighter squadrons for the defence of Great Britain, he reminded the CAS that the Air Council estimate of 52 was endorsed by the CID. He added:

> "On September 3, I had 25 Regular Squadrons and 14 Auxiliary Squadrons in various stages of inefficiency, say a total of 34. Consternation when I learned that four squadrons of Hurricanes [are] to be dispatched to France." [7]

A further threat to Dowding's forces arose when an airborne invasion of the United Kingdom was being considered by the government, which thought it unwise to ignore it completely, and ordered the Air Staff to prepare contingency plans. At a conference on 31 October to discuss the role of Fighter Command, Dowding emphasised that the commitment of fighters already undertaken in France and those in connection with the Fleet bases had drawn all the blood to the extremities and left the heart of the country exposed.

18 September was a red letter day for the WAAF when the very first trained plotters arrived at Stanmore from Leighton Buzzard and were met at the entrance to Bentley Priory by the Director of the WAAF, Air Commandant Jane Katherine Trefusis Forbes. The plotting school had opened on 4 September after a tour of WAAF companies for suitable candidates by Senior Commandant Dacre, who had travelled to Oxford, Reading, Farnborough, Hook, Brighton, Kenley, Kidbrooke, and Loughton. Arrangements had been made with the local police to billet the expected number of 65.

Eventually, a large house was requisitioned in the nearby village of Heath and Reach where the volunteers spent the first four days on an induction course while their backgrounds were checked by MI.5; a few occasions arose when some were returned to their companies. The daily routine at the hostel was:

0700 Reveille, beds stacked, room swept, tidied and dusted.
0745 Breakfast.
0850 Parade, roll call and prayers.
0900 P.T.
0930 Fatigues – cleaning paint.
1045 Break.
1100 Assemble front drive for route march.
1200 to 1355 Lunch period.
1400 Drill.
1500 Lecture.
1600 Respirator drill.
1630 Little Tea.
1730 Lecture.

1815 Put up blackout boards.
1830 Supper.
2100 Roll call
2200 LIGHTS OUT. SILENCE.

On Sunday there was free time after 0920 and for girls who were out for the day: THEY MUST BE BACK AT THE HOSTEL BY 1830 HOURS.

Training for the RAF remained at the RDF School, Bawdsey, already open 24 hours a day. With only one receiver the number of trainee operators was limited to 27 and when the second one arrived the number would be increased to 36. But to meet the demand the course had been cut from three to two weeks at the end of which the trainees had little idea of anti-jamming methods, height measurements, IFF responses or counting. Many of them selected from Yatesbury were posted directly to a CH station to await the next course. Mechanics fared no better – the students received a sound theoretical training but there was no transmitter to obtain practical experience or knowledge of the setting up adjustments.

The importance of RDF was reflected in the way that any changes had to be approved by the Air Staff, major ones by the CAS. The war altered many things, and one of them was a meeting held at the Air Ministry on a Sunday, the 24 September, to discuss the various proposals for defence of the CH stations. The Army CIGS, the counterpart of the CAS, had suggested that the vital parts of the CH stations should be buried in order to release part of the Light AA defences that were being provided by the Army and which were in very short supply.

The CAS considered the findings the next day and made the following rulings: (a) there was NOT to be any deep burying of the technical buildings, (b) all the living quarters at present inside the technical compound were to be dispersed at least a mile away, with separate self contained accommodation for 35 WAAF at each CH station, (c) the present 'Intermediate' transmitter and receiver when replaced by the 'Final' equipment were to be installed in buildings sunk to ground level at least 300 yards from the main site, turfed for concealment and protected against blast, splinter, and 25lb incendiary bombs and (d) a mobile to be provided and kept in reserve to provide cover should the station be put out of action.

With just over a month passing since the declaration of war there had been very little enemy air activity, certainly not the 'knock-out blow' on London that the government was expecting and against which all defences, land, sea and air had been carefully arranged. The German Air Force had confined its activities to the bombing of shipping along the east coasts of England

and Scotland. On 16 October when Drone Hill was off the air, naval vessels in the Firth of Forth were attacked without air raid sirens being sounded. Dowding explained that he was aware of enemy activity in the area and that patrols were investigating, but his first knowledge of the raid came from the Admiralty. He judged that no good purpose would be served by issuing an 'alert' at that late stage.

Vice-Admiral James F. Somerville had been recalled from retirement to organise the naval defences of the Orkney and Shetland Islands. He asked for the immediate installation of a CH set at Wick to cover the southern approaches to Scapa Flow, for higher power and all round looking for Netherbutton and a CH station in the Kinnairds Head area (Hillhead). A few days after the beginning of the war he had witnessed at Bawdsey, on Watson Watt's invitation, the detection of a submarine with the prototype CD set. The Admiral was now asking for CD sets to be sited on the approaches to Scapa Flow from the east with the primary object of detecting submarines plus additional air cover.

There was only one CD set in existence; it was at Bawdsey but owned by the Army and waiting to be transferred to ADEE Christchurch, soon to be re-named the Air Defence Research and Development Establishment (ADRDE). The War Office scientific officers there were also joined in October by scientists from the Cavendish Laboratory, Cambridge, headed by Dr J.D.Cockcroft. Watson Watt telephoned the Superintendent to ask him to arrange for facilities to be made available for Cockcroft to produce six copies as a matter of great urgency, and who set about his task unhindered by Civil Service regulations. The Superintendent wrote later:

> "We have only acted as hosts to Dr. Cockcroft and his party, but the urgent and often irregular provision of a great number of stores, components and tools, etc., is building up a packet of trouble with the Finance branches." [8] (It took over three years to be sorted out.)

Cockcroft went to MetroVick where a number of GL transmitters that had been completed could not be delivered because Cossor were delayed in clearing obscure faults in the receivers. According to him the wavelength change from 7 to 1.5 metres had been made with a hacksaw, a humorous reference no doubt to the shortening of the tuned Lecher bars: the receivers were handmade and copied from the Bawdsey model. The sets were renamed Coastal Defence 'U' boats (CDU). The construction of the wooden equipment cabins, built to a 'back of an envelope' design, was given to a local contractor who was building huts and other work at ADRDE. His estimate was £1,920 and as soon as the cabins were completed the contractor submitted his bills for labour and materials costs. The superintendent wrote to his superior:

"I have taken the exceptional course of paying roughly 80% of this bill, £1,500, from my Imprest [the station cash supply] that I appreciate is entirely illegal, but it should not be the contractor to suffer who, by producing the structures at very short notice, has been the sole means of Dr. Cockcroft's special work being got underway." [9]

A month later the Imprest was still in deficit and remained so until April 1940 when an alarming situation occurred, the Paymaster at Southern Command disallowing the payment, an action that in theory required the officer concerned to settle the deficit from his own pocket. There was immediate and urgent correspondence until the Ministry of Supply paid the full amount two months later.

On the evening of Sunday 15 October an incident arose that was to have repercussions right throughout the RDF chain and like all such events was insignificant in itself. At Stanmore the Filter Room log recorded that Drone Hill went off the air at 1608 as one of the transmitter silica valves developed internal sparking with the only replacement valve having a faulty filament. The laid down rules were that the maintenance section allocated to Drone Hill, which was at RAF Driffield, would supply replacement valves and, if required, technical assistance which, if out of office hours, could be contacted through Staxton.

There was however a misunderstanding as it was thought by Staxton that maintenance was now from Dundee, and the matter remained unresolved until Stanmore phoned BMHQ at 2100 to enquire the reason for the delay. BMHQ confirmed that although it was not until some four hours later that they knew of the situation, it was now in hand. At 2115 BMHQ telephoned Staxton to learn that a Corporal Lowery had left the station for Driffield, some eight miles away where the technical staff were in lodgings. He telephoned back after 15 minutes to say that Driffield would send two valves the next morning, Monday; Stanmore agreed.

Eighty minutes later BMHQ received a call from the Filter Room that the Senior Air Staff Officer was insisting that the valves leave Driffield at once. A Magister aircraft there was attached to the CH maintenance unit that could have flown the valves to RAF Drem near North Berwick but as it was not certified for night flying Driffield were instructed to send the valves immediately by van, a distance of 160 miles. Also at 2330 Stanmore arranged directly for Ottercops to send their one available spare by van. Drone Hill reported serviceable at 2359 but with reduced power. At 0200 a van left Driffield for the eight hour journey, the 'Ottercops' valve arrived at 0900 followed by the 'Driffield' ones at 1030 but Stanmore would not allow the transmitter to be closed down until 1200. The 'Ottercops' valve was found to be faulty and the two 'Driffield' valves would only give an output of about 15kW, way below the maximum of 50kW. Technical assistance had been asked for but the scientific staff at Driffield were on their way to Danby and were redirected to Drone Hill where they arrived at 2230. It was not until midnight that the transmitter was serviceable and the station operational on full power.

On 16 October the officer in charge of BMHQ wrote a letter to DCD, copied to AMRE, Sigs 1A, 2.IU and Fighter Command, expressing his dismay at the ever lengthening list of spare parts that were on order and the time that it was taking for contracts to be completed with some spares not even ordered. The supply to the chain was literally on a hand to mouth basis and the very serious insufficiency of spares could not be overstressed:

> "This deficiency is causing the unserviceability of the chain for unnecessarily long periods, [and] entails emergency action on manufacturers for individual items. It can be said that were the chain to suffer the effects of hostile action, its maintenance might become an impossible problem with the limited spares at our disposal." [10]

Dowding, on 19 October, in a letter to the Air Staff, referred to the BMHQ letter and its effect on the maintenance of the chain with specific attention to Drone Hill. He was also aware of a suggestion that as transmitting valves were in short supply their life could be increased by the simple expedient of reducing the filament voltage; the range would only be reduced by a small amount:

> "Whether I accede to this request or not, it is obvious that the Air Defence of Great Britain is put in jeopardy....I request that this vitally important subject may receive immediate attention at the hands of the authorities concerned and that I may be informed what steps can be taken to ensure a flow of spares adequate to maintain the R.D.F. cover." [10]

A second letter to the Air Staff followed the next day from Dowding, who emphasised that more was necessary than just the supply of adequate spares; he was responsible for operating the chain but the organisation for maintenance was not under his direct control. He partially blamed the Air Staff for their insistence on a 24 hour watch for the chain six months before the outbreak of the war that had largely prevented the modernisation and proper calibration of the chain:

> "I should like to suggest that a small committee should be formed, under the chairmanship of Sir Henry Tizard, if he would consent to undertake the duty, to investigate the working of the R.D.F. system and to make recommendations for its improvement." [10]

The CAS was advised by the Director of Signals that the mushroom growth of what was already a very large and complex organisation had outstripped the present resources of the administrating and directing machinery: the time was ripe for a small committee to investigate the workings of the chain. This was the opportunity for Signals 'empire building' :

> "Is it not time that Mr. Watson Watt was relieved of the above responsibilities and confined himself to research and design...Questions such as the substitution of women operators for men...the defence of R.D.F. stations are clearly outside Mr. Watson Watt's province..." [10]

As a result of Dowding's letter, the CAS ordered the formation of a small committee, which Tizard agreed to chair, to investigate the working of the chain from the technical and operational aspects and to make recommendations for improvements. At its first meeting on 1 November, he obtained a complete picture; Watson Watt and his department, the DCD, were responsible for research and development, production, planning, construction, equipping, commissioning and maintenance, all civilian staffed to a great extent. DCD's unique and anomalous position had arisen through the phenomenal rapid development of RDF and the Air Staff's decision to put it into service while the equipment was still in the research and development stage.

On training Tizard heard that the best of the trainees from the Wireless and Electrical schools at Cranwell (the RAF College in Lincolnshire) and Yatesbury were sent to Bawdsey for RDF training – six weeks for the mechanics and two for the operators. But many had to wait until vacancies arose and meanwhile were posted direct to chain stations. Problems had, therefore, arisen there because of the lack of operator training for some and the short course for those at Bawdsey; they were uncertain and hesitant in determining sense when the echo was small and the noise heavy, when the echo was beating and when the aircraft were well clear of the station Line of Shoot.

Signals had plans to introduce large numbers of women operators to alleviate the grave shortage of RAF operators and train them at Bawdsey until WAAF accommodation and facilities were provided at Yatesbury, where the RDF school was under construction. The biggest burden on the chain was the supply and training of filterers, which had met with little success, with great difficulty being experienced in selecting airmen of suitable intelligence and characteristics without mis-employing tradesmen; one outstanding filterer was a corporal in the trade of equipment accounting, while airmen in the wireless operator trade had proved to be quite indifferent even though experienced as operators on CH stations.

In his interim report of 28 November Tizard outlined the history of the chain; the first three RDF stations on the east coast were in existence just two years ago and, due to the political crises in Europe in late 1938 and early 1939, the Air Staff had ordered that very hurried steps had to be taken to erect and operate the remainder of the chain along the south and southeast coasts of England in the shortest possible time. As a result of that decision it was necessary to establish improvised equipment in temporary accommodation and place it on continuous operation. Every effort was being made to complete the stations with the Final equipment, but only seven out of the twenty stations had the high power transmitter (½CH), with none having the approved receiver (RF6) or the second wavelength. Tizard commented:

> "In all the circumstances it is not surprising that there are technical imperfections at the stations. The surprising fact is that the stations are working so well. We only have to consider the state of affairs that would exist in the absence of R.D.F. information to realise to the full the great technical achievements of the last few years." [11]

The shortcomings were well documented by Fighter Command. There were permanent echoes from fixed objects at Douglas Wood, interference at Dunkirk from the London Balloon barrage, insufficient coverage in the Humber and Firth of Forth areas, 10% D/F errors at Stenigot and Dunkirk and at Ventnor and Staxton some tracks disappeared due to gaps in the cover. There was no detection of low flying aircraft and an inability to detect aircraft flying above 25,000ft. Other criticisms on technical reliability and the training of personnel raised indirectly the whole question of responsibility for the chain. His report concluded:

> "..that a change in the present system of responsibility is necessary, both from the point of view of technical and of operational requirements...From the point of view of any Commander-in-Chief, it appears to us that his chief need is to acquire correct information without necessarily knowing how that information is obtained...and in our opinion there is much to be said for the formation of a separate Command solely for the purpose of organising the various means of tracking aircraft." [11]

Tizard was also of the opinion that there was too much control in the hands of the DCD, which was a result of the need for secrecy. In his report to the CAS on 1 December he wrote:

> "We envisage the eventual separation of the operation of the chain, or indeed, of any responsibility for it, from Fighter Command. It does not follow from this that we are unanimously convinced that this responsibility should be removed now (although Air Marshal Joubert is of the opinion that it should be). I feel that the C-in-C will have strong arguments for saying that as he is responsible for the Air Defence of Great Britain, he cannot accept the view

that one of the most important instruments enabling him to discharge his responsibility is taken away from his direct control." [11]

The CAS disagreed with the formation of a Command and suggested the formation of a group in Fighter Command to take over all the installation and maintenance of the chain from DCD, which would remain responsible for research, development, production and for the interpretation of the Air Staff requirements.

The problem at Dunkirk was a serious handicap as the display from 27 to 53 miles was full of beating echoes, some two to three centimetres in height, with the same effect at Canewdon but on a much reduced scale. The situation was quite unexpected and had only shown an appearance on the day that war was declared when balloons were fully raised over London for the first time. If there was no solution, Dowding threatened to close the station and consider another one near North Foreland at a cost of £150,000; the matter was handed to Wilkins for action. As the echoes were produced by leakage from the rear of the transmitting aerial, Wilkins designed a small horizontal diamond shape aerial that was erected behind the main array 100ft from the ground pointing towards London. Connection to the transmission line was made in such a way that a small proportion of the power, about one fifth, was radiated in opposite phase to the main array; the effect was reduced to 2 to 3 millimetres.

Equipment began to arrive to provide air cover for the naval base in Scapa Flow. Any hindrance to progress official or otherwise was quickly removed by the password 'Ring Admiral Somerville at this number'. For the southern approach, Wick had been surveyed in early October and an area selected at Thrumster, four miles south, one mile from the coast. To provide Advance CH (ACH) equipment, but without heightfinding, the Army 7 metre GL sets were modified by 2.IU to extend the range from 30 to 90 miles and renamed GM. By mid October the first CDU was on its way to the Shetlands Islands where a naval crew with a sub-lieutenant in charge was sent from Portsmouth to meet AMRE scientists at Sumburgh airport. A good site was quickly found at Sumburgh Head, 300ft above sea level in the grounds of the lighthouse, which also had the advantage of ease of access and security.

One of the two CDU sets earmarked for Fair Isle was diverted to the Isle of May, in the Firth of Forth, to detect enemy aircraft on mine laying missions; a survey was made on 22 October and a note made of the possible transportation difficulties of a generator and transmitter that weighed two tons each, two aerial arrays that required eight men to lift, the receiver, plus three prefabricated huts and stores. A special visit was made to the island on 24 October by AMRE personnel to look at this particular aspect, which was not part of their professional work, and the conclusion they reached was that shipping should be made available from Leith Docks in Edinburgh in a suitable wind and tide.

Inclement weather at that time of the year forced the abandonment of the landing, which was considered arduous enough in fine, and an alternative site was quickly found on the mainland on 8 November at Crail, near Anstruther, on the Fife coast. (It is understood that a different version for the move to Crail exists– the ship's company was 'unwell' !) The station was erected by a naval crew in record time under the supervision of a scientific observer, Dr M.V. Wilkes, MA PhD (now Sir Maurice), and was ready on 17 November awaiting an air test.

On 30 October at Duxford, RAE were ready to demonstrate the prototype VHF R/T to Fighter Command. Six Spitfire aircraft were available, in two groups of three, for the station controller to make range, manoeuvres and 'homing' bearing tests. Communication was established as soon as the groups became airborne without tuning calls as needed for the TR9. Each group leader reported the other group's transmissions for at least 100 miles, until, at that considerable distance apart, they became unintelligible.

From the ground, good two-way communication was maintained, just over 140 miles at 10,000ft. Bearings had a high degree of accuracy that would require larger scale D/F maps. As expected, the reception of speech was exceptional, the observers being of the opinion that it was as good, if not better, than the Post Office telephone network. A comparison was made by a Spitfire with a TR9D immediately after the conclusion of the trials, which was very unfavourable compared to VHF, whose demonstration was considered an outstanding success.

It was recommended that immediate action should be taken to re-equip all sectors without delay and the Director of Signals wrote to ACAS the next day of his approval. He added that there could be no doubt that even this Mark 1 equipment opened up a completely new chapter of R/T aircraft communication:

"I think that you will agree that the successful outcome of this hard fought battle, after the various difficulties that have arisen including two appeals to the C.A.S., is a matter of great satisfaction and reflects the greatest possible credit on all concerned particularly No. 10 Department of R.A.E., who have evolved in a matter of 10 months a completely new scheme, which previously has taken four years or more to produce. All the representatives of Fighter Command present ...were most enthusiastic regarding the results obtained and are only too anxious that the equipment shall be generally introduced as quickly as possible..." [12]

Air Marshal W.Sholto Douglas wrote to the CAS on 3 November that the conclusions drawn from the air trials were that the introduction of VHF for fighter aircraft would permit a remarkable advance in the present scope of squadron control and his authority was requested for immediate implementation. The CAS replied the same day that there was great credit on all concerned and to proceed; he would like to know when requisitions would be issued and contracts placed and perhaps the ACAS would report back by 15 November. However casual the reply appeared it was in effect a CAS instruction and the relevant departments in the Air Ministry acted swiftly. By November 9 all the major requisitions had been ordered and the ITP, the Intention to Purchase contracts, were placed on the 14 and 15 of November.

On 1 November Joubert received a private note from the DCAS that on his return from France he was to be attached to the Air Staff for special duties as the Air Co-ordinating Officer for RDF. He was to examine the operational, technical and administration details of the chain and to advise the Air Staff of any deficiencies, as there was no command organisation or document or order which laid down who was in charge. He was responsible for co-ordinating all the aspects of RDF and for seeing that action was taken to remedy the deficiency of equipment and personnel with the utmost dispatch.

His other duties were to advise the Director of Signals on re-organisation and training and also the Director of Communications Development of the expansion of RDF to meet the needs of the RAF. Although at this stage Joubert was only an adviser he began to play an increasing part in the direction of policy as he would now attend all the important meetings and committees, many as the chairman.

One of Joubert's first actions was to suggest to the CAS that Dowding's control of the chain should cease at the filter room and, in a letter on 12 November explaining his view, he suggested that the operation of an RDF station was a technical matter best removed from control by Fighter Command;

> "...[Dowding] has different views, [and] he regards the R.D.F. chain as one of his functions to be controlled and administered by himself. He is only prepared to give up the training to an outside organisation." [13]

But in his reply, the CAS stated that he agreed with the C. in C. Fighter Command that the chain was as much a part of Fighter Command as was the Observer Corps:

> "The success of his operations depends to a considerable extent on the efficiency of the chain and, rightly I think, he wants to be able to ensure that its efficiency is of the highest order. He can only do that if he controls and administers it." [13]

Dowding was always conscious of the number of fighters in the air, as many as 160, just to provide air cover for the many convoys of ships proceeding along the east coasts, with one of the hazards of being shot at by naval vessels, which were on convoy duty. On 27 September, when HMS *Valorous* and HMS *Hastings* were exercising off the Isle of May, they were attacked by enemy aircraft believed to be Heinkels. 603 Squadron were sent out as the patrol and while flying in formation at 1,000ft were fired on by one of the vessels. In a similar incident off Skegness, on 17 October, a patrol sent out for protection of the convoy received the heaviest fire from naval ships with one aircraft being hit.

He wrote to the Air Staff to complain that there had been no expression of regret from the Admiralty, and he was thinking of ordering all his fighters to remain outside the range of HM ships unless he was convinced that the Navy was honestly attempting to co-operate and educate its personnel in the difficult process of recognition. He added:

"I have repeatedly heard the expression from the most senior officers of the Navy – we shall open fire first and ask questions afterwards....In my opinion any [RAF] officer giving vent to this sentiment should be court-martialled." [14]

Dowding had earlier tried for RDF coverage in the Highlands of Scotland, where it was impossible to establish the Observer Corps, but now he was no longer content with the bare statement that RDF could not be provided in the Highlands; that it could not be used due to the hilly country. He wrote on 26 October:

"It seems reasonable to suppose that if the chain station will not give an echo from an object less then 1000ft in height, then an R.D.F. station on top of a hill should not give echoes from other hills which are lower than its own site...The danger of our Firth and Clyde defences being outflanked without our being able to keep track of raids is so great, that I recommend that one of our portable R.D.F. stations be erected on the highest accessible ground in the Highlands so that a practical trial can be made as soon as possible." [15]

It took five months to be organised. By the end of June 1940 an exercise had been held in the Scottish Highlands to test Dowding's theory that an RDF station on top of a hill would be free from permanent echoes. Using a GM mobile set the ranges achieved were well below those usually obtained, 22 miles at 5,000ft, 45 miles at 10,000ft with the first 12 miles useless on account of the large numbers of local echoes; further trials were abandoned.

From the beginning of October the German Air Force began to attack coastal shipping in the North Sea, mainly small craft of 500 to 2,000 tons, coal carriers not yet fitted with guns, and lightships. Towards the end of that month and the beginning of November the number of ships, especially those in harbour, that were sunk began to increase causing the Admiralty to suspect that mines were being dropped by parachute. The first definite evidence came on the night of 21 November when twin float seaplanes, Heinkel 115s, operating from the islands of Sylt and Borkum, were seen to drop mines in the Humber and the Thames Estuary. Planes were heard and seen in bright moonlight approaching at a great height and then, with the engines switched off, gliding down to about 600ft above the sea.

One was seen to drop a large object attached to a parachute into the sea near Shoeburyness, north of the Thames Estuary, and the Admiralty was advised that it could be recoverable by 0400 hours. A party was organised of two naval staff officers, soldiers equipped with lights, rope and tackle, with two photographers; the mine was recovered and taken to HMS *Vernon* at Portsmouth. Churchill gave orders that work was to proceed night and day until the answer had been found. It was a magnetic mine and within hours the secret of its operation revealed and neutralising action taken immediately. Much success had been achieved at first by the Germans. On 4 November the new cruiser HMS *Belfast* was mined in the Firth of Forth, the destroyer HMS *Blanche* mined and sunk in the Thames Estuary on 13 November, and on 21 November the destroyer HMS *Gipsy* suffered the same fate at the entrance to Harwich. By December a total of ten Royal Navy vessels had been lost.

The seriousness of the situation regarding the detection of low flying aircraft was quickly conveyed to the Air Staff. On 22 November the Director of Signals chaired an urgent meeting to discuss ways and means by which RDF cover could be very quickly provided. The Director asked if any time could be saved by robbing the French of allocated training sets and converting to CHL, but, after a discussion, they concurred that no such useful purpose could be served. Cockcroft was immediately requested to survey a site north of the Thames at Walton-on-the-Naze (Essex), and south at Foreness (Kent). AMRE quickly carried out site surveys at Dover, along the east coast at Dunwich (Suffolk) to cover Harwich, Happisburgh (pronounced 'Haysboro' by the locals), to cover the Wash, Easington to cover the Humber, Shotton to cover Tyne and Tees and Cockburnspath near St Abbs Head to cover the Firth of Forth. Joubert ordered GM sets to be rushed at breakneck speed to the selected sites where a Line of Shoot was given for the aerials to face and for the CHL aerials to be secured in windy weather.

Within weeks of starting CHL production a major modification took place, the first of many that followed. A second tube was added that showed an expansion of the original trace for easier isolation of the selected echo for 'split' to obtain the bearing. DCD had accepted the view that a single tube display was unable to meet the possible contingency of multiple raids separated by only a few miles as the echoes would be closely spaced and the application of 'split' would cause confusion.

The German Air Force tactics in the bombing of defenceless merchant ships caused the writer of Fighter Command's Air Staff Diary to comment that 'there would appear to be, on physical evidence alone, a Mongolian trait in the Prussian and in general it could be said that Germany only felt to a limited extent the impact of classical Rome, and so missed most of an important chapter in the civilisation of Europe'. He added:

"The routine of the Filter and the Operations Room is like the general routine of the Great War [the 1914-1918 war], long periods of inactivity interrupted by short bursts of excitement. At some times particularly about midnight and dawn and, more particularly throughout days of fog and rain, there is a lotus land tranquillity during which on the ground floor in a pre-digested atmosphere, the men and women plotters would be engrossed unravelling a tale of deception or murder in a newspaper or novels, or in dropping or purling stitches in some elaborate knitting.

On the first floor the controllers with their multifarious colleagues, naval, bomber, coastal, civil observers, gunners and wardens would watch wearily and monotonously for a sign from heaven which the Germans would not give. Then, suddenly, from one of several sources there would come intimations of a raid, it was plotted say one or more aircraft, flying at 15,000ft at 250mph towards the estuary. An unknown quantity, it was labelled 'X' and given a number to distinguish it chronologically from its forebears and its followers. The C. in C. deputy would be summoned from his office to the scene, meanwhile the three Fighter groups had the same plot in their Operations Room and, within their own area, they were exercising the executive. The C. in C. did not interpose except where the responsibility of a Group might be in doubt. His primary function was to issue or withhold air raid warning red or green.

Fresh plots would appear. They will identify it as a friendly or as a hostile, more and more plots appear on the table. It has been identified as a hostile and everybody knows that patrols are up to intercept it. The matter is now out of the hands of the controller and must await a combat report which will give the last chapter of the story, the raider has been shot down or has escaped to Germany. There are now no more observations or plots, all the ground floor eyes are trained once more to newspapers or knitting." [6]

An ex-sector commander, who was posted to Stanmore, wrote to Hart on 27 November that he had received a rude shock regarding the reliability of RDF;

"...we had a childlike faith in the absolute accuracy of a plot which appeared on our table. I had no idea that there were limitations as regards height and numbers, or that there were certain areas in which aircraft might not be picked up. What is worse...I assumed that if the [Operations Room] table was clear then there were no aircraft about." [16]

Hart replied that he had taken vast steps to spy continuously on the chain:

"The mysterious civilians who devote their time making notes in the Filter

Room are the only visible members of this 'spy' system, but there is a complicated system of analysis applied to their observations which has already produced some most valuable results." [16]

Park wrote to Dowding that the RDF limitations in respect of height should be issued to sector controllers and a personal talk to them by Hart was suggested. Dowding replied that it depended on what he was going to tell them:

"If he says that the R.D.F. is very capricious and unreliable, but better than nothing as being the best evidence we have of what is going on over the sea, I don't mind, but we could tell them that by letter!" [16]

Park wrote to the four Groups on the limitations of RDF:

"Range and position is accurate to within a mile, height readings in the Thames Estuary are ±1,000ft, elsewhere ± 2,000ft. For the number of aircraft 1 to 3 is accurate, 1 plus means more than one aircraft up to any number, 3 plus means 3 to 9, and 9 plus means more than 9. There is a time lag of 1½ minutes from the operator at the R.D.F. station to the plot appearing on Sector or Group tables." [16]

AMRE were busy on surveys in Scotland as the Air Staff had approved the defence of Glasgow from the west and the south, which had resulted in sites being selected at Greenock, where a local golf course was requisitioned, and at Gleniffer Braes, Paisley, where a site 150 yards north east of Sarjeants Law was pinpointed. For general cover in the Scottish Highlands it was believed that the top of Ben Nevis would be suitable where there were the remains of an observatory that had been closed since 1904. At Tobermory a Post Office station could be used to give cover across the north and the west. However, none of the sites became stations because it was eventually decided that Stranraer would suffice. There was another visit there with a local farmer complaining that a previous siting team had caused damage to his grouse shooting and he was claiming compensation. Earlier, there was a visit to Fraserburgh in Aberdeenshire where Hillhead, near Memsie, was selected and a revisit to West Prawle to prepare a layout for two Lines of Shoot of 107 and 130 degrees.

By the beginning of December the CHL sets were being installed by 2.IU with supervising scientific officers; each station required two locations, one for the transmitter and one for the receiver hut spaced about 75 yards apart. Straddling each hut was a 20ft wooden gantry upon which was bolted a metal turntable fitted with a metal cradle into which the aerial assembly, 26ft by 13ft, was secured. It was rotated by a 36ft (11m) length of bicycle chain connected to a sprocket wheel fixed to an upturned bicycle frame secured to the floor of the hut. Stops were fitted so that the sweep, which took eight minutes to complete, covered a range of 200 degrees that ensured overlapping with adjacent CHLs. The sole duty of the transmitter operator was to ensure that the direction of the array was identical to that of the receiver. As he was inside the trailer there was a simple meter scale that indicated the direction of the aerials relative to each other. When the needle was dead centre then both arrays were in line, but if left or right then turning was required to bring the needle back to the midpoint. The tedium of the task was made worse by access holes in the roof for the chain that provided an unwelcome entry of the outside weather. The linkage was the weakest part of the aerial system as the arrays were quite impossible to control even in moderate winds, and above certain wind speeds had to be lashed to the ground.

In December the CDU sets at Foreness and Walton (known as CHL because they were used for the location of low flying aircraft), were in operation and carefully watched; at first the transmitter and the RF tuners required periodical adjustments and were checked every two hours for drift.
It was reported that:

> "The [handmade CDU] receiver is the worst piece of workmanship ever seen, dry soldered joints, over run resistors and condensers [capacitors] and instability caused by missing grid stoppers. The design did not favour a rapid change of anything, least of all the Acorn valves that took 30 minutes." [4]

Periodic inspection of all aerial joints was deemed essential and all the steel screws, now rusting from the salt sea spray, would have to be replaced with brass. The maximum range at Foreness was ships at 17 miles, aircraft 24 miles at 500ft, 34 miles at 1,000ft, 53 miles at 4,000ft and 65 miles at 5,000ft, but the results were erratic.

There, at a later date, 600 Squadron repeated the 'Lamb' interception experiments with day and night flying. The technique was for the operator to watch the echo of the 'bomber' and to disregard the fighter echo, which was moving under radio instructions from the controller, who was sitting next to the operator at the tube console. The lack of height information was a serious drawback and the HF R/T communication channel with the fighter suffered from high interference resulting in poor contact between ground and aircraft.

Although considered to be inconclusive, Hart and other RAF officers remained convinced that the future of quick and effective interceptions would be direct from the tube, not through the time delaying filter-to-operations room chain. The one big disadvantage of interceptions from the tube face was that the station could not then perform its original function of reporting plots to the filter room.

Operational at the end of the year, Dunwich in performance was found to be far below that of Foreness, aircraft at 10 miles fading at 2,000 – 3,000ft, which was eventually found to be due to the station being substantially off-tune; there was no wavemeter available. Maintenance was the greatest problem as no stations had an Avometer and few with a Megger.

One of the main reasons for the move of BRS to Dundee was the nearness of the CH station at Douglas Wood, which was expected to be the least active of all the CH stations, and so would serve as a part experimental station. But since the beginning of the war it had been in the zone of maximum enemy activity with long periods on 'standby', making it unsuitable for research; wind and the very cold weather had also seriously delayed field work there. The young Fl/Lt in charge of Douglas Wood was, of course, completely unaware of the background of AMRE, the reason for the sudden influx of scientists and the need for them to get familiar with RDF. On 1 December he wrote to Rowe complaining of the AMRE scientists who appeared in the wooden receiver hut from time to time; he wanted the number reduced:

"Some of the younger members of the research staff do not perhaps realise the importance of the operational work done here, and are apt to gather in the receiver hut just as on-lookers without adequate duties to justify their presence..." [18]

Rowe sent him a private and personal letter on 8 December:

"I quite realise what a nuisance the research staff must be to you, and I will make a point of telling the C-in-C [Dowding] the position when next I see him...Your station, as well as the others, have been made possible as a result of research, and a great deal of research remains to be done; we cannot stop research in war... I think it will make it clear to you if I say that we are having considerable additions to the scientific staff and that these are men who know nothing of our work, and it is important that they should, in fact, do nothing but look on for a day or so in order to see how the station works...We will be as understanding as we can, but I am afraid we must, as I say, continue to be a nuisance for another two months." [18]

The Fl/Lt's reply was that he did not intend to belittle the importance of AMRE:

"All your staff must be working under considerable difficulties...I can assure you that everything possible to assist them will be done here." [18]

On 6 December Rowe heard the news that the transfer had been approved in principle, Watson Watt told him the next day that it was all in his hands and he was free to contact the various headquarters sections direct. One thing that Rowe emphasised to his staff was that there would be no action until the accommodation was complete; he would not repeat the mistake of the move to Dundee. He appointed an officer to follow up all aspects of the move and in the file already opened, titled '*The move from Dundee*', Rowe inserted:

"I should like a report on the position of the move on the file every Monday morning, more often if anything is holding up the move." [3]

The first groups of WAAF operators to the CH chain had been enthusiastically received. At Poling they had proved very much more satisfactory than the officer in charge had anticipated and he noted that their ability to read through interference was exceptionally good. On 26 December, the officer at Dover wrote that in his opinion the WAAF in time would be able to take over all the plotting and operating.....provided there was an RAF corporal RDF as the girls had little or no technical knowledge and did not understand the various adjustments on the receiver. A policy decision had been made that when one WAAF watch on each CH station had been completed then a second one would be posted in until the station was wholly manned by WAAF operators. The training sums were simple – 54 WAAF at each station, 23 stations, so nearly 1,300 women required. The main problem was the accommodation, it being provided exclusively for the RAF and there were limitations to the number of requisitioned properties that were available nearby.

Cockcroft was actively involved in the installation of three CHL stations. The first one was at Happisburgh where the aerials had been erected and connected by 21 December but as there was trouble with the receiver the station was not functioning until 24 December. Cockcroft and two assistants had left for Shotton and had to wait for the aerials that arrived the next day, 23 December at 4.30pm. If there were thoughts that they could all go home for Christmas, and this included the riggers and labourers from 2.IU, it was not to be as the aerial assembly and erection could not start until 24 December, the station not completed until 27 December. When two scientific officers arrived at Easington on 24 December the aerials had not arrived, half coming in the evening and the remainder the next day, Christmas Day. Boxing Day was no holiday either as it was work as usual. It was not until the end of the year that the three stations were passing plots to the nearest CH station.

There had not been sufficient time to obtain Army guards so airmen were quickly posted from the nearest RAF station. At one site on a cliff edge an inspecting RAF officer found them huddled together in a packing case to escape the biting wind– there had not been time to order a guard hut. They had to live on site under canvas inside the compound unlike the RAF operators and mechanics who were billeted in the nearest village.

The Army representative at the Ministry of Supply wrote on 18 December direct to Joubert that he was experiencing endless trouble of a petty nature, but none the less irritating, in soothing contractors who had not received official orders for goods that had been supplied weeks before, and also from his contract branches, which he had short-circuited by ordering from the firms direct:

"All these grouses I have to try and settle personally, all I need is a written request to supply. I feel that you will probably be able to move more quickly.....and it does want straightening out quickly." [19]

Joubert, with the authority of an Air Marshal, soon settled the matter with advice to the Air Ministry departments that if action was not taken quickly, then the Ministry of Supply 'would make difficulties the next time we wanted something in a hurry'. Little did he realise that it would be sooner rather than later. Another headache for Joubert to sort out was the crash programme of the CHL installations initiated by DCD on advice from Larnder at Stanmore. Fighter Command was made aware of the extra cover and had agreed on the locations but did not take part in the selection of the sites and Signals were unaware of the extra stations until requests for telephone lines were received. Furthermore, Dowding had complained about the AMRE site proposal on the Isle of Man – the summit of Snaefel:

"The site has been selected on purely scientific grounds with no regard at all to the considerable expense and administrative difficulties involved, least of all the operation of the railway to the summit." [20]

In rejecting it he also refused to accept any future recommendations unless represented on the survey party. At a meeting on 17 December Joubert agreed: AMRE for the technical aspects of the site, Works for tower suitability, land acquisition and services, Signals for installing the equipment and telephone lines and Fighter Command for admin and control of the completed station; the area Post Office official would also be in attendance. AMRE would communicate the survey results to the relevant HQ sections plus the AOC Fighter Command and BMHQ by the use of a proforma signal on the RAF teleprinter network that conveyed all the site information but did not compromise the secrecy of RDF.

Rowe had arranged for monthly meetings at Dundee for the scientific observers who were at the CH stations and a few of the remarks are taken from their reports:

"At Stenigot the Fl/Lt adopts a difficult attitude in not allowing scientific observers to operate the receiver. At Danby the Fl/Lt needs backing up as the F/Sgt who previously ran the station resents his arrival. At Ottercops, Fl/Lt S.F.Evans, Ph.D., a short wave research man, wishes he could be used less for admin and more on radio work. Noisy echoes when turning the goniometer due to dirty slip-rings are cleared by the operators using a fire extinguisher rather than wait for maintenance." [21]

(It is thought that this unofficial mini-maintenance was responsible for the issue of an instruction that the 'Improper use of fire extinguishers is to cease forthwith.', but it alerted others to the fact that they were a prime source of carbon tetrachloride that was ideal for the cleaning of switch contacts.)

There was a continuing delay in the supply of IFF sets. DCD had decided that no set was to go into operation without the provision of an explosive charge for its destruction, which could be set off by the pilot, or automatically, if the aircraft were shot down. To obscure the regenerative nature of the set, the essential components were grouped together and provision made for sliding an explosive cartridge underneath them. The redesign was given to RAE, which commented adversely on the original BRS set as they were the designers of airborne equipment. Such was the dire need for IFF, however, that 1,000 sets were ordered without the explosive, which would be added later. The contractor, Ferranti, was requested to provide the materials for a further 10,000 sets.

On 21 December one of Dowding's worst fears was realised. Twenty-four Hampden bombers had flown from two Lincolnshire aerodromes for a reconnaissance over northern Germany, and had returned in four formations of six apiece in the afternoon. But, unexpected by Fighter Command they approached in the guise of raid X37 at 15,000ft, a yellow air raid warning being given. 13 Group sent up three squadrons, 72 and 602 from Drem and 43 from Acklington to investigate. Over the Firth of Forth with the light deteriorating at 1515, one section of fighters thought they were Dorniers, while another section of 602 delivered an attack and shot down two Hampdens. Bomber Command had not advised Fighter Command of the time and their point of return and the fighter pilots had been unable to recognise one of the most striking of their own bomber force.

A complicated identification system was already in operation; the bombers leaving their airfield had the radio set tuned to the HF band with the wireless operator maintaining a listening watch to and from the target until reaching about 100 miles from the coast. The navigator then instructed the wireless operator (W/Op) to change to the MF band to send an identification signal and this involved him changing the coils, retuning and also running out a trailing aerial. After it had been sent the set was retuned to HF to obtain instructions and for direction finding back to base.

By December two steel towers were completed at 18 sites, many with four, but at some stations not on the same Line of Shoot as the wooden ones. At

Drone Hill the T towers were 22 degrees further east and at Dunkirk the T towers were 44 degrees towards the north. All the 2.IU effort was directed to the rigging of the transmitting aerials, known as a 'star' array, a six element end fed array with one reflector, between the 350ft and 220ft cantilevers with transmission lines down the tower and into the T building, a task that took eight men eight days. As calibration was not necessary, the ½ CH transmitter was in use as soon as scientific officers had completed the commissioning tests. Fighter Command reported that limited experience at Bawdsey had shown that the increase in power achieved a success in excess of that anticipated. Range was slightly improved, over 100 miles at 10,000ft but the accuracy of D/F was exceptional with the precision of heightfinding good at ± 1,000ft above 6,000ft. These improvements were entirely due to the three to four times increase in echo height that enabled the tube operator to find the 'minimum' with confidence. Except for Netherbutton and Schoolhill, all the R blocks had been completed and ready for an RF6 and aerial arrays on the third tower. Calibration was under way but was made precarious by the intense German air activity along the east and southeast coasts that required fighter escorts for the calibrating aircraft. Larnder advised AMRE that it was 'extremely essential' to devote immediate thought and research towards simpler methods of calibration than that of the present practice of using balloons, which had to be flown at considerable heights from vessels at sea. An Autogyro fitted with a pulse transmitter was suggested and in under a week Hart advised Rowe that three Autogyros with two qualified pilots were being hired for six months from the manufacturers, who were on the point of closing down the factory because of the lack of work.

   Rowe had received a letter from his scientific officer at Staxton Wold on calibration, which was representative of many stations:

   "Progress is slow, aircraft are difficult to get... yesterday we had one flight but owing to an error somewhere it started at the wrong place and only passed by the edge of us... Today is not good [for test flights] because of mist. New [½] CH transmitter being installed." [22]

The post of Inspector-General had been revived by the Air Council in 1935 in order to assist the Chief of the Air Staff in the work of supervising the rapid expansion of the Royal Air Force. The I/G had enormous power as the post was usually held by a very high ranking officer who had 'retired' prior to leaving the Service. He reported, if that is the correct word for an Air Chief Marshal, to the CAS on training and matters affecting the efficiency of the RAF and the current state of air defence – virtually everything. Little known perhaps by the rank and file, he certainly was by the officer commanding of any station due to the thoroughness of his inspections that could range from ablutions to workshops.

At the beginning of the war the second I/G, Sir Edward Ellington, who had earlier retired as the CAS, had visited the CH station at Dunkirk where he found that ground defence was provided by 32 men of the Buffs Regiment, and air defence by 60 gunners with the three Bofor LAA gun and two Lewis gun posts without guns. In charge was one RAF Sergeant with other ranks, 12 technicians and three civilians, all living out. At Canewdon the gunners were living under canvas in bad conditions and at Poling the airmen, civilians and the Warrant Officer were in billets but the Royal Artillery gun detachment slept in huts beside their guns.

He found at Yatesbury that the technical buildings and barrack blocks were not 'blacked out' because of the shortage of materials. That was a serious matter as a vast number of hours of instruction were being lost during the hours of darkness when all activities ceased completely; the only lighting available for reading or games was in the canteens or messes (Service dining rooms). He made a few more visits after Christmas. At Schoolhill there was one Fl/Lt in charge with 14 airmen, the officer and NCOs billeted locally but the airmen travelled daily to and from RAF Dyce, a few miles north of Aberdeen, where, as no beds were available, the men had to sleep on palliasses (straw mattresses). There was no electricity except for the RDF equipment or running hot water, cold water being conveyed daily from Dyce in a 500 gallon tank then re-issued in two gallon cans; cooking took place in a temporary building. Sanitary conditions were primitive with the widely dispersed points served by Elsan closets and the main camp with field latrines.

At Stenigot he found that the huts for the RAF and the WAAF were being constructed to the north on a by-road; the site was very exposed and was bitterly cold at the time of his visit. There were no 'comforts' (welfare and indoor games, dartboards and radio sets) received from the Central Fund nor had they been asked for as the officer in charge, an ex-schoolmaster, had thought that others had more need of comforts than the men on his station. There were two or three radio sets in use but these were on hire by the users.

Attempts had been made to visit Staxton Wold but without success owing to the approach road being very steep and covered with ice and snow. Vehicles had also failed to get access but the I/G had been assured that there were reserve rations on the station. At Ottercops Moss the huts for the RAF billets had been lying on the site for some time as no decision had yet had been made on where they would be erected; the RAF were at present being billeted in houses at a considerable distance from the station that was causing a measure of dissatisfaction. At Drone Hill he was told of the intention to substitute 35 WAAF for RAF which he considered to be undesirable at such an isolated station; huts had been constructed but as they were without electricity, lighting was by hurricane lamps.

Freeman received a letter from the Ministry of Supply, that had only been formed in June, to the effect that it wanted to take over the production of RDF equipment:

"The Supply Minister is now in some doubt whether a Directorate so fully occupied in research and experiment embracing the requirement of all three Services, and dealing with a subject so complex and still so embryonic, could at the same time deal adequately with the pressing needs of production..." [23]

There was also Admiralty backing for the proposal. Freeman wrote to the CAS:

"It is clear that if we do not accede to the suggestion for a separate directorate for production, the Ministry of Supply will have a strong political case for taking over R.D.F. production which will be disastrous. With only one Director and deputy, the great increase in quantity and the general urgency on the development side has resulted in a serious loss of drive and supervision on the research side. It is proposed to rename the directorate as the Directorate of Research and Development of Communications and a new Directorate of Communication Equipment Production." [24]

The CAS agreed, adding that he considered the reorganisation most necessary and urgent.

On 27 December, the CDU at Sumburgh began to pass plots by W/T to HMS *Greenwich*, moored in Scapa Flow, which also had a plotting line to Netherbutton, but the plots were solely for the Admiralty to alert naval vessels. Aircraft were detected at 70 miles and submarines at 25 miles. The convenience of the site had now revealed two disadvantages; the nearness of a 1 million candle power light and the foghorn tower, which on occasions emitted a seven second blast every 90 seconds.

At Fair Isle conditions were found to be rudimentary in the extreme: no telephone lines, only a single line for sending telegrams to Orkney or Shetland and no motor transport. Using ox carts at a speed of two miles per hour, the two CDU sets were taken to Ward Hill, 712ft above sea level and sited back to back to give maximum coverage. Installation was by naval ratings under the supervision of scientific officers that continued into January and February 1940. The very severe weather, however, delayed the operation of one set by blowing the aerial assembly away but both were eventually in service by the beginning of March 1940.

Joubert, in his capacity as the Air Co-ordinating Officer, had put forward to the ACAS that there was justification for an individual who would ensure that the Air Staff received the best scientific advice on telecommunications, and who was free from the responsibilities of research, design and production. He added that experience gained by the actual users should be made available to Research and Development and the Directorate of Production should be rapidly informed of requirements not being fulfilled covering W/T, R/T and RDF. An advisor to the Dominions and the Colonies on telecommunication matters was also vitally necessary; he recommended the appointment of an Inspector of RAF Telecommunications.

The ACAS agreed but a meeting that followed it was proposed that the name be changed to the Scientific Adviser on Telecommunications (SAT) to the Air Ministry. In a memo to the CAS, Joubert advised him that the DCD was to retain Research and Development but that production was to be made into a separate directorate because of the rapid and huge increases in demand for RDF; he also put forward the proposal for a scientific adviser:

"The new applications of R.D.F. in its various forms require constant scientific advice and very large developments in R.D.F are anticipated in the future: it is proposed that Mr. Watson Watt, whose knowledge and experience is unique, should be given the post." [25]

The CAS did not like the proposed title which he thought rather long-winded, preferring instead 'Technical Adviser of Signals Air Ministry'.

REFERENCES

1	AVIA7/600	2	AVIA7/533	3	AVIA7/601	4	AVIA7/448
5	AIR16/262	6	AIR24/520	7	AIR16/677	8	AIR2/2965
9	AVIA7/3269	10	AIR2/3143	11	AIR20/189	12	AIR2/2946
13	AIR2/5086	14	AIR16/263	15	AIR2/4489	16	AIR16/19
17	AVIA7/445	18	AVIA7/496	19	AIR20/2272	20	AIR2/3271
21	AVIA7/243	22	AVIA7/294	23	AIR2/2942	24	AIR2/4257
25	AIR2/3181						

Chapter 8   *January to June 1940*

A LETTER to the Treasury on January 4 from the Air Council contained the proposal for the split of the DCD into Research and Production:

> "and it is further proposed that the Signals Directorate under the Air Staff should have a full time scientific adviser, and authority is requested to appoint Mr. Watson Watt, whose knowledge and experience are unique, to the post with increased pay, from £1,500 to £1,600. In the place of Mr.Watson Watt it is proposed to appoint Sir George Lee, recently retired from the Post Office as Chief Engineer, to be paid £1,700 from Air Funds and £300 from the Paymaster General [Pensions fund] to make up to the £2,000 he drew as Chief Engineer." [1]

The Treasury were not, at first, in full agreement with the proposals as they queried the necessity for a scientific adviser and wanted to know what particular duties he would perform that were not covered by Air Marshal Joubert and the new director of R and D:

> "We are at a loss to understand the appointment of another director who, as far as we know, has not been in touch with the development of R.D.F. It is agreed on the separation of production from research and development, but why cannot Mr. Watson Watt concentrate on research and development and thus avoid the necessity for creating a new post? " [1]

A reply to the Treasury followed:

> "R.D.F. is now so wide and the extensions in manifold directions so important, that we have no doubt that the new post is urgently necessary and that Mr Watson Watt is the proper person to fill it." [1]

The Treasury gave way at this second application and agreed to the appointments but had the last word regarding salaries:

> "We see no justification for increasing the remuneration of Mr. Watson Watt, as it is thought that the responsibilities of the new post could be less than the post of D.C.D. and, but for the fact that Mr. Watson Watt is to occupy the post, we would have pressed for a lower salary than £1,500. In our reluctance in agreeing to the appointment of Lee, we insist that only £1,500 can be taken from Air Funds leaving the Paymaster-General to find the difference." [1]

At a meeting on 9 Jan to discuss RDF matters, Watson Watt conveyed to Joubert his grave objections to the SAT title change, stating that the difference between a scientific and a technical adviser was the difference between a philosopher and a plumber, and he insisted on remaining a philosopher. Joubert forwarded Watson Watt's objection to the CAS adding that there was general agreement with his view and, in recommending that the original title be retained, he added that the word 'telecommunication' was now acceptable and well understood by both signaller and scientist. The CAS was content to leave the choice with the Secretary of State, who endorsed the SAT title.

In early January the Germans increased the number of air attacks along the east coasts of England and Scotland by using low flying aircraft against merchant shipping and, to counter these moves, Joubert ordered a second emergency programme of seven CHL installations. Within days AMRE had sent back signals for locations in northern England at Ingoldmells, Flamboro' Head, Bamburgh, Cresswell and in Scotland at St Cyrus, Doonies Hill and Rosehearty. Signals wrote to Pye:

"We are relying on you to produce seven C.H.L. receivers in the next three weeks and to provide and assemble the aerial arrays for 200 Mc/s [MHz]." [2]

and to Works:

"We hope all Works Services will be completed by January 25...advise of hold-ups." [2]

The installations by 2.IU were done amid the coldest weather that the country had experienced for over 40 years. Temperatures of -12C were common; the River Thames was ice-bound for eight miles, the sea had frozen along the shore line at Bognor Regis (in West Sussex) and snow had fallen so heavily that some low lying villages were buried up to the roof tops. At Yatesbury the schools had closed because the camp heating had failed, there was no electricity, roads were impassable and instructors could not get to the station. Over 4,500 students were sent home on three weeks' leave.

At Dover the CHL area was covered with deep snow and the turntables and cradles had to be unloaded 200 yards from the huts and dragged into position with the Lister generator manhandled to the site. At Cresswell there were 12ft snow drifts that were worsening by the hour making transport almost impossible; at Bamburgh the lorry driver had to wait there for two days before assistance arrived to unload, while those on the way to Scotland had seemingly disappeared. At Doonies Hill there was masses of snow and ice and at Rosehearty the trailers were bogged down in snow. Joubert was concerned with the delays in completing the stations and complained to the DCD on 6 February:

"Actual technical process of getting C.H.L. on the air [is] taking long, do you want Professor Cockcroft's assistance in the future?" [3]

Lee, the new director, replied:

"...the weather...[was] of unprecedented severity over the whole of the country; through confusing instructions, equipment was delivered before the buildings were ready." [3]

But by mid-February all the seven stations were operational. The performance of CHL was uncertain; there had been no time to find the best siting conditions. To assess the optimum working conditions, AMRE had laid down a number of checks to be made at all CHLs before the test flight: the plotting of the horizontal and vertical polar diagrams, the evaluation of the permanent echoes, the azimuth calibration, the maximum range of aircraft echoes and the identification of shipping. One vital non-scientific task was the setting-up of the motor generator's voltage regulator for, if not done properly, the receiver power supply went dangerously high when the transmitter tripped. A vital daily chore quickly made itself known, the careful drying of the insulators used as spreaders to maintain the transmit line spacing, for when these got wet from rain or sea sprays the output power dropped by nearly 90%.

Before the appearance of the CHL chain a number of trawlers were positioned in the North Sea to form a screen, which reported aircraft movements by W/T to Staxton and Stenigot, but Joubert was not convinced that they were dependable. He wrote:

"The trawler screen is unreliable. A south-east gale sends them scuttling back to harbour, the system vulnerable to weather conditions and cannot be relied on. C.H.L. is still in infancy, still learning about limitations...[it] seems clear that present equipment at heights in excess of 200ft a.s.l. [above sea level] give ranges up to 60 miles. We made the initial mistake of siting the first part of the C.H.L. chain at sea level, [which is] now being corrected, and before long C.H.L. should fill the C.H. gaps [below 5000ft]." [4]

The CHL stations detected aircraft 25 miles away flying at 500ft and 15 miles flying at 100ft except for Ingoldmells and Flamboro' Head, which gave poor ranges due to bad siting and would have to be moved. The Dover CHL was excellent at 350ft above sea level and 150 yards from the cliff edge with a sweep of 015 to 230 degrees; Blenheims were detected at 25 miles at 200ft. The speed of the two top-priority CHL programmes caused Rowe to complain to Joubert that:

"... because of them there are delays in the installation of additional C.H. stations. C.H. has fallen into the background [and] C.H.L. is taking its place. I cannot see the sense of that as research into obtaining accurate tracks towards the coast is outstanding." [4]

Joubert's reply was that he would like nothing better for Rose (2.IU) to get on with CH;

"...unfortunately the Hun has sprung two surprises on us which has necessitated emergency action along the coast." [4]

Watson Watt, in his new post as SAT, also expressed his anxiety:

"C.H. installations are being delayed by C.H.L., [and] concern is being accentuated by the fact that C.H. has given valuable military results whilst C.H.L. has not yet, I think, done so. Moreover, a good C.H. system which we have never yet had is almost essential to a good C.H.L. system and is vital to good A.I." [5]

Perhaps Watson Watt was being a trifle unfair. He was of course pointing a finger at those responsible for the slowness in the completion of the chain to four wavelengths. Had he overlooked the fact that compared to the years that the CH chain had been gathering expertise, the CHL chain was barely two months old and with stopgap equipment? There was also disruption for the Army that is best summed up in the short correspondence between Rowe at AMRE, Dundee and Colonel Colbeck at ADRDE, Christchurch. To Rowe on 6 February:

"Can you tell me the present position [on CHL] please, it has all been rather a nightmare these last few months with these emergency demands and so on, and we do want to get the picture cleared up so that we can get on with C.D., which has become the Cinderella of the piece. When do you hope to be at Swanage? it's the devil being so far away from each other – this cold weather has held up the building work, [and] you must have been frozen up there." [6]

Rowe replied a week later:

"I do not know whether to laugh or cry at your letter, we are very much in the same state and we do not know the nature of the organisation for C.H.L.... We are looking forward to being on your doorstep." [6]

Colbeck wrote to the War Office:

"We are in despair at getting any answers to our queries on C.D. I wrote to Rowe who seems to be in the same state of haze as we are. C.H.L. has been run by an ad hoc medley of scientists, the Navy and the Air Force using Cockcroft and our Cavendish staff as and when they please." [6]

There was also concern at ADRDE because events had not only forced the Air Ministry to take the Army CD and modify it for CHL, but also to fully occupy Pye with CHL receiver manufacture for many months. Colbeck had outlined the cumulative effects of the delay; there was hope that the 1.5 metre CD prototype receiver would be ready by May; Pye would take four to six months to design a production model and another three months to get it into manufacture so the earliest that could be hoped for was January/March 1941.

Freeman had written to Joubert that he had heard that he was complaining about the delay in the production of RDF equipment. Joubert replied:

"My dear Wilfred, I make no complaints, only moans of despair when promises are broken like pie crusts and excuses carry no conviction. Not one single programme has been up to schedule, the future grim beyond words....Desirable but unessential modifications are allowed and interfere with production, and nobody seems to have a grip of the whole situation, Yours, Philip." [7]

The wintry weather had also hit the CH chain with many aerial arrays damaged by the weight of excessive ice, radiators frozen in standby generators, aerial phase variations due to the stretching of feeder wires and, when the thaw came, the replacing of burst coaxial lines. Like many CH stations, West Beckham was off the air because the transmitter power was being almost completely absorbed by the iced array. The enterprising scientific officer there made a few calculations then connected the aerial array across the transmitter mains supply. Within a few hours sufficient heat had been generated for the ice to crack, aided by vigorous shaking, for the station to return to normal.

German air activity had not only produced two totally unexpected CHL installations but also a major clash between Dowding and the Air Staff. The CAS was concerned at the disturbing amount of immunity that the German bombers appeared to have on their side. He called a meeting on 12 January attended by Dowding and others to comment on the opinion of the Air Staff that there would be more fighter interceptions if the time lag, which occurred between the receipt of the RDF plots and the dispatch of fighters, was removed or reduced. After discussion an agreement was reached that the first arrow on the filter room table representing the approach of aircraft would be immediately 'told' to groups and sectors without waiting for a specific identity ie, friendly, hostile or unknown.

When Dowding received the minutes of the meeting he was surprised to see that there were three conclusions: (1) that Fighter Command would henceforth pass raid plots to groups as soon as the directional arrow was in place on the table; (2) that the C-in-C would consider the possibility of RDF plots being passed direct from the Chain stations to groups, and they would 'tell' plots to Fighter Command with an experiment to be arranged; and, (3) CHL development should be for plots to be passed direct to sectors, they being immediately responsible for taking tactical action without prior reference to Groups or Fighter Command.

He wrote back the next day that from his point of view the minutes conveyed a very misrepresented account of what had taken place. He was aware that the CAS nevertheless wished an experiment to be carried out for filtering at Group Headquarters, which he asserted was thoroughly unsound and would lead to a grave loss of efficiency. Dowding explained that the existing RDF intelligence system had been built up as a result of 3½ years of unremitting work. He had considered group filter rooms to avoid centralisation and to effect economy in land lines but found there were practical difficulties so the idea was abandoned:

"My system is now being criticised at the Air Ministry by officers who do not know the circumstances in which the system was evolved and are even unaware of the existing facts. If the Air Council have some experiment that they wish me to try, it is for them to say what they want to do and how they want to do it... Those [proposals] put forward at the meeting, viz., filtration on existing Group Operations Tables, I can only describe as fantastic." [8]

Dowding concluded his letter with a mild admonishment to the Air Staff:

"The R.D.F. system, with all its imperfections, is of inestimable advantage for the land defence of this country on account of the warning which it is generally able to give of enemy approach. It does not, however, in its existing state, afford a reliable method of making interceptions over the sea, and I suggest that the best service that the Staff at the Air Ministry can perform is to concentrate on the improvements to the apparatus and the elimination of its defects. As the efficiency of the apparatus improves so will the percentage of over the sea interceptions increase." [8]

A further letter from Dowding informed the CAS that his group commanders were unanimous in declaring that they could not contemplate the possibility of filtering taking place on their operations room tables:

"I am sure that this view will be endorsed by anyone who is familiar with the circumstances." [8]

He outlined the problems of the proposed experiment; three filter rooms would need to be built and placed underground, it would be useless to use untrained staffs and the organisation at his headquarters would be broken up. He strongly recommended the idea to be abandoned. He did not agree that CHL stations should be connected to sectors. A reply followed the next day; there had been some misunderstanding on the proposal for group filtering, but it should be considered because of the possibilities of any disablement at Stanmore and Leighton Buzzard, and the saturation of raid movements on the filter room table; another meeting was suggested. Dowding's final letter conveyed his resistance:

"It is the principle in this Command that tactical control is delegated to Groups. Groups detail raids to Sectors and indicate the strength in which they are to be met, and Sectors select the units to be employed. In certain conditions, particularly at night, Groups delegate complete control to Sectors... My contention is that the Air Council have the right to tell me what to do but should not insist on telling me how to do it so long as I retain their confidence. I have spent a very great deal of time on this subject, starting with the proposal to form a Communications Command. I calculate that I have devoted about 30 hours to the subject, and a great deal of nervous energy which might have been otherwise expended. I therefore deprecate the suggestion that a further meeting should be held to discuss the subject, since there are several matters of great importance which I have had to put aside pending the discussion of this issue." [8]

Dowding did not receive a reply to his last letter although one had been drafted; the policy of Group Filtering, however, was far from being forgotten and would reappear when Dowding least expected it. Joubert saw the correspondence and wrote:

"I am still of the opinion that the existing system is neither safe nor adequate ...I therefore adhere to my desire that the experiments asked for by the C.A.S. should be put into execution and that the Air Ministry should continue to control closely the development and application of R.D.F." [8]

Dowding had decided on a centralised filter room because it would give him a greater measure of control and, very close to his heart, economy in air operations. It was his view that plotting by groups and sectors would inevitably increase the number of fighters in the air at a time when such resources were at an irreducible minimum. Now an academic question: would the Battle of Britain have been won with Group filtering?

The rapid installation of CHL and mobiles had highlighted the shortage of operators and mechanics. When the sums had been calculated Joubert was alarmed to realise that there were only 250 mechanics available against the 1,000 required, and that figure did not include those needed for airborne equipment. He ordered a speedy recruitment programme by the placing of advertisements in national newspapers offering civilian posts to trained radio and television service engineers aged 28 or over (under that age they were liable for 'call-up' service in the Army), for the sum of £3.15s. 0d (£3.75p) a week.

One Scottish newspaper advert alone produced over 83 replies that resulted in 58 acceptances. The successful candidates, who had been screened by MI.5 and were mainly experienced radio service engineers, were interviewed at their local Labour Exchange and were asked to: (a) draw a box diagram of a 10 valve superhet marking the function of each box, (b) indicate what Intermediate frequency would be used and show the frequency of the local oscillator for an incoming frequency of 30 Mc/s [MHz], (c) draw the circuit diagram of a pentode and explain how the valve gets its auto-bias and indicate typical currents and voltages in the circuit.

Notes had been prepared for the guidance of the local interview boards, who were non-technical, of which the following is an extract:

"It is considered that such qualifications may be possessed by professional radio service engineers and by amateurs who have had a close and enthusiastic study of radio. In this connection it is worth noting that one of the most successful appointments as a radio mechanic was that of a bookmaker's clerk, who had dabbled in wireless as a hobby and picked up a certain amount of theory, as well as a working knowledge of wireless repair and overhaul." [9]

Applicants were paid their travelling expenses for the interview, but according to Civil Service rules would not be paid their rail fare to the CH station after completion of training, with a consequence that few took the posting. Joubert was quickly made aware of this objection, which he took up energetically with the Treasury, which eventually agreed that despite the rigid principle at stake, they were prepared to allow the issue of railway warrants at public expense on the strict understanding that there was no consequential entitlement to removal expenses. There was a major difference between being a serviceman in the RAF and a civilian in the Air Ministry as the latter had to pay for meals and accommodation. Eventually most of the civilian mechanics at the CH stations resigned or volunteered for the RAF and returned in uniform.

The rapid expansion in numbers had overloaded the RDF School at Bawdsey and, what no doubt was considered by many to be a retrograde step, training was transferred to the vast expanse of Yatesbury, in the wilds of Wiltshire, a place never to be forgotten by the thousands who went there. To ensure secrecy, huts were erected in a remote part of the camp surrounded with barbed wire and guarded at all times, mainly by the incoming students. An Air Ministry instruction was issued that the RDF school would open on Friday 19th January complete with an instructional staff of 14 Officers, three Grade 2 technical assistants and eight other ranks, mainly drawn from the RAF Education Branch.

For months the students had a trying time as the buildings were not complete and there was very little equipment. The distance from the airmen's quarters was nearly 1½ miles by road or ¾ mile across a grassy track and during inclement weather the trainees would arrive so wet that they were unable to work efficiently. Joubert soon heard about it. He wrote to the AOC in charge of Training:

> "I am very disturbed about the report... of the inadequacy of the special R.D.F. school. If I cannot get satisfaction in regard to the existing arrangements at Yatesbury, I shall have to raise the question of taking up a suitable building in a civilised centre, where valuable equipment and rare and civilised trainees can be housed and instructed in conditions which enable effective work to be carried out. I cannot emphasise too strongly that it is not possible to handle R.D.F. matters on a normal organisational basis, and exceptional measures are for the present normal procedure." [4]

Many of the civilian trainees had resigned and a very concerned Joubert wrote again to the AOC:

> "I cannot afford to have a number of valuable men resigning their job with the R.D.F. organisation which is what happened in the case of 38 W.E.M.s [Wireless and Electrical Mechanics] that were sent to Yatesbury, many of whom have

SIR HUGH C.T. DOWDING

The first AOC-in-C of Fighter Command, he was responsible for the prevention of surprise enemy air attacks. To meet that commitment he ensured that the radar was under his control.

(IWM D1417)

SIR ROBERT A. WATSON-WATT

His second memo to the Air Ministry showed that the location of aircraft was possible using existing techniques that had not been used collectively before.

(IWM CH13862)

SIR HENRY T. TIZARD

Chairman of the Committee for the Scientific Survey of Air Defence, he quickly recognised the potential of radar and gave his full support to its development.

(IWM HU42365)

PLATE I

A.F. WILKINS

As a scientific officer at the NPL, Slough, he provided the calculations for the production of a 'death ray' and the level of re-radiation of radio energy from metal aircraft. He was also responsible for the success of the Daventry Experiment.

(Photograph by courtesy of Mrs Nancy Wilkins)

A.P. ROWE

As Personal Assistant to Wimperis, he had unrivalled knowledge of radar policy. He was appointed Deputy Superintendent of the Bawdsey Research Station in 1937 and became its Superintendent from 1938 to 1945.

(Photograph by courtesy of DERA)

H.E. WIMPERIS

The first Director of Scientific Research at the Air Ministry from 1925 to 1937. His approach to Watson Watt in January 1935 for an evaluation of the 'death ray' as a war weapon led to the initiation of radar.   (Photograph by courtesy of

the Royal Aeronautical Society Library.)

PLATE II

THE SOUND MIRRORS AT DENGE, KENT (Above) The curved 200ft mirror with a maximum range of 25 miles. (Below) In the centre a 20ft mirror and to the right a 30ft mirror with a range of 8 miles. Built in the early 1930s the site is slowly collapsing due to the removal of the shingle beds. (The photographs taken in 1988 are by courtesy of Charles.W. Snowdon)

PLATE III

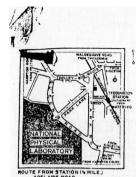

TELEGRAMS:-
"PHYSICS TEDDINGTON."

TELEPHONE:-
MOLESEY 1380 (IF-LINES)

The National Physical Laboratory.

Teddington. Middlesex.

YOUR REF:	OUR REF:
	787/S/HB.

12th February, 1935.

S 35 290.

SECRET.

A. P. Rowe, Esq.,
    Air Ministry,
        Adastral House,
        Kingsway, W.C.2.

Dear Mr Rowe,

        1 enclose, herewith, a memorandum on the "Detection of Aircraft by Radio Methods" in accordance with your letter of 6th February. It turns out so favourably that I am still nervous as to whether we have not got a power of ten wrong, but even that would not be fatal. I have therefore thought it desirable to send you the memorandum immediately rather than to wait for close re-checking.

        Yours faithfully

        R.A.Watson Watt

WATSON WATT's covering letter for his second memorandum is the first enclosure in a secret Air Ministry file titled 'Aircraft Detection – Investigation of Radio Methods'.

(PRO AIR2/4483)

PLATE IV

Date	Machine	d (km)		Angle of Neglecting Curvature.		Elevation True.		Remarks.	Height (ft)
July		Lost	Found	Lost	Found	Lost	Found		
8	Valentia (λ50cm) (on 26 metres)	37.5			4° 39'		4° 30'	noise	10,000
9	Valentia	49	48	4° 20'	4° 22'	4° 03'	4° 09'	"	12,000
10	"	47	25	4° 41'	4° 50'	4° 26'	8° 43'	"	12,500 L
10	Wallace	42	51	4° 47'	3° 50'	3° 36'	3° 33'	morse	12,600 F / 11,500 L
11	Valentia	53	46	4° 07'	4° 45'	3° 51'	4° 30'	noise	11,000 F
12	"	53	46	4° 13'	4° 52'	3° 59'	4° 42'	morse	12,400
16	Bristol H120	67	60	3° 56'	4° 24'	3° 37'	4° 09'	noise	12,800 L / 12,900 F
18	Vildebeeste	39.5			5° 48'		5° 35'	not lost	15,200 L / 15,000 F
18	"	27		0° 40'		0° 31'		noise	13,000
19	Bristol H120	43	22	5° 29'	11° 00'	5° 18'	10° 55'	noise	1,000
19	"	43	20.2	5° 30'	11° 45'	5° 18'	11° 39'	" receiver fault	13,500 L / 13,800 F
22	"	34.2	32.4	2° 33'	2° 42'	2° 24'	2° 33'	morse	13,500
23	Wallace	34.2	25.4	2° 33'	3° 26'	2° 24'	3° 12'	heavy morse	5,000
24	"	55.7	62.1	4° 37'	4° 13'	4° 22'	3° 57'	morse	5,000
26	"	59.6	63.9	4° 24'	4° 06'	4° 09'	3° 49'	noise	15,000

ORFORDNESS The first known record of the experiments during July 1935. Note the change of wavelength on July 9 – see text.

(AIR2/4481)

PLATE V

THE DOVER CH STATION IN 1937 A rare photograph of one of the original five Thames Estuary stations. The single 240ft wooden tower in the foreground is nearest the sea and supports the transmitting aerial with the equipment at the base in the wooden hut. The receiver hut is in the centre of the two rear towers. Note the palisade fencing around two of the towers with the third tower and the site uncompleted. The photo was taken to show the ease of recognition from the air. (PRO AIR2/2216)

PLATE VI

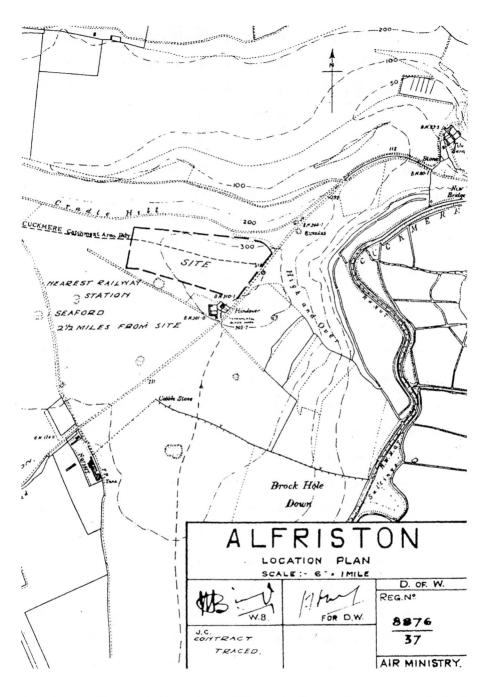

SITE PLAN of the intended CH station at Alfriston, East Sussex. The proposal was 'leaked' to the Secretary of State for Air (see text) who requested an alternative which was found at Poling, near Littlehampton, West Sussex. (AIR2/2685)

PLATE VII

THE THREE SECRETARIES at BRS, Miss H.Brooker (left), Miss N.Boyce (centre) and Miss M.Girdlestone (right) whose expertise in plotting at the Dover CH station in February 1939 after a few weeks' training supported Watson Watt's view that women would be superior to men in plotting and observing. It led to the introduction of the WAAF into operational areas that hitherto had been the exclusive preserve of the RAF.

(IWM E(MOS) 1426,1427)

PLATE VIII

3 SEPTEMBER 1939 RADAR COVERAGE 60/100 MILES AT 15,000FT SHOWING THE DIRECTION OF THE STATION LINE OF SHOOT

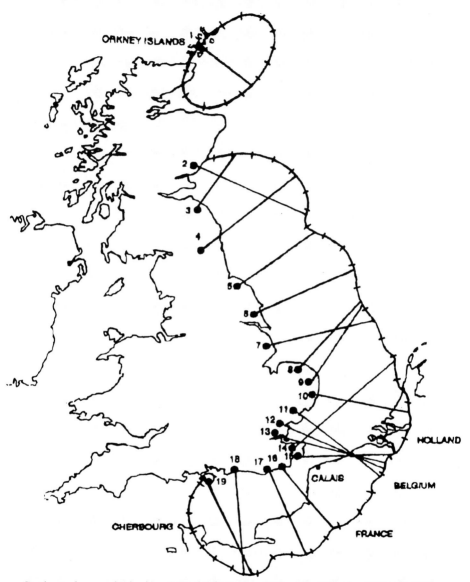

Stations shown clockwise. **1** Netherbutton **2** Douglas Wood **3** Drone Hill **4** Ottercops Moss **5** Danby Beacon **6** Staxton Wold **7** Stenigot **8** West Beckham **9** Stoke Holy Cross **10** High Street **11** Bawdsey **12** Great Bromley **13** Canewdon **14** Dunkirk **15** Dover **16** Rye **17** Pevensey **18** Poling **19** Ventnor

PLATE IX

THE FIGHTER COMMAND OPERATIONS ROOM (Above) In the ballroom at Bentley Priory, Stanmore, in 1939. Officers of the Air Raid Warning Group on the left are waiting for the first arrow to be placed on the table that indicates enemy aircraft. (Below) The new underground Operations Room that was opened in May 1940 just two months before the start of the Battle of Britain.   (IWM MH27893 and IWM C1869)

PLATE X

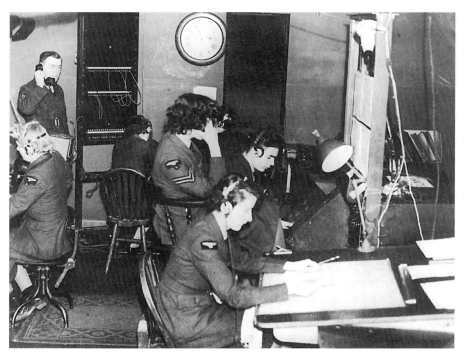

PLOTTING (Above) In the wooden R hut as at Ventnor during the Battle of Britain. (Below) In the permanent R building showing one of the two receivers and the Mark 3 console.

(IWM C1868 and CH15176)

PLATE XI

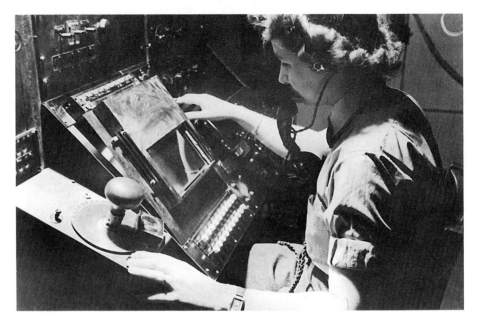

THE BAWDSEY RECEIVER ROOM (Above) Denise Miley 'on the tube'. Her right hand has selected direction or heightfinding and her left hand ready to register the gonio setting to the calculator. (Below) Left to right, Sgt K. Sperring, WAAFs Joan Lancaster, Elaine Miley, Gwen Arnold and Joyce Hollyoak. Standing is Section Officer Peggy Wright.

(IWM CH15332, CH15331)

PLATE XII

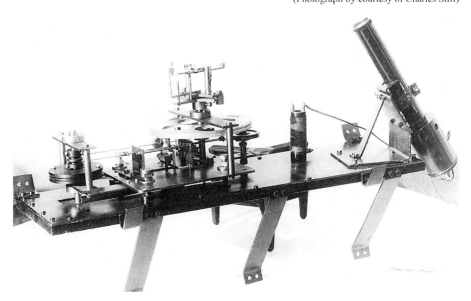

```
Y Z V W X Y Z        1 2 ③ 6 9 12 18 +   (DS) (H) (NH2)
                       Below
D E A B C D E        ○         F          ○  ○  ○
J K F G H J K        ·5- ·5 1·0 1·5 2·0 2·5 3·0 3·5 4·0 4·5 5·0
O P L Ⓜ N O P        6·0 6·5 7·0 7·5 8·0 8·5 9·0 9·5 10 10·5 11
T U Q R S T U        12 12·5 13 ⑬·⑤ 14·0 14·5 15 15·5 16 16·5 17
Y Z V W X Y Z        18 18·5 19 19·5 20 21 22 23 24 25 26
D E A B C D E        28 29 30 30 +
```

```
1 2 3 4 5 | 1 2 ③ 4 5 | 1 2 3 ④ 5 | 1 2 3 4
6 ⑦ 8 9 0   6 7 8 9 0   6 7 8 9 0   6 7 8 ⑨
```

THE CALCULATOR LAMP DISPLAY was fitted in the console facing the 'teller'. The left hand side is a block of 7 by 7 letters each representing a 100km square of the Cassini grid. The centre letter is the station reference, in this case M for Bawdsey, Great Bromley, Canewdon and High Street. The four groups of 1–0 digits along the bottom show the vertical and horizontal co-ordinates. The centre group of lamps indicate height from below 500ft to over 30,000ft. The lamps above show the number of aircraft as decided by the operator with F for friendly, DS for a plot stored and ready for display, NH1 to change the aerial to obtain a height, NH2 that no height is available and H that height information is being displayed or in the process of display. The indications above show 3 aircraft at 13,500ft at M73,49.

THE OPTICAL CONVERTER without the ground glass screen fitted above.

(Photograph by courtesy of Charles Stiff)

PLATE XIII

THE CH TRANSMITTER was in two sections, the RF output unit (above) and the oscillator and drive (below) duplicated for main and standby. Maximum pulse power was 350kW which was raised to 750kW in 1941 and for some stations in 1944 increased to 1 Megawatt.

(PRO AIR16/935)

PLATE XIV

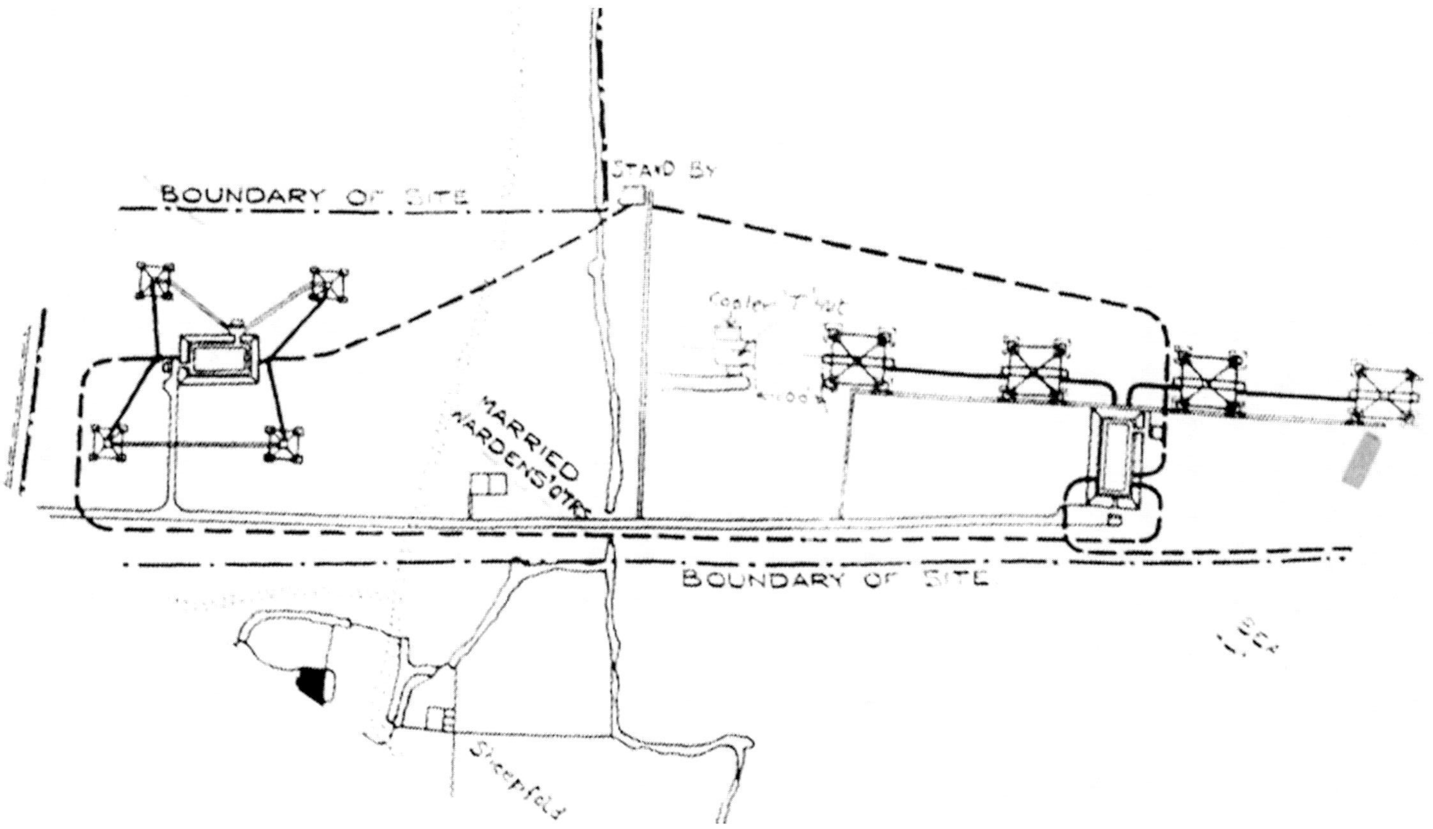

THE SITE LAYOUT FOR THE RYE CH STATION showing the arrangement of the 240ft wooden receiving towers on the left in a rhombus form and the in-line 350ft steel transmitting towers on the right (see text).

(PRO AVIA7/266)

PLATE XV

POLING – AN EAST CHAIN CH STATION The receiver building is in the centre of the four 240ft wooden towers on the right and the transmitter building is in front of the three 350ft steel towers facing the sea. This photo was taken after the fourth steel tower had been removed (see text).

(IWM CH15173)

PLATE XVI

A MOBILE RECEIVER shown fitted into a trailer which was also the operations room. The boxes bolted on the left side are for IFF Mark 3.

(IWM CH15202)

AN MB2 TRANSMITTER in a West Coast CH station. The canopy was needed to extract 7kW of heat in what was a totally enclosed semi-sunk building. Note the two pairs of RF outlet feeders on the wall that connect to the aerial array through the side of the building.

(PRO AIR16/935)

PLATE XVII

TWO WEST CHAIN STATIONS (Above) Saligo Bay, Islay, showing the dispersal of the two pairs of the 325ft guyed steel masts. In the foreground is one of the two 240ft wooden towers. (IWM CH16469) (Below) Sango, Lairg, Scotland, showing one of the two earth covered and semi-buried receiver blocks in 1998. (Photograph by courtesy of Tony Wintringham)

PLATE XVIII

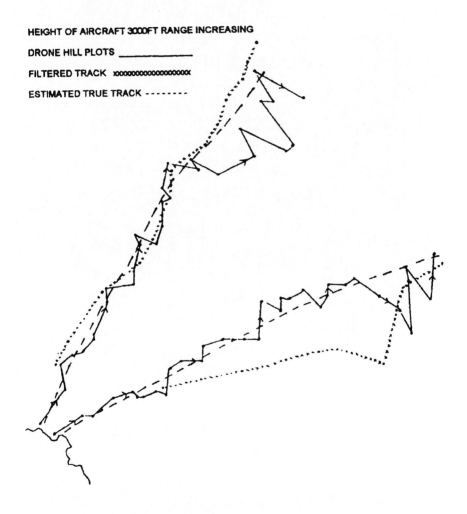

SECRET

HEIGHT OF AIRCRAFT 3000FT RANGE INCREASING

DRONE HILL PLOTS _____

FILTERED TRACK xxxxxxxxxxxxxxxxxxxx

ESTIMATED TRUE TRACK - - - - - - - -

DRONE HILL CH STATION One of the test runs made during the transfer from the Intermediate to the Final stage on 6 September 1940. Calibration was not welcome by Fighter Command as the station was off the air for seven days.

PLATE XIX

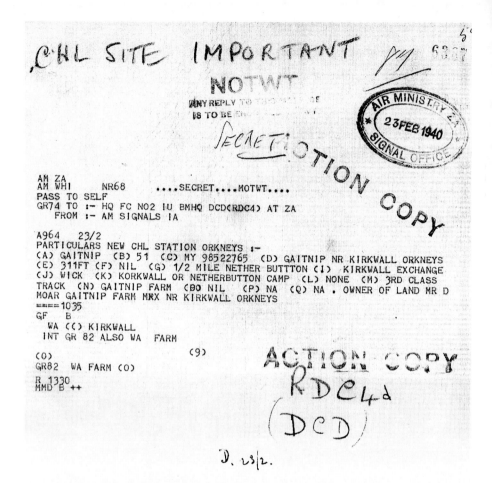

CHL SITE IMPORTANT

NOTWT

ANY REPLY TO THIS ... IS
IS TO BE ...

SECRET

AIR MINISTRY
23 FEB 1940
SIGNAL OFFICE

ACTION COPY

```
AM ZA
AM WHI      NR68      ....SECRET....MOTWT....
PASS TO SELF
GR74 TO :- HQ FC NO2 IU BMHQ DCD(RDC4) AT ZA
    FROM :- AM SIGNALS IA

A964   23/2
PARTICULARS NEW CHL STATION ORKNEYS :-
(A) GAITNIP  (B) 51  (C) MY 98522765  (D) GAITNIP NR KIRKWALL ORKNEYS
(E) 311FT (F) NIL  (G) 1/2 MILE NETHER BUTTTON (I) KIRKWALL EXCHANGE
(J) WICK  (K) KORKWALL OR NETHERBUTTON CAMP  (L) NONE  (M) 3RD CLASS
TRACK  (N) GAITNIP FARM  (BO) NIL   (P) NA  (Q) NA . OWNER OF LAND MR D
MOAR GAITNIP FARM MRX NR KIRKWALL ORKNEYS
====1035
GF    B
   WA (() KIRKWALL
   INT GR 82 ALSO WA   FARM

(O)                           (9)
GR82   WA FARM (O)
R 1330
MMD B ++
```

ACTION COPY
RDC4d
(DCD)

D. 23/2.

SITING SIGNALS were introduced in December 1939 to convey RDF siting information using the RAF teleprinter service. For security a code was in force.
(A) Name of station (B) Number of station (C) Grid reference (D) Postal address (E) Height above sea level (F) Nearest power supply (G) Nearest telephone (H) Nearest filter room (I) Nearest telephone Exchange (J) Nearest Fighter Command station (K) Nearest billets or accommodation (L) Nearest railway station (M) Road access (N) Water supply (O) Sanitation facilities (P) Mean line of shoot (Q) Number of personnel

PLATE XX

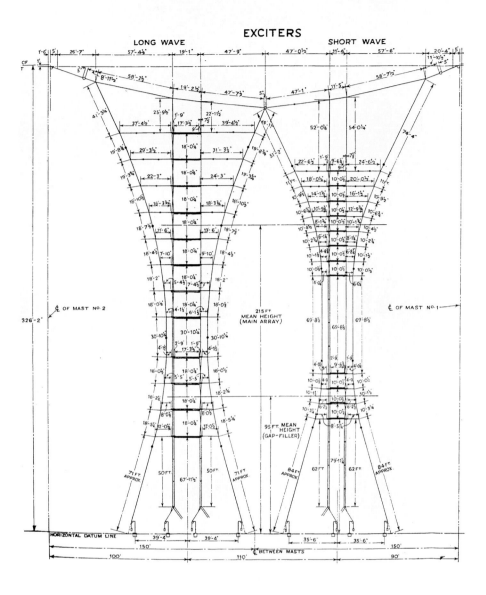

THE WEST CHAIN transmitting curtain showing the constructional details of the exciter array with the dipoles thickened for clarity. A reflector curtain of almost similar dimensions was positioned a specific distance behind the exciter array. 'Long Wave' was notionally 10 metres and 'Short Wave' was 5 metres. (PRO AIR10/3561) The East Chain arrays between the towers and feeders were upgraded by thicker wire to match the increased transmitter output.

PLATE XXI

WORTH MATRAVERS April 1943 'C' Watch ready to move off to the CHL. The ladder was a concession to the WAAF.

FOUR CTC MEN at Cranwell, December 1941. Knoel Cragin, Jim Farrior, Louis Davis and J.B.Clark ready for a long bike ride in bleakest Lincolnshire.

PLATE XXII

THE '1941' VERSION OF CHL showing the power turned five tier four stack dipole array on top of a 20ft gantry with a RDF mechanic looking for cracked and broken insulators. The Army guard is at 'attention' for the benefit of the photographer.   (PRO AIR16/935)

PLATE XXIII

THE GREAT ORMES HEAD CHL in North Wales was conveniently situated in the local hotel with a special eight tier five bay aerial array on the roof. (AVIA7/320)

PLATE XXIV

THE CHL TRANSMITTER in the familiar MetroVick style, which was completely enclosed and needed forced air cooling. The open wire feeder is visible above the transmitter.

(IWM CH15196)

A TWIN WATCH CHL STATION. On the right the PPI and Range consoles and at the centre the Air Plotting board. The resident WRNS, left, with the naval PPI and plotting board off-left, passed shipping plots to the nearest naval plotting room. Similar arrangements were provided for the Army Coast Defence.

(IWM CH15185)

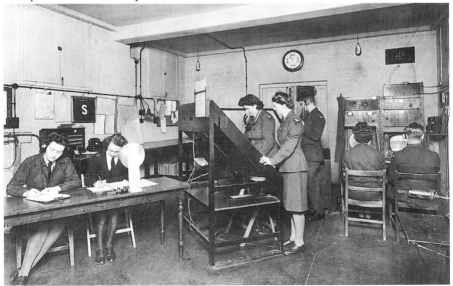

PLATE XXV

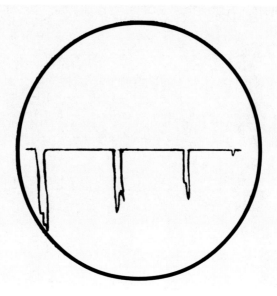

THE CH DISPLAY shows all the aircraft ranges but some 24 seconds were needed to evaluate bearing and height of each echo that had to be repeated every two minutes. The number of aircraft depended solely on the ability of the operator to interpret the echo shape which was constantly changing. Far left is the transmitter pulse.

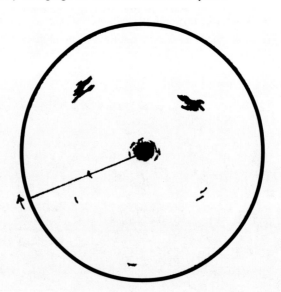

THE PPI DISPLAY shows range and bearing. The long persistence of the tube afterglow ensured that plots remained in view while the aerial was turning with a slight movement between sweeps that indicated direction. Local clutter is at the centre of the tube with permanent echoes top left and right. Height was obtained from a separate tube.

PLATE XXVI

A GCI MOBILE with the aerial array fixed to the side of a trailer, at first manually turned. The complete station was erected or dismantled in 12 hours by unit personnel – no Works services were needed. (IWM CH15199)

THE INTERMEDIATE TYPE 8C with power turning of two 35ft arrays that improved the range at 5000ft. Like the mobile only one interception at a time could be controlled. Many were replaced in 1943/1944 with the Final Type 7. (IWM CH15197)

PLATE XXVII

THE GCI FINAL TYPE 7 showing the aerial system with the large and camouflaged operations room in the background. Known as the 'Happidrome', a total of eight interceptions could be positioned by two controllers. (IWM CH15188)

THE TYPE 16 was a 50cm Fighter Direction station with a range of 200 miles. A single fighter could be detected anywhere from Le Havre, France, to the Dutch Islands.

(IWM CH15204)

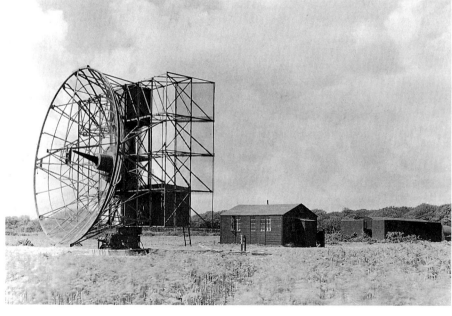

PLATE XXVIII

PLATE XXIX

THE TYPE 13 MARK 2 HEIGHTFINDER seen here as an experimental version.

Previous page

EARLY 10cm SETS

(Top) The first Army mobile set with waveguide feed to separate transmit and receive dishes.

(Bottom) An experimental model on the roof of a War Office CD/CHL building.

(PRO WO33/1822)

PLATE XXX

THE 'GIBSON BOX' A 10cm radar developed by the Army as a mobile or fixed station. Also used by the RAF for the detection of very low flying aircraft.

/P.U.S. / 04A.

10, Downing Street,
Whitehall.

PERSONAL MINUTE

SERIAL No. M.158/3

SECRETARY OF STATE FOR AIR.

Your minute of the 12th March refers -

The King mentioned this subject to me when he came to Chequers last week, and we both felt rather cool about the proposal.   Smuts has never been identified with the Air in any marked manner except in the way you mention as a Member of the 1918 War Cabinet.   He was made a Field-Marshal because he had commanded armies and campaigns.   It would be just as natural for the Navy *as Air Chief Marshal* to make him an Admiral of the Fleet.   On the whole, therefore, I prefer not to go forward with the plan.

WSC

13.3.43

PRIME MINISTER WINSTON CHURCHILL'S change of mind after earlier agreeing with the Secretary of State for Air, Sir Archibald Sinclair, to make General Smuts an honorary Marshal of the RAF for his recommendation in July 1917 to form an Air Ministry.

(PRO AIR2/7842)

PLATE XXXI

THE WORTH MATRAVERS CH STATION under demolition in 1962. No sign now exists of the station.

(Photographs are by courtesy of Tom Hatcher)

PLATE XXXII

been on the chain for two months and are already in possession of a great deal of secret information." [4]

In January, the CAS had approved plans for further extensions of the CH and CHL chains to close the gaps between Weymouth to Torquay, cover for the Isles of Scilly, Liverpool to the Clyde, for central Scotland and the Shetland Islands, where there was no Observer Corps. The Navy also required coverage in the areas of Cromarty, Devonport and Port A, the last a code name for the navy anchorage at Loch Ewe on the northwest of Scotland, where the Fleet had been hastily re-assembled after the torpedoing of HMS *Royal Oak* in Scapa Flow in October 1939. The broad outline of the plans, known as the Air Staff Requirement, accorded top priority by the Prime Minister, were passed to DCD, who decided where the additional areas would be and prepared recommendations for a meeting to be held the following month.

Survey teams for CH stations in the Shetland Islands had selected land at Skaw, on Unst, the most northern island and in the south at Noss Hill near Sumburgh: in the Orkney Islands a CH station at Whale Head on the island of Sanday. These three stations were built to the existing East Chain standard of 'above the ground' equipment blocks but for two wavelengths only as Joubert considered that the jamming danger was not such as to justify the retention of four wavelengths when 'we are so short of timber, time and money.' The steel towers were provided in a most unusual way. At the request of Joubert, Works had estimated that the cost of dismantling an existing tower, providing new foundations and re-erection would cost £3,600, compared to the cost of a new tower of £6,500, with three to four months to complete. Wooden towers also could be moved at a cost of £1,900 but there is no record of further action. Joubert was in favour of removing two steel towers from three CH stations, later amended to one tower from six stations. In May work began on the removal of one 350ft steel tower from Ventnor, Poling, Pevensey, Rye, Great Bromley and Staxton Wold. (Uncorroborated information is that the Rye tower had only been erected for seven days when it was dismantled)

At Netherbutton work was proceeding to install and commission the ½CH transmitter. Air Ministry Contracts branch wrote to MetroVick that the installation was to be completed at the earliest possible date and to be given the highest priority:

"Use any means at your disposal such as overtime, extra shifts and the employment of extra staff ." [10]

In April, with the new transmitter in operation, 'all round looking' was achieved by simply removing the reflector curtain from the transmitting aerial on one of the steel towers that halved the range to 40-50 miles, fading to 65. Joubert called for vigorous and decisive action to remedy the situation that he considered was not a success. The map showing radar cover in September 1939 that appears on page 236 of Watson Watt's book *Three Steps to Victory* is in error in showing cover all round the Orkney Islands, a mistake also unwittingly made by a number of other authors. The southern approaches to Scapa Flow would be covered by a CHL at Wick, (Thrumster) and a CH and CHL at Helmsdale; Port A would be covered from the east with a CHL at Cromarty in the Moray Firth and a CHL at Greenstone Point would protect the northern entrance, but the latter was only surveyed as the Royal Navy had returned to Scapa Flow before the station could be constructed.

The research work at AMRE was mainly for CHL ; gap filling, provision of heightfinding, increase of power, reduction in pulse width and assembly of aerial arrays on towers. While waiting for a CHL to arrive, work commenced on a 53cm version with 3kW of pulse power and a 2.5μsecond pulse. Other effort was directed to the design and production of desperately needed training equipment, the first of which was to produce echoes to simulate CH and CHL displays, the second was to produce films that showed echoes under various conditions of interference and enemy activity. Another belated need was for a wavemeter in the 3-20 metre band.

The MB2 transmitter had been developed at BRS during 1939 to use the Admiralty NT77 silica envelope tetrode that in a pair produced 300kW at 5 metres. GEC had designed a similar valve but with a metal to glass seal, the VT114, with a production rate by the end of 1939 of over a 100 a week. MB2 manufacture was changed to the VT114 with the first 15 modified to take either type. Further developments by GEC on advice from BRS enabled a pair of modified valves to produce 750kW, a combination of a thoriated filament and a 35,000 anode voltage.

AMRE continued further development of higher output power without obtaining authority from DCD. (It was a wry comment from Watson Watt to the effect that when AMRE asked if they should perhaps begin working on another project, he then knew that they had already done six months' work on it.) The Megawatt amplifier as it became known was an arrangement of four VT114 valves in parallel push-pull that produced 1.5 megawatt of pulse power. When it was completed, but not air tested, as there were no aerials at Dundee, it was taken to Bawdsey to await the installation of a high power aerial array on one of the steel towers. Ready in March the results showed that compared to the CH transmitter the echo size had increased by 1½ times, the output power limited by corona and flashover to a maximum input of 900kW to the aerial, which was without a reflector, but expected to be 2½ times with a completed array. Rowe was somewhat disappointed that DCD showed little enthusiasm for the project and discouraged further development.

There was one project that did not get past the laboratory doors at AMRE and that was the concept of the 'split receiver' to eliminate the time consuming aerial phasing checks; the 'front end' would be in the aerial tower with the 'IF' output cabled into the receiver building for the display. A prototype was made using remote controlled goniometers but DCD was of the opinion that the electronic equipment would be impossible to maintain if outside the building.

Two methods suggested for CHL heightfinding were two wavelengths or tilted arrays but at the experimental site at East Seaton near Arbroath, the CH system was under construction. Two sets of vertically spaced aerial arrays hand winched inside a pair of 70ft guyed masts to evaluate the optimum spacing but before the equipment reached AMRE a signal was received, signed by Joubert, with instructions to redirect it to Rosyth Dockyard for onward transmission to Gaitnip Farm, half a mile from Netherbutton. The inadequate mechanical features were being redesigned by RAE; the first for the hand turned mechanism, the second for a power turned double aerial array on a single shaft. The project to support and turn three arrays on a common axis had yet to be considered.

In January the Admiralty had reported excellent results of the Sumburgh CDU, 300ft above sea level, which was detecting aircraft flying 50 miles away at 500ft. As at that time the policy was for CHL to be on the same site as CH, there was a possibility that CHL aerials would have to be placed on the 200ft platform of a steel transmitting tower at low level CH sites such as Bawdsey, Rye and Pevensey. The experiment, which confirmed the Admiralty results, had to wait until CHL equipment arrived in April when the aerials were assembled on to two of the steel towers at Douglas Wood. They were set on a fixed Line of Shoot with one above the 200ft cantilever and the other below the cantilever on the adjacent tower. The manufacture of the steel aerial gantry was undertaken by a local firm at Dundee, the Caledonian Shipbuilding and Engineering Company to an AMRE design, with £150 being quoted, and a caution that priority would be required to be obtained from the Admiralty for the supply of steel tubing and bearings.

The concept of a display that rotated in synchronism with the aerial had been recognised to be of the greatest potential in the first six months of work at Orfordness, but it was not practical until the advent of short wavelengths that complex aerial arrays were sufficiently small to be rotated and, more to the point, the production of adequate pulse power. In the autumn of 1939 work had commenced at BRS by G.W.A.Dummer and H. Franklin on the development of what was known as a radial time base for both magnetic and electrostatically deflected cathode ray tubes: the display showed the range line with the zero from the centre of the screen to the tube edge. The screen was blacked out, apart from the rotating line, but any echoes increased the brightness as a elongated spot on the line, according to the range. The centre of the tube was in effect the position of the station relative in miles to the operational cover; it was known at the Plan Position Indicator (PPI). As an 'add-on' cabinet it was placed alongside the existing display in the CHL receiver hut. The ability to see the range and bearing of the echoes simultaneously was a major step forward in the development of RDF and, with many improvements in presentation, remains in use to this day.

ADRDE had obtained an Admiralty 53cm transmitter for the next stage of improving the bearing accuracy of CD, with the eventual possibility of using RDF for coastal artillery. The last 1.5 metre CDU receiver was modified with a simple frequency changer stage to make it suitable for 50cm. The single display was retained; a special cathode ray tube had been designed for a spiral time base that expanded the nine inch horizontal time base to seven feet, which materially increased the reading accuracy. The low power, which was the initial limitation with the lower wavelength, was of no consequence for the Army as CD was not required to exceed a 20 mile range.

At Birmingham University work was being undertaken for the Admiralty on the development of two centimetric devices, the American Klystron and the Magnetron Diode, for higher output powers. The magnetron had been invented in 1921 and was essentially a diode that would oscillate in a very intense magnetic field and development by the early 1930s was obtaining 20 watts of continuous power at 40 to 60cm. In 1939 it was used in a naval transmitter for ship to ship communications. The Klystron was in use as a low power device as the first oscillator in 50cm receivers with development in America for higher power in pulse transmitters. Dr J.T.Randall and Mr H.A.Boot came to the conclusion that enclosed resonators, which were the feature of the Klystron, were absent from the magnetron; the way forward was to incorporate resonant cavities. Their calculations indicated that the generation of a 10cm wavelength needed a supply of 16,000 volts and an axial magnetic field from a 50lb weight magnet: a continuously evacuated pump had to be built for the DC rectifying valve and the cavity magnetron.

On 21 February an event of major importance occurred in the development of RDF when power was slowly applied to the rudimentary assembly. Success was immediate with the burning out of an increasing number of car headlight lamps that had had the caps removed and the lead out wires attached to the output line for a dummy load. The magnitude of the power being developed was not at first thought to be a good sign, looking suspiciously that the generated wavelength was perhaps in the metric region. It was not until the next day that measurements indicated, with much relief, that the wavelength was 9.8 cm with a continuous power output of 400 watts. There was one aspect that remained untested – could it be pulsed, as that was the failing of the earlier types of split anode magnetrons? Within five months GEC had produced a sealed-off cavity magnetron with an oxide coated cathode and an existing permanent magnet producing some 7 to 10 kW of pulse power, sufficient for work to start immediately at AMRE on the basic design of ground and airborne equipment. In contrast to the unlocked laboratory doors at the university, the cavity magnetron assumed the highest security; in transit they were guarded by military police.

The cavity magnetron has, rightly, been called the greatest single contribution in the radar field and has received marked attention in all books about radar, but this has tended to push into the background another, but equally essential component, the first detector in the centimetric receiver without which a working system would not have been possible. The thermionic diode had been found to give good results down to 50cm but for lower wavelengths development was needed for a closer clearance diode in a coaxial line.

Research was already directed towards a crystal for the prototype 25cm airborne systems especially for stability and, equally important, to be able to withstand vibration, rough handling and resistance to 'burn-out' from nearby transmitters. Successful 10cm crystals were eventually produced using silicon and a tungsten 'cats whisker' in handmade prototypes by Dr H.W.B.Skinner at AMRE in November. (Continuing research after the war, especially into purity and improved methods of manufacture, laid the foundations of the solid state industry, which is still producing a revolution of its own. The magnetron has not disappeared; it is also playing a part hidden inside the microwave oven in millions of kitchens around the world.)

Resulting from the objection of the CAS to the formation of an RDF Command, the Air Ministry announced on 23 February the formation of 60 Group, under Fighter Command, with Air Commodore Gregory in charge. At Oxendon Lodge, a country estate near Leighton Buzzard not far from Carlton Lodge, 60 Group took over the Bawdsey RDF School, BMHQ, the technical maintenance of 21 CH and 16 CHL stations and the direction of

2.IU. Fighter Command retained operational control and, through the parent station that each RDF station was attached to, all non-tech admin including discipline, rations, pay, welfare and non-tech stores. It was the beginning of the end of the closeness that had pervaded all sections of BRS with individual members of the RAF bonded by the need for secrecy and the sense of urgency – ground RDF was now out of the experimental and interesting stage and into the cold atmosphere of uniformity.

The CH and CHL chains were isolated from the conventional way that radio equipment was introduced into the RAF. These procedures were undertaken by RAE, that took a great deal of time for extensive test trials, the writing of handbooks, maintenance schedules and other technical information. Every piece of apparatus had replaceable component parts identified by a number and when faulty, and not on the station as a spare, was available from RAF stores. This ordered system did not apply to RDF as only BRS/AMRE could supply spares and place orders for replacement items direct to the Air Ministry, whose contract branch ordered direct on MetroVick, Pye or Cossor, a slow and cumbersome arrangement.

In the early days when there were only five estuary stations the amount of maintenance was small, but from 1938 when the remainder of the chain was being installed, the amount of paper work increased tremendously. When 60 Group took over BMHQ, the RAF Equipment Accounting officers found a mass of technical equipment, largely unidentifiable except by highly qualified personnel, housed in inadequate and unsuitable buildings for which there were no reliable records. Without an identification number, none could be placed in equipment depots so all the spare parts for the CH and CHL chains that were at Leighton Buzzard had to remain there and be distributed direct to the stations by road, rail, sea and air. There were a number of occasions in the past when Drone Hill received spares that had been dropped off at Berwick by the night train from King's Cross to Scotland making an unscheduled stop at Leighton Buzzard. The practice had to cease; it was unprofessional, and the RAF were now in charge.

An RDF policy meeting was convened on 27 February with Dowding, Joubert, Watson Watt, Sir George Lee, the new Director of the DCD, and representatives from Works, Signals, AMRE, the Admiralty and others, to discuss in detail the expansion approved by the CAS. Dowding explained the reasons for the additional cover. There was the possibility of enemy attacks in the Western Approaches by aircraft having a ceiling of 34,000 ft, and since shipping might be diverted to the route north of Ireland, it followed in principle that RDF cover was required to be continuous from Land's End to the North Channel (between Northern Ireland, Stranraer and the Isle of

Islay). He also wanted protection for 50 to 60 miles all round the Shetland Islands plus further cover at Wick and Sanday for Scapa Flow.

For economy in landlines, which was always Dowding's first consideration, he had decided that all stations in the Orkney and Shetland Islands, plus Wick on the mainland, would have their plotting lines terminated at the combined Observer Group Centre and Filter Room associated with the Gun Operations Room at Kirkwall; information would be 'told' to the Wick Operations Room and, later, to a new fighter group to be set up at Inverness; he would be satisfied with information at Stanmore from there. With prior knowledge of the expansion, DCD had prepared a map showing the cover, both high (CH), above 2,000ft with flying heights at 3,000ft, 10,000ft and 20,000ft and low (CHL), below 2,000ft. A total of 13 additional CH stations were required and would, at first, be the 'Advance' type or a mobile, followed by the two wooden tower Intermediate stage then to the Final version, all without a break in service and to take some ten months to a year. The CHL discussion covered a wide area from the outermost point of the Shetland Islands, Saxavord, to the Isles of Scilly. A total of 22 additional CHL stations were required plus six resites.

The agreed policy for CHL siting was in the CH compound; the receiver would be installed in the permanent R block with the aerial array above the building and the transmitter sited outside the protective traverse; Works had already begun to modify the buildings for aerial access. Where the CH station was near ground level the CHL aerial array would be placed on the 200ft cantilever of a 350ft steel tower. The completion date depended on two factors: the availability of equipment and personnel to man the stations.

At the beginning of the year Works had asked DCD for a replacement of the 350ft steel towers due to the wartime scarcity of steel, the labour to erect them and the cost, but towers had been preferred to guyed masts as they could deter aircraft from flying too near and make a partial or complete collapse unlikely. But early in 1939 BRS had already made the decision that steel towers would be inappropriate for overseas CH installations, known as CO, and had proposed the use of guyed masts, based on a commercial design, which had the merit of a much lower cost, minimum Works services and fast erection. Agreement was now reached that they would be used for the West Chain with DCD confirming from Marconi that the 325ft triangular section masts that they had supplied and erected at Daventry for the BBC were easily modified to a square section.

A new design for the transmitting aerial, which became known as a 'curtain array', was placed on RAE. Rigged between two masts, it provided the main and gap-filler array for two wavelengths and for the increase in the power output of the MB2 that now equalled the MetroVick CH transmitter. With markedly reduced maintenance because of the absence of vacuum plant, water-cooling systems and a greater ease of operation, the MB2, and later the MB3, became the standard transmitter for all new CH stations both at home and overseas. There were other minor differences from the East Chain; Works had redesigned the wooden 240ft tower to use less wood and at a lower cost but able to withstand an 100mph gale. AMRE had improved the receiving aerial array design by adjustment of the phasing by electrical methods, eliminating the check half way up the tower and adding a further set of aerials at 45ft to reduce height ambiguities.

In the first three months of the year siting surveys were in progress for the extension of the chain west of Ventnor; all final CH stations would be twin beam. A CH and CHL at Worth Matravers for AMRE, at West Prawle a CHL, to cover Plymouth a CH at Hawks Tor and a CHL at Rame Head. Goonhilly Downs was found to be highly suitable for a CHL and a CH but Signals suggested a change of name to Drytree so as to avoid confusion with the Met. Office station. At Carnanton, Newquay, a CH and a CHL but the Coastal Command aerodrome of St. Eval was only three miles away. Further north a CHL at Trevose Head, a CH at Warren, in South Wales, and nearby, St.Twynells for CHL and further north a CH at Hayscastle Cross and Strumble Head for CHL. A CH site had been found at Bryngrwan in Anglesey but the ACH under construction had to be abandoned due to the nearness of a proposed airfield; it was moved to Nefyn (Nevin) on the Lleyn Peninsula.

The Isle of Man would watch the approaches to Belfast and enemy aircraft overflying the west of England; south of the island with a CHL at Cregneish near Port Erin and a CH at Scarlett Point near Castletown, and north with one at Bride. To complete the coverage there would be a CHL at Prestatyn to cover the southern approaches to Liverpool and a CH at Stranraer and a CHL at Glenarm in Northern Ireland, as there was no suitable site at Stranraer, for the approaches to Belfast and Glasgow from the west

There was slow but continuing progress in coverage for the defence of the approaches to Scapa Flow from submarines and low flying aircraft. In the last few days of February the two Fair Isle CDUs were on the air after many trials and tribulations, not least with one aerial array being blown away. It is believed that Saxavord in Unst, the most northern of the Shetland Islands, was the personal choice of an esteemed guest with the visiting scientists – Admiral J. Somerville. This site was ideal for a CDU at 950ft above sea level; it was almost inaccessible but not considered insurmountable by the doughty admiral.

Work began in March on the approach road and to save time the road was terminated some 200ft below the summit, then continued upwards with a 2ft width railway, driven by a winch, to the top. Construction began in April on two reinforced concrete huts, each 16 ft square with 10 inch thick walls and a 12 inch thick roof, and completed in July. To cover the eastern entrances the Admiralty had asked for a CDU on the summit of Ward Hill, 389 ft above sea level, on the Orkney island of South Ronaldsay which began in the Spring of 1940; all buildings were of brick and concrete with 13½ inch solid walls. To complete the cover east and west of the Orkney Islands and across the Pentland Firth a CDU site was selected at Dunnett Head on the Scottish mainland.

The Air Staff had discussed the necessity of 'bending all our efforts towards the urgent solution of the night fighting problems as soon as practicable' with the formation of a Night Interception Committee. The first meeting was held on 14 March and attended by Dowding, Watson Watt, Tizard and others with the DCAS in the chair. In opening the discussion he said that the defence against night air attack was one of their biggest responsibilities that had to be faced. He was quite sure that even if the enemy began by raiding in large numbers by day our ground defences would force him to adopt night bombing. Dowding assured the meeting that CHL was a preliminary to AI, 'If CHL does not work, AI is useless',[11] and Watson Watt gave his opinion that there was no prospect of an early solution to provide heightfinding for CHL. There was general agreement with Dowding's suggestion that the meetings be held fortnightly.

In March, Signals wrote to the BBC suggesting that when large scale enemy bombing began all programmes should be recorded and played from a safe place. Their reply was that such an arrangement would incur financial penalties because of the extra high engineering costs and new contractual arrangements with artistes that would cost nearly £200,000 a year. The BBC explained the strict legal rights in that it was a criminal offence to record an artiste without his/her written consent, and so far the Variety Artistes Federation and the Musicians Union had refused even to discuss it:

> "They might agree to recording if the records were destroyed immediately afterwards and if they were paid full performing rights fees. Without some compulsory powers, a single artist in a cast or orchestra refusing to record could have something like the vote of veto on the programme; as regards copyright there is a performing and a recording right, and if records were made as routine, a recording right would have to be paid. The owner of a single copyright in a production of a mosaic of rights could veto the recording. Nothing

less than an Act of Parliament giving compulsory powers as regards recording and copyright could remove the difficulties." [12]

The BBC had made provision for a single national programme on two wavelengths with synchronised transmitters to make their use for navigation confusing to hostile aircraft, and in addition it was arranged that if enemy aircraft were in the area of a broadcasting station where the strong signal could be used, the transmitter would be closed down. The schedule for the single broadcasting station Athlone in Ireland, where it was thought that the Irish Government would be unwilling to close it down during enemy raids, is interesting; the broadcast was monitored in Northern Ireland then sent by land line to broadcasting stations in Somerset, Anglesey and Aberdeen.

All broadcasting since its inception was 'live' and steps had been taken to ensure that outside broadcasts such as concerts should not radiate the air raid warning sirens. The usual procedure was for the programme to be faded out with an announcement – 'We regret that we are unable to continue this programme' and commercial recordings substituted.

The AOC of 60 Group quickly found a number of things that were not to his liking, one of them being that AMRE and DCD were sending staff to the stations without his knowledge and what they were doing there. On 11 April he wrote a private letter to the Director of Signals:

"If this is ever to be a Group and do what you require, which I understand is to take over all the troubles of the Chain, we shall have to have very shortly a clear show-down of who's who, which and where. Lang's branch [the section responsible for RDF in Signals] and 60 Group Headquarters should control the whole outfit. We should know what is going to happen, plan what we can get out of it, and get good prior information of any proposed alteration on any station. The Chain must be led to look on the Group as their father – at present they don't know where they are and frankly nor do I. To begin with D.C.D.'s Department sends men to do things on stations without informing anybody.

Recently, work was done on, I believe, four stations which affected their calibration – no word to Fighter Command...Lardner found out about it by accident and stopped it... [I was asked] if I could organise a rush re-calibration...You see the state of confusion this divided control is producing...Next. Before elaborating this point I don't want to say a word against Hart. He is an excellent fellow, he is helping all he can and liaising well but he has a master [Dowding] with his own definition of 'operational control'. Hart has been a good father to the Chain since its inception. I appreciate his advice and propose to use him to the full but the more he goes round stations the harder it is for my staff to assume control.

All stations still look to Hart as the father....Now I am given to understand that the C. in C. [Dowding], interprets 'operational control' as sending Hart to

A.M.E.S. to see the crews are working as they should, that the gear is being used to the best advantage, etc., etc. I put it to you that this is a hopeless position. Either (1) Hart is transferred to my staff... or (2) that he stays where he is and advises the C. in C. on the best operational use of R.D.F. and reports to Group the dissatisfaction of the C. in C.,(or his compliments?) on the output and conveys back to the C. in C. the action we are or propose taking.

Hart, in view of his knowledge of the chain, has another dangerous aspect from the Group point of view. He communicates to Sigs. 4 details and names for proposed postings, officers and men. I am then sent these as a 'fait accompli' under A.M. authority. How can I operate like this. I know its all done by both sides with the best intentions but I must be sent the requirements and I will work it out.... But I can't go on and get any organisation or efficiency when any of the following can butt in and change things:- Dundee, 2.I.U., D.C.D and Fighter Command. I have spoken of my ideas as to F.C.'s position and require an A.M. definition of "Operational Control ". Much as you dislike this it must be provided. As to D.C.D. and his branches, it must clearly understand that he does nothing unless 60 Group is given notice. This is absolutely necessary...Can you please do something about the points raised. I feel only you can do this...By all means show him [Lang] this, though its contents must not get into any file. I forward it to you, the points are sticky, as the hardened old diplomat." [13]

On 21 April an instruction was issued by the Director of Signals that all visits to chain stations had to be cleared by 60 Group and, despite efforts by AMRE and DCD to be excluded, they failed.

The inevitable incident arose later when Wilkins, Dr C.Wynne-Williams, and others, arrived at Stenigot requesting admission, which was initially refused, as they were not in possession of valid passes and notification of their arrival had not been received by the officer in charge. A letter arrived for Rowe from 60 Group to advise him that, in order to conform to the regulations with regard to security, no personnel would be allowed to enter a station unless in possession of official passes and notification of the impending visit had been received by the station concerned. Rowe dictated a reply, surely with a smile on his face:

"Your letter not entirely understood. These members of the staff of this establishment are lent to 60 Group for the inspection of completed stations. The release of these experienced officers is a loss to this establishment and it is asked that you should give every facility for their work. If special passes are necessary you will no doubt provide these gentlemen with them." [14]

The electric calculator was under test at Poling and in April Dowding was asked to attend a preview but, as urgent Cabinet business prevented his arrival he wrote:

"The outstanding defect of the whole R.D.F. system is its inability to measure height even approximately, and the provision of some apparatus to enable this to be done is an urgent requirement." [15]

He asked for a private demonstration for himself at a later date adding, at the same time, that he felt the matter had gone so far that no objection by him was likely to prohibit its installation. As the RF6 was designed before the calculator, modifications were necessary to extract the range and angle (gonio) information. The range spindle was fitted with a wiper blade that passed over banks of switch contacts as the knob was rotated, and the gonio spindle was also fitted with a wiper blade that swept over 400 contacts in one revolution. The display panel was fitted in the receiver to the right of the tube operator and showed all the data by miniature lamps behind an engraved screen. Because of the changing lights of the display when the calculator was in operation, it was dubbed by the WAAF as the 'fruit machine'; the name stuck and was used by all and sundry. The calculator was capable of passing seven plots a minute, which was too quick for the filter room and twice that obtained by manual methods.

The scientific officers in the operations and filter rooms continued daily to labour on for hours after the raids had finished and the plotting tables cleared to examine all the paper records of the enemy tracks including the plots recorded at each CH and CHL station that were sent to Stanmore the following day. In January a scientific officer there wrote that the technical function of RDF was not finished until the plot was assessed. He commented on:

> "...the appalling low standards of filtering which has been a curse of the Filter Room for the past nine months. The writer of this memo is quite convinced that a complete breakdown of the Filter Room will occur if the enemy attempts a large scale attack of even half the magnitude of that tried during the RAF air exercises of 1939. All the few expert personnel of the Filter Room have been, or are being, posted away...[and] there are not enough for 24 hour working." [16]

Hart had written in November 1939:

> "One of the weakest links in the R.D.F. system is the filterers in the Filter Room. In peacetime every effort was made at Stanmore to train filterers during major and minor exercises, but unfortunately the material trained was not of the right calibre, therefore at the commencement of the war, Fighter Command were faced with conducting operations in the Filter Room with a very inferior staff of N.C.O. filterers. A special effort has been made to select filterers thought suitable for training...the situation is not completely satisfactory in that the method that should be employed for selecting personnel...is not yet clear. There does not appear to be a trade in the R.A.F. from which personnel can be drawn with a certainty who will prove to be satisfactory filterers." [17]

The poor standard of filtering was not wholly the fault of Fighter Command as every change for the rank of filterer had to be approved by the Air Ministry. In December 1939 a request had been made for approval to recruit civilian clerical officers as filterers, with the rank raised from corporal to sergeant so as to obtain the right type of man and to give them disciplinary control over plotters. The Air Ministry did not agree. One officer commented:

"In the course of my frequent visits to units, I have found that there is a general feeling of dissatisfaction throughout the Service against this practice of bringing in people from civil life and giving them relatively high rank. Promotion is therefore denied to Regular personnel and, moreover, I am convinced that the system will eventually have serious disciplinary repercussions." [17]

Something had to be done and done quickly but a forceful argument was needed and accepted before the Air Ministry would agree; it was in preparation. As early as 14 February, Wing Commander J.N.T. Stephenson of the Air Ministry Operations Branch and civil servants in the Finance Branch had visited the Stanmore Filter Room to see and hear the situation at first hand; he wrote to Finance the next day with a summary of the findings.

It was now becoming apparent that, compared to the early days of RDF, when the whole system from CH station to the filter room was in the hands of hand picked enthusiasts and had produced such excellent results, the rapid expansion in 1939 had diluted the experience and technical ability of the RDF personnel. The consequence was that the vastly improved equipment at the stations, and a more highly developed technique, were producing markedly inferior results to that obtained in the early days. The deterioration was, had to be, ipso facto, due to the quality of the personnel.

Fighter Command had arranged for tracks to be made on tracings by the scientific personnel from the complete series of raid plots given by different stations, that were compared to the tracks produced on the filter room table by the filterers and, from which, the fighters had failed to make interceptions. The analysis made it clear beyond any possible doubt that from the tracks produced by the filterers the fighters never had a chance of making a successful interception, a conclusion that was no surprise to Fighter Command. Three technical assistants with physicists' backgrounds were put in as experimental filterers and after a short period of training showed a remarkable aptitude for the work. Their mathematical and scientific experience enabled them to produce from plots passed to them from stations, the operation of which they understood and the technical vagaries of which they fully appreciated, the most probable answer.

The word 'probable' was the key word, in fact it was 'the assessing of a probability' that was of supreme importance. The officer entrusted with the investigation and analysis was of the opinion that the most accurate assessment of the probability depended on many factors, the comprehension of which would never be found in the ordinary airman or, indeed, to the highest degree in the ordinary officer. The Wing Commander continued:

"You know as well as I do the vital importance of accurate filtering. At only one point in the vast network of the R.D.F system does the information collected and forwarded by the R.D.F. Chain assume a tangible form upon which fighter action may be taken. At that point stands the filterer and it is his responsibility and his alone that this tangible data is the most accurate which it is possible to obtain and, unless he has the peculiar knowledge and the ability to profit by the experience which is ultimately the medium through which a Filterer becomes an expert, we shall never get good filtering and the maximum of interceptions. Without such filtering the whole of our fighter defence of this country will be most seriously handicapped, and the ten and a half million pounds of capital sunk in the R.D.F. organisation itself will never give the results of which we know it should be capable." [18]

He proposed that steps should be taken:

"...to recruit as filterers the type of man now known to be necessary for the proper discharge of these duties...[and] make it imperative that we should establish the posts of Filterers as for officers and I suggest we should take this action now, fixing the rank as of Pilot Officer/Flying Officer. Owing to the length of time which Fighter Command have taken to come to the conclusion that an inquiry into this matter and a consultation with us was necessary, this requirement is now most urgent." [17]

A reply from the Finance Branch, which followed a few days later, was in total agreement with the Wing Commander, well, almost:

"Efforts have been made in the past to get the right type of man for filtering duties, but unfortunately they have failed, and unless filterers who are capable of assessing the degree of probability with reasonable accuracy are employed, the R.D.F. organisation might just as well not exist.... We came to the conclusion that the duties of the filterers were such as to justify the appointment of junior officers and there is, therefore, no financial objection to the appointment of Pilot Officers/ Flying Officers to these posts in lieu of the Corporals established." [18]

But, there was disagreement on the number of filterers; they recommended that the existing four watches of five persons should be reduced to three watches with five persons plus three for relief. That was not all; they raised the question that with filterers of officer status was it then necessary to retain three sergeant floor supervisors? However, the Wing Commander was not prepared to give way and on 23 March he wrote to Finance, his patience clearly exhausted:

"I am not disputing your acknowledged responsibility for examining the establishment in detail or your right to criticise any proposal and to offer what you may consider is an acceptable alternative, but where I am convinced that a replacement is essential to meet an operational commitment in war, I must ask you to remember that I am fully aware as you are of the need for economy in manpower and in money – that I will not support any extravagant requests, but I cannot agree to the same lengthy, academic and delaying examination of establishment proposals which was possible and acceptable in peace time." [18]

After a few weeks of silence the Wing Commander was informed on 8 May by Finance that:

"... in view of the unquestioned importance of the Filter Room and for the necessity for ensuring that there is no risk of breakdown, we accept your view that the Filter Room staff must be established on a four watch basis... there is therefore no financial objection to the establishment." [18]

The beginning of the Battle of Britain was just two months away.

A Stanmore Research Section (SRS) report had commented that height finding by CH operators was 'an epic event', a judgement on their avoidance and little understanding of the hand calculator. The angle reading on the gonio was converted to height by the combination of range, a correction due to the curvature of the earth and site irregularities, but there were limitations. There was a minimum of angle of elevation that could be read, usually 1.5 degrees but varying between stations, but all angles below that figure all read the minimum, ie, an aircraft flying at 5,000ft at 30 miles and one flying at 3,000ft at 30 miles both gave the minimum angle. At angles above six degrees, height measuring was insensitive and turned over, an angle of eight degrees reading as four and, at bearings greater than 45 degrees either side of the station Line of Shoot, the accuracy sharply deteriorated.

Dowding had written on 27 March to the Air Staff to complain about the limitation of heightfinding and its importance as an aid to interception; he reminded them that most interceptions were over the sea where no indication of height, other than that given by RDF, could be obtained. He continued:

"I think it is not generally known how very limited is the capacity of R.D.F. to give height. It is generally known that raids under 2,000ft and over 25,000ft are likely to be missed altogether by the Chain Stations, but there is a comfortable feeling that between these limits the Chain Stations give height with approximate accuracy. This is far from being the case... 15,000ft is about the best height, but even at this optimum altitude there are important areas where blanks occur. The situation is much worse at 10,000ft; but, when we come to 5,000ft there is practically no part of the coast North of the Humber where height can be read at all...." [19]

Rowe felt that he had to defend the operational performance of CHL and wrote on 6 May to DCD:

"If there has been some doubt in many minds regarding whether C.H.L. stations are contributing their fair share to the defence effort, and we at Dundee have not escaped an element of doubt on this point, intelligence reports covering 7 to 26 March have been analysed and materially assisting the plotting of hostile raids was C.H. stations 56 times and C.H.L. stations 42 times. When the newness of the stations and their crews are taken into account it is considered that the analysis affords a striking and...unexpected tribute to C.H.L. Stations." [3]

On 9 April there was a sudden and highly dramatic change in the conduct of the war with the invasion of Norway and Denmark by German armed forces, with such rapidity and effectiveness, that opposition in Denmark was crushed within a day, and Norway in a few weeks, despite Allied assistance and Norwegian resistance. The calamity provoked a debate in the House of Commons on 7 May when speakers from both sides attacked the Prime Minister, Neville Chamberlain, in particular Mr L.S.Amery who quoted, amid ringing cheers, Oliver Cromwell's imperious words to the Rump Parliament on 22 January 1654,

"You have sat here too long for any good you have been doing. Depart I say and let us have done with you. In the name of God, go."

The debate continued the next day with the Government surviving a vote of censure. Chamberlain decided the next day to form a National Government with senior political figures from the Labour and Liberal parties, but before any moves could be made the Germans invaded France, Belgium, Holland and Luxembourg on 10 May. This unexpected enemy action expedited the Parliamentary crisis, Chamberlain being told by his Cabinet colleagues that he could no longer continue as Prime Minister. In those days the outgoing Premier named his own choice of successor to the King and Chamberlain only had two choices, Lord Halifax and Winston Churchill, but the former declined because of his title. Churchill became Premier without the consultation of the Conservative Party who, it is thought, would not have supported him, and the announcement in the House of Lords was greeted with complete silence. He made himself the Minister of Defence with undefined powers that included the supervision and direction of the Chief of Staffs Committee and, among other Cabinet changes, Sir Archibald Sinclair, the Liberal Party leader, was appointed as the Secretary of State for Air.

For the public the danger was all too clear, with the announcements that aliens were to be interned, policemen to be armed against parachutists, place names to be removed from signposts, shop fronts and tradesmen's vans. Restrictions were placed on the sale and possession of maps and guide books, arterial roads and those leading to ports and aerodromes to be blocked and bridges prepared for demolition. Air Staff Intelligence had correctly surmised the course of events:

"German strategy has followed the Christie plan with remarkable similarity, and after the Scandinavian expedition I think that we can believe that an air attack on the Low Countries in the almost immediate future is probable, with the object of drawing closer to this country, giving depth to the defence of the Ruhr and bringing German bases so close to this country that a heavy and constant scale of attack could be maintained with ease. Primary facets of the Christie plan subsequent to the vigorous attacks on industry, ports and main centres of the country, is a landing of German troops on our soil with the object of bringing intense pressure on the British people to sue for peace. The possibility of the Germans having air superiority between the Low Countries and this country is so that established naval operations by surface craft in daylight would be impracticable. The possibility of the invasion of this country in the second German war is by no means a fantasy." [20] (Christie was a retired air attaché living in Berlin.)

At the beginning of the year agreement had been reached that guyed steel masts would replace self-supporting 350ft steel towers for the West Chain on the grounds that the increased cost was not justified by any additional security that they might give against various forms of air attack. On 14 May, Lee, the Director of DCD wrote to Joubert:

"...that 325' guyed steel masts fabricated to an existing Marconi design will be employed for the Western chain. It is understood that W3 [Works] reported ...that the Marconi firm were 'blackmailing' us for the use of the designs. In this connection the Director of Signals instructed the Works Director to go ahead with all plans and to report any further difficulties immediately so that Air Staff authority could be given to 'take' the designs if necessary." [21]

Shortly afterwards, Works reported, after placing an order for eight 325ft masts that:

"...we have obtained possession of the drawings. We are consulting a number of suitable contractors with a view to placing further orders for the masts of this design and have at present ordered eight masts from J.L.Eve Construction and hope to place additional orders within the next few days." [21]

Works had started on AMRE's next home at Worth Matravers but the harsh winter had delayed all the building work. The sudden appearance of the towers gave the locals in Swanage the idea that oil was being prospected and some of them looked on the change positively by writing in to offer accommodation. One wrote negatively by repeating a rumour that had supposedly come from one of the site workers that when he was in the Shetlands doing the same job the German aeroplanes had come down and bombed them, killing 15 men and blowing all their half-built works, masts, etc., to blazes.

To aid the staff at Dundee to arrange accommodation they were told that the new station was approximately four miles from Swanage; starting from sea level and rising to about 400ft the outward journey by bicycle was 25 minutes, the return journey ten minutes! At Dundee, Rowe was impatiently waiting for the signal to start the move, which was received on 3 May, and, after a 'marching out' ceremony was performed, the research staff began their long awaited return to the south. The next day stevedores hired from the Dundee docks began removing all the heavy packing cases from the third floor of the Teachers' Training College and from the Physics Lab. at the University and loading the railway wagons, which arrived at Swanage on Monday 6 May. Two days later the AMRE scientific and technical staff were organising the installation of a double site CHL and a CH station. Determined resistance from Dr Bowen failed to prevent his AI group returning to Worth, where they were also joined by the VHF development section from RAE.

Rowe wrote to DCD that in his opinion a letter of thanks should be sent to the Principal from the Air Council as they had received every possible assistance from the college authorities, and one was duly sent. In his return letter the Principal reminded the Air Ministry that they had not yet received any rent for the period of occupation. Rowe reported to DCD that the site and neighbourhood were liked by the staff and the facilities provided made those at Dundee appear lamentable in comparison. At AMRE the irony of realising that now they had just moved to within striking distance of the Germans was perhaps overshadowed by another unforeseen change. A new state department was announced on 14 May, the Ministry of Aircraft Production (MAP), to take over not only the production side of the Air Ministry but also research and development. Churchill had put forward the name of Lord Beaverbrook as the Minister, which did not meet with the approval of the King; nevertheless Churchill insisted. Now taken over by the MAP, Freeman's directorate staff including the DCD perhaps let out a silent cheer when they were told that they were moving from Harrogate, their wartime home, back to Millbank, London. AMRE became MAPRE but the change appeared to be ignored; for many months incoming and outgoing letters, committee minutes and even letters from MAP headquarters at Millbank, London were duly addressed to AMRE. Many training films were simply titled as AMRE Swanage.

The first indication that the Germans were on the English doorstep was on 10 May when a single aircraft dropped a bomb on Canterbury, and on 25 May the first raid occurred on the northeast industrial town of Middlesborough. The swiftness of the German offensives had produced many instructions from the Director of Signals. One message on 21 May was addressed to DCD, 60 Group, 2.IU and AMRE:

"Imperative you proceed with the immediate manufacture of six M.B.2 stations in final form. This work to proceed on the highest authority with a view to completion and readiness for duty on site by 1st June....Most likely further calls for Mobile M.B.2s will be made at short notice....Progress report to be signalled to D of S daily." [22]

A signal followed for 60 Group to immediately recondition the five sets of GM mobiles returned from France and to place the three GMs allocated to the Norway campaign, but never used, into the standby pool. Rowe was advised that the resources of his establishment had been placed at the disposal of the Director of Signals, through 60 Group, for the supply of scientific officers if needed at the new CH and CHL sites.

On 27 May at AMRE a meeting was convened to provide cover in the quickest possible time with priority for the defence of London, the Straits of Dover to the Humber, from the Lizard to the Bristol Channel, from Liverpool to the Clyde and from the Humber to the Shetlands. 60 Group found themselves arranging for the installation of eight CH and 15 CHL stations almost overnight. An 'Immediate' signal ordered a mobile to Hawks Tor to provide cover for the naval base at Plymouth: it left Kidbrooke on 30 May at 1700 hours and arrived the next day at 1500 hours; on 6 June, one Warrant Officer and 22 RAF arrived from Yatesbury to open a 24 hour watch. A survey for part of the West Chain had already been conducted by Wilkins in March and the stations were being planned with ACH, but now mobiles would be used to move forward the operating date as Works were then not needed to provide huts and mast footings; ACH would follow at a later date. At Stranraer, the original site at Mid Moile was abandoned because the approach road could not be built fast enough and another site found along the sea shore at North Cairn. A semi-mobile station, which formed a convoy of ten vehicles complete with tented accommodation, field kitchen and workshop, was dispatched on a near 1,000 mile journey to Skaw, in Unst, the most northerly of the Shetland Islands. The Admiralty began to supply depth charges for the demolition of their CDUs in the event of invasion; the German occupied Norwegian coast was just 220 miles away.

There was insufficient time for CHL aerial arrays to be placed on the 200ft cantilevers of the steel towers at Rye, Poling, Pevensey and Dunkirk so alternatives were found at Fairlight, Beachy Head, Truleigh Hill and Whitstable. Two CHLs were useless and as Fighter Command would not allow the sets to be closed down and re-erected, a new station would be installed at Skendelby, eight miles inland, to replace Ingoldmells, which had been positioned too low at 15ft and was on a sandbank provided to prevent flooding by Spring tides, with another at Bempton, three miles inland, to replace Flamborough, although at a height of 140ft it was too near the sea.

A further two CHL stations were also to be moved but these would have to wait until equipment and effort was available – Anstruther to Drumrack Farm, three miles north at 378ft, and Foreness, ten yards from the cliff edge and suffering from sea reflections that gave rise to unpredictable fading of echoes, to 200 yards inland and to be called Foreness 2. Gaitnip, which was useless due to its position in the middle of islands that gave excessive permanent echoes, would be re-erected nearer the sea at Deerness, 280ft, six miles east of Netherbutton.

Fifteen CHLs were required very urgently: the War Office and the Admiralty handed over their transmitters and receivers and all spares were taken from Pye; there would be no further supplies until mid-July. As there were only 16 turntables available there could only be one aerial at each site and, knowing that two broadside arrays could never be turned by hand, AMRE, as an experiment, had earlier replaced the transmitter array with a 13 director Yagi aerial fixed on top of the Worth CHL receiving array.

Watson Watt had given an assurance of his personal conviction that Yagi T arrays would prove satisfactory and it was recommended that they should be fitted to all CHL stations even before the test results from AMRE were known, which were due on 1 June. DCD protested that the Yagi aerial had not received approval but to no avail – RAE were requested to supply drawings in two days for manufacture by Pye. The installation consisted of a single 12ft by 12ft wooden hut for the receiver under a 20ft wooden gantry that supported the aerial, one 30ft by 18ft hut for the transmitter and another for stores and offices. A further improvement was the replacement of the inadequate chain turning of the aerial array. Known as the Hopkins modification, a metal frame supported a vertical column with universal joints that was turned by a motor car steering wheel, with a handle attached, coupled to an Austin 10 car type gear box to transpose the rotary motion. All installations had to be completed by 8 July with AMRE scientific officers attached to ensure optimum performance.

A few stations gave very poor results; at Fairlight and Truleigh Hill the scientific officer discarded the Yagi aerial and replaced it with a single dipole tier isolated from the, now, three tier receiver broadside array. There was a great improvement with Truleigh Hill reporting that aircraft were being plotted to 40 to 50 miles on wet and 85 to 95 miles on fine days. When the CHL arrived at Hopton the Yagi aerial was missing so the aerial array was split into two separate tiers that gave a working range of 40 miles with occasional plots to 70 miles. Fighter Command forbade any further alterations. The very rapid increase in the number of CH and CHL stations west of Ventnor had forced the setting-up of two filter rooms, one at Rudloe Manor, Box, the headquarters of No 10 Group near Bath in Wiltshire, and the other at Barton Hall near Preston, Lancashire, the headquarters of No 9 Group. A telephone line was provided to the Filter Room at Stanmore to alert the Air Raid Warning section there.

The German Army meanwhile had continued their rapid advance into France and along the English Channel forcing the retreat of over 325,000 British and French soldiers to the beaches of Dunkirk from where they were miraculously evacuated, but without their stores or equipment. France fell with an humiliating capitulation on 18 June. In the space of two months the strategic situation of the war had changed quickly and, almost unbelievably, in favour of the Germans. It brought home to the British people that a very serious situation was now on their doorstep; just how serious they were never allowed to know.

Air Staff intelligence reports had suggested that the German Air Force had nearly 2,000 bombers, 500 dive bombers and 1,400 heavy and light fighter aircraft. They were capable of flying from the coasts of Brittany and Norway to any part of the United Kingdom including all the West Country, Scottish and Irish ports, the dive bombers with a range as far as the Midlands. The resources of Fighter Command were well known to the Air Staff; 700 first line fighters of which 600 were a mixture of Hurricanes and Spitfires, with 230 in reserve. Fighter Command had lost over 400 Hurricanes and Spitfires in the last few weeks of the fighting in France, 106 during the Dunkirk evacuation, and with them the VHF sets that could not be quickly replaced. Their loss became so serious that the Secretary of State, Sir Archibald Sinclair wrote to Lord Beaverbrook, the Minister of Aircraft Production, on the 28 May to complain of the breakdown in supplies.

On 1 June, Dowding wrote to the Air Staff to explain the reason for his signal on 26 May that withdrew VHF R/T from fighter squadrons:

"...that to have to abandon the use of our most successful form of fighter communication...is a deplorable necessity. The result must be to reduce the operational efficiency of Fighter Command. The necessity which has forced me to resort to such drastic action is due entirely to the inadequacy of supplies...I am required to operate fighter patrols over the Channel and parts of France and Belgium from bases in the South – East of England; losses are unavoidable ... I am informed that no further equipment...will be available until late Summer. I must maintain complete flexibility in the operation of all my Squadrons under the present exceptional conditions...it is not practicable for a Squadron to keep changing from one type of equipment to another....the continued use of the admixture of V.H.F. and H.F. is unworkable." [23]

It was not until 19 August that Dowding approved the return to VHF. The beginning of June saw a sharp rise in the number of reported 'hostiles' to the Filter Room at Stanmore. The Air Staff Diary recorded:

"June 5 [has been] a hot and busy day in the underground Operations Room at Stanmore, the work of plotting and identifying the raids in the evening almost exceeding the physical abilities of airmen and W.A.A.F. plotters and of the Controller and his staff of officers. Between 0900 and 1100 eight unidentified raids plotted in the Straits of Dover, and over the coast of France between Dieppe and Boulogne, between 1100 to 1300 there were eight similar raids plotted either over the North Sea or over the Dunkirk, Abbeville and Calais region, between 1300 and 1600 there were nine unidentified raids plotted over France, between 1600 and 1800 seven unidentified raids plotted over Ostend, Dunkirk and Abbeville, between 1800 to 2100 13 unidentified raids plotted over the coasts of France and Belgium between the mouths of the Seine and Scheldt. But the watch 2100 to 0300 was a masterpiece of activity, no less than 134 'X' raids plotted, very heavy enemy activity largely by Ju88s from the Orkney Islands to the Isle of Wight, the main area effected between Flamborough Head and the Isle of Wight....

German bombers now finding targets by night and day and dispersed over a wider and more inland areas of England, Scotland and Wales than ever had been contemplated....Enemy aircraft were now operating from Stravanger [Norway] to France, laying mines off North Foreland and the Downs, Humber and the Tees....Films taken by cine-camera guns were to be shown at stations, not so much for their instructional value on tactics, but for the morale value of seeing a German aircraft shot in bits and its pilot taking to his parachute. On 18 June bombs were dropped on the C.H. stations at Bawdsey, Canewdon and Stenigot." [24]

Park complained to Rowe on the poor counting technique; one raid was reported as 3+, then 6+, finally 9+ but turned out to be about 80 and on another occasion two squadrons were surprised to find out that they were engaging about 40 to 50 enemy aircraft.

The nearness of the German army to the English coastline raised the possibility that the CH and CHL stations would be liable to capture, if only for a short time, so destruction orders, which had been prepared for stations in the Orkney and Shetland Islands, were now applied to those on the south coast. It was emphasised that action was only to be taken when it was clear beyond all doubt that the station was in imminent danger of being seized. Scientific officers with their knowledge of RDF would have to make every effort to avoid being taken prisoners and other station staff were to refrain from panic measures that would lead to premature demolition of the equipment.

The overriding parts for destruction were the pulse elements of the transmitter such as the modulator panel, the receiver cathode ray tube to be smashed using a nearby fire axe, and the CHL motor-driven aerial switch. At Beachy Head the charge next to the motor was accidentally fired during a mock demonstration destroying the aerial array. Documents such as the

RDF manual, the Cossor receiver handbook, circuit diagrams and other secret papers were to be destroyed in an acid bath. To make it appear that the CH stations were high powered W/T stations the receiver rooms were supplied with signal pads and headphones, and in the transmitter room a Morse key would be fitted with broken wires attached. Watson Watt gave his opinion that complete destruction was unnecessary as it was highly likely that a re-occupation was bound to follow. Fighter Command had issued code words for invasion:

Blackbird – surface vessels, submarines and motor torpedo boats sighted but not identified,

Gallipoli – enemy are landing from ships, boats or caterpillars,

Parasols – enemy landing by parachute, and

Starling – enemy air transports landing on our aerodromes.

SRS issued a report covering 18-26 June during which the German Air Force had raided the country on five occasions during the hours of darkness. With an average of 80 planes a night, single aircraft spaced at intervals of a few minutes, the practice adopted by Bomber Command, the attacks were in two waves with the second approximately two hours after the first and, for a portion of the night, when both of them were over the country. It was considered that all aspects of the chain had functioned in an extremely satisfactory manner but it was pointed out that there were too many tracks without height. The report added:

"It would appear doubtful that the R.D.F. chain missed more than 10% of the total number of aircraft invading the country, and as R.D.F. tracks were generally available for 30 minutes or one hour before any aircraft crossed the coast, the Chain served a very useful purpose in giving advance information to the effect that an attack was on its way, as well as giving information as to where the attack would make its landfall...it was noticeable that a small proportion of their aircraft proceeded down the southern side of the English Channel to Cherbourg and then turned north towards the Bristol/ Cardiff area... The new R.D.F. station at Worth has proved invaluable in dealing with these aircraft, and without it the gap to the west of Ventnor would have enabled them all, at least, to reach the coast of England without being observed.

During the first three nights, the majority of German aircraft effected a landfall between Dover and Cromer, those that were directing their attention to targets on the south coast then proceeding down the English Channel, well within 20 miles of the coastline, and often only five miles from land. Those that were after more northerly objectives proceeded northwards, hugging the coast as they went...aircraft, when proceeding parallel with the coast at a comparatively short range out to sea, were in general more difficult for the R.D.F. chain to track than those that were well out to sea, the C.H.L. stations suffering from permanent echoes when swung to look up and down the coast and the C.H.

stations suffering from their general inability to discriminate sense when viewing aircraft at right angles to their line of shoot: luckily, the Observer Corps are quite good on tracks within five miles of the coast..." [25]

The WAAF Directorate was circulating a report on the hardships that were affecting the WAAF at certain RDF stations, which drew a first reaction that perhaps it was not such a good idea to have them there. The report said, in essence, that the accommodation and working conditions provided for the RAF were certainly not good enough for the WAAF. The stations presented a special case that had received little attention as a one day visit gave very little idea of the danger of ennui from living on one, month after month, the same crew working, sleeping, eating and taking their recreation together, shut off from the world. The huts were two to four miles along a rough track from the technical compound where the women worked. Transport was an open van with a canvas top and wooden seats. The nearest village was often three or four miles distant, while a town with a hairdresser and a cinema might be 15 miles away. Even if there was a train or bus service within a reasonable walking distance, airwomen earning 1s 4d (7p) a day such as mess or kitchen grades could not afford even the half fare very often and free rides were not forthcoming. Apart from the isolation, the work done by the WAAF on the stations was of a nature calculated to try their nerves to the utmost:

> "Everything should be done to mitigate these nerve-wracking working conditions. At present, not only do the airwomen receive no special consideration, but too often it happens that, owing to the great distance from the Parent station, and to difficult local conditions, they receive less. Their equipment, rationing etc., should be a matter of the greatest importance if their physical and mental welfare is not to suffer from the intense strain under which they work." [26]

One of the main criticisms was the lack of recreation that was enjoyed at the majority of RAF stations, which were less isolated, and no social life within reasonable distance. Isolation was relevant in that even in summer it was undesirable for airwomen to be out alone after dark on the moors, or in the woods or upon the marshes after seeking a little amusement from the nearest village:

> "In winter, however, it is really dangerous for airwomen to be out without an armed male escort after about five o'clock in the afternoon in some places; and not all airwomen number an armed escort among their special friends." [26]

The all-male food came in for censure as;

> "...totally unsuitable, being much too heavy for airwomen engaged on sedentary duties; it is frequently lacking in suitable vitamins. A carefully chosen diet is required, including less meat and more fruit and vegetables and plenty of milk,

if the airwomen are to be kept fit for their exacting duties." [26]

Nor were the barrack huts comfortable or warm enough:

"...there is nothing to stop the wind whistling through the barrack-rooms on bitter winter nights...[that] were hastily constructed in an emergency and have ill fitting doors...[existing] stoves are totally inadequate for winter conditions...[The] present issue of four blankets for each airwoman is not enough...even in June...all personnel [should] be issued with at least six blankets each before the autumn." [26]

Even the laundry service was not straightforward:

"It is not sufficiently realised...that the airwomen, having only two sets of clothing, cannot spare one set for a week at a time if the laundry is delivered and collected on the same day, as this would entail an airwoman wearing no underclothes for one day." [26]

The report concluded by observing the lack of medical services, with some detachments ten miles away from the nearest doctor and no telephones in the barracks, yet the airwomen worked and lived in a danger zone with a high casualty risk as most A.M.E.S. were visited by the enemy almost nightly. There was one concession in that the Director of the WAAF no longer insisted on the erection of barbed wire fencing between the RAF and the WAAF hutted camps.

A letter had been sent in April by the AOC 60 Group to all stations:

"I have been asked by the W.A.A.F. authorities to see that the girls are not mollycoddled. It is the idea of their service to replace men and do men's work, not to have men set aside to make their lives more easy. The officers would like to be treated as a male officer of equivalent rank and not as a lady at a social gathering." [26]

Joubert had spent many months as the Air Co-ordinating Officer but he found that he was more of a sightseer than a player. He wrote to the CAS:

"The situation described is considerably worse. Sir Henry Tizard's resignation has been effective and there is 'war' between Sir George Lee [the DCD] and Mr. Watson Watt. Mr. Rowe is in open mutiny. Further, Mr. Watson Watt has departed from the arrangement made some months ago whereby you decided that he was to advise the Air Staff on telecommunications, and is now inserting himself into Sir Frank Smith's organisation. I understand the latter has taken over all Sir Wilfred Freeman's responsibility for R.D.F. production. My position has become impossible. I have responsibility without authority and the R.D.F. sheep, harried by the Lindemann wolf, are rushing madly in every direction. No one knows who to go to for orders and it is my opinion that it is time that I was given authority as well as responsibility. I suggest that for the future period of the war, that an A.C.A.S. (R) be established to run the Service side of R.D.F. and Communications generally and be responsible to V.C.A.S." [28]

The CAS agreed and the post was grudgingly approved by the Treasury as they had suggested that the post was more suitable for an Air Vice Marshal, but they eventually agreed to Joubert's appointment in July. The (R) indicated the word 'radio', which was introduced in February to enable distinctions to be made between those working on RDF, now radio, and those on 'wireless'.

On 22 June, Works received a letter from Messrs J.L.Eve, who had manufactured four 350ft steel towers for the French CH chain; worth £13,500, two were at Southampton and two at the steel works and in view of the invasion and collapse of France they were asking for disposal instructions and payment. Works quickly made use of this unexpected good fortune by earmarking two for AMRE at Worth and two for North Cairn where it had been found that there was insufficient space on the sea shore to set up guyed masts; it was discovered at a later date that the two towers had been erected without the correction of the magnetic variation.

A potential invasion was the major concern of the Chiefs of Staff and, in particular for the CAS, the possibility of one by gliders. Intelligence had been received that over 100 of them were being assembled in Belgium and in Norway it had been reported that at Trondheim they had been seen in the tow of Ju52 aircraft. The detection of gliders was in Joubert's hands and he, with others, was anxious to see the effect on the CH display tube when they became separated from aircraft. A flying officer, a renowned glider expert, was called to the Air Ministry to discuss the aspects of gliding with Joubert; the expert thought the Germans would use an 80ft wingspan glider that could carry eight men, cast off at 10,000ft and glide for 20 miles landing at 65mph. Ten experimental flights were made, which were a great success and carried out under dangerous circumstances, as they were liable to enemy intervention across the English Channel. They clearly showed that the echo on the CRT display could be seen to split at the point of release with the glider echo moving slower than that of the aircraft. Joubert's view was that as the invasion would occur at night and, as the existing CH chain would be fully occupied by aircraft location, a second chain should be established some 20 miles behind the existing one.

Moves were made to check if the coastal CH stations could be arranged to look backwards but this would require another receiver and a special receiver aerial. The Observer Corps were given additional duties for the watching of Ju52s, which were used exclusively for the carrying of parachute troops and supplies while those near harbours were told to keep a sharp watch on people landing from vessels. On one occasion the police were alerted only to find that the persons being brought ashore in the early hours of the morning were two local ladies who had earlier paid a visit to a ship.

At a meeting at the Air Ministry to discuss gliders the chairman suddenly realised that Joubert had not been sent the papers or invited to attend and could not be contacted. In a letter of apology and explanation to Joubert, the chairman wrote:

"Dear Air Marshal, We held a meeting today on gliders and when we were all assembled I found to my horror that owing to a slip up you had not been sent the papers or asked to come to the meeting. I went along to see if I could get you to come at short notice but you were away. I am very sorry as I know that you are interested and I particularly wanted you to have an opportunity of attending. I can only hope that when you get the minute you will say that all your points are covered and that you are happy, Yours, in a white sheet, R.Saundby."

Joubert replied the next day. "Dear Saundby, It is quite alright." [29]

With the exception of Schoolhill and Hillhead that were at the Intermediate, and Wick (Thrumster) at the ACH stage, the East Chain was operational with the ½CH transmitter in the T building with an aerial on one of the 350ft towers and the RF5 in the wooden hut. An RF6 was installed in the R building with an aerial system on the third wooden tower but waiting for calibration. The Post Office had also commenced the fitting of one electric calculator with priority for the south and estuary stations. Aircraft were located between 70 to 95 miles at 10,000 ft, with 50 miles at 4000ft and 25 to 30 miles at 500ft by CHL. Although without a heightfinding system the operators were able to judge the height of single aircraft by ± 10% when followed through two minima that caused the echo to fade, and for very low levels of height an outdoor visual confirming check had to be made. Installation progress had to be reported by signal every 48 hours and the state of readiness of the two chains had to be reported daily. Watson Watt had given his assurance to the War Cabinet that the five estuary stations would be completed on one wavelength by 7 July and the latest chain extensions would be in operation by the end of that month.

REFERENCES

1	AIR2/3181	2	AIR2/7117	3	AIR2/7151	4	AIR20/2267
5	AIR2/3271	6	AVIA12/146	7	AIR20/2271	8	AIR2/5056
9	AIR2/4059	10	AIR2/3271	11	AIR2/7180	12	AIR2/5067
13	AIR20/1484	14	AVIA7/737	15	AVIA7/161	16	AVIA7/183
17	AIR2/3143	18	AIR2/3461	19	AVIA7/438	20	AIR20/295
21	AVIA15/217	22	AVIA7/562	23	AIR2/2946	24	AIR24/525
25	AVIA7/439	26	AIR2/3023	27	AIR16/882	28	AVIA46/58
29	AIR20/2265						

Chapter 9   July to December 1940

THE appearance of the German army in northern France, opposite the south coast of England, caused many problems for the Air Staff, one of which was the nearness of AMRE. DCD wrote to Rowe that packing cases should be ready to ensure a quick departure to a place of safety with only files and essential research material to be taken and the remainder destroyed. Rowe's reply was to question a move to an unorganised place – the effect on morale would be like depriving an infantryman of his rifle; his preference was to set up research in Canada or disperse it throughout the UK. Another quandary was the half ton of secret files and documents and 150 tons of equipment as AMRE was completely unprepared to cope with their destruction on any scale and, in an emergency, could do nothing.

The DCD's opinion was that research should be dispersed and he had selected three places for investigation by AMRE: the research and development section of the Distillers Company at Epsom, the Anglo-American Oil Company at Sunbury and a detached building in the grounds of the Royal Holloway College at Englefield Green, Egham, all in Surrey. AMRE reported that all the locations were occupied and would require orders under Defence Regulations to evacuate them, which at short notice was impracticable. At Holloway College the lighting was 110 volts DC with no AC points, which would necessitate a new AC supply and a complete re-wiring of the building, and at Epsom enemy aircraft had been in the vicinity an hour before the arrival of the AMRE team.

The idea was not abandoned by the DCD. Rowe was urged to make a further search for alternative accommodation and he made his opinion felt in a letter to DCD stating that the evacuation of AMRE to other than a fully prepared position would be catastrophic to their work, but agreed that some preparations had to be made as a contingency. He suggested three possibilities: the first was a purpose-built place somewhere with 53,000 square feet of floor space, towers and a cliff for CHL work, which could all be made available in three months; the second was a return to Bawdsey and the third to split the work between RAE and specified CH and CHL stations.

The situation was clarified by a directive from the Ministry of Aircraft Production which decreed that offices and laboratory accommodation should at once be found for about 200 people at Swanage: dispersal not evacuation. Worth Matravers village was to be used and properties requisitioned 'with Mr. A.P.Rowe armed with the necessary authority.'

From the beginning of July the German Air Force had been preparing and re-grouping its formations on the French and Belgian airfields. Now understood to be the start of the Battle of Britain the Germans increased their air attacks with daylight raids on towns, on convoys in the English Channel especially in the Straits of Dover, and at night with repeated mine laying. These activities showed a deficiency in the cover between Worth and West Prawle so a mobile set was hurriedly taken to Branscombe, near Sidmouth, in Devon; it was not without incident.

On July 18 the convoy left AMRE but when it had reached Wareham it overshot a turning and, as it was found impossible to reverse, an alternative route was taken. A low hanging tree carried away the dipole and insulator packed on one of the top of the towers so a spare was delivered by a dispatch rider from AMRE the next day. A little later one of the vehicles developed magneto trouble to such an extent that the convoy was forced to stay overnight in Dorchester Barracks for repairs. The next day it arrived at the site in a heavy rainstorm but work started straight away in erecting the guyed masts and by the 22nd the station was in operation but waiting for the telephone lines to be connected and a flight test to be made; by the 24th the station had been handed over to the RAF.

The CHLs at West Prawle and Drytree were giving poor ranges due to bad siting and were scheduled for a resite, the first to Kingswear, the second to Pen Olver, on the coast near Lizard village. As the ACH and CHL at Carnanton were too near St. Eval aerodrome AMRE confirmed that the CHL would have to be moved to Trevose Head and the CH to Trerew. At CHL stations along the Channel the importance of ship detection was emphasised as the possibility of an enemy invasion grew daily.

Preparation work was continuing to fit CHL at all CH stations but the height of the sites was the main stumbling block. Above 200ft two 40ft gantries would support two broadside aerials with synchronous electric drive, and for sites below 200ft the aerials would be on 200ft towers but it was not known if these towers were to be steel or wooden until after tests on a prototype being fitted on a 200ft cantilever of a steel tower at Bawdsey. The two display units would be in the R block and the transmitter in a hut adjacent to the gantry or tower.

West Beckham was representative of many CH stations; the new R building had been ready for five weeks, the RF6 installed but awaiting calibration. Barrack huts were being constructed for the RAF and the WAAF about two miles away. The station strength was RAF – 2 Officers, 64 NCOs and Airmen, WAAF – 1 Officer, 32 NCOs and Airwomen, Army –g 2 Officers and 63 men of the Norfolk Regiment plus a detachment of the Royal Artillery. All rations had to be fetched from Bircham Newton, the parent station some 26 miles away.

Ottercops with a range of over 100 miles had the first 25 miles of the trace full of fixed echoes that was not considered serious as the station was the same distance from the coast. Dunkirk had a Final 'passing out' conducted on 8 August by Wilkins; the plotting line to Stanmore was shared by another three CHL stations, Foreness 1 and 2 and Whitstable, the last with calibration delayed because of the presence of hostile aircraft night and day. Runs had been arranged for July 20 and 21 but were cancelled at the last minute. On 22 July one aircraft on a 40 degree course was plotted 30 miles at 500ft, 50 miles at 1,500ft, 60 miles at 5,000ft; the maximum range was 75 miles. At Ventnor aircraft were frequently seen at ranges of 155 miles, while at Stenigot there was severe R/T interference from Moscow (USSR), which, fortunately, was removed by slight retuning otherwise the station would have been unworkable and out of action until another wavelength was allocated and new transmit aerials fitted.

In July the naval authorities at Kirkwall complained that bombs had fallen without any RDF warning, the third time within 14 days that low flying aircraft had been undetected. The CHL at Gaitnip was unusable and waiting to be moved to Deerness but held up because of the vital work by 2.IU on CHL installations along the English south and southwest coasts. The growing use of the northern route by convoys was the reason for increased enemy activity in the Wick area. Inspection of 'X' (unknown) raid tracings by SRS had suggested that enemy aircraft were continuing to fly from Norway, round the north of Shetland and/or Orkney Islands and return eastwards to their bases over the Orkney Islands and north Scotland.

A scientific officer reported:

" On August 1, Unst received a signal – Close down, prepare to embark August 4." [1]

A few hours after the receipt of this signal the controller at Sumburgh rang Unst to make an enquiry and was told that the station had ceased operating and was now packed up on the shore.

"I feel that this alacrity is expressive of the Unst personnel's opinion of Unst."[1]

The rapid growth of expansion can be gauged from the fact that only five months from the formation of 60 Group to take over the maintenance of 21 CH and 16 CHL stations, there were now an additional 23 stations in operation. Also, eight had been overhauled and a great deal of minor repair work completed at 21 others. The four groups of maintenance units that were based on the pre-war number of CH stations were now completely overloaded and were expanded to eight, all demanding skilled men and officers. The daily routine at each unit was: Reveille 0700, Breakfast 0800, Working parade 0845, CO's parade (Wed. only) 0900, 15 minute break on arrival of the YMCA van, Dinner 1230, Working parade 1320, Tea 1700, Lights Out 2215.

At the beginning of August the German Air Force began specific day raids on RAF airfields and other military targets and at night on many towns from southwest England to east Scotland. A raid over Somerset and Hampshire was unique in that leaflets printed on yellow and green paper were dropped, appealing to the British public for reason and to accept peace terms.

On 12 August there were precise attacks on CH stations; the first, by three aircraft on Pevensey, managed to cut the power supply cable, and caused concern there by demolishing the NAAFI hut. The second on Rye at 0947 by six Me110s succeeded in destroying all the wooden huts and private cars in the technical compound but left the permanent buildings untouched – the station was off the air for three hours. At the same time Dover was also bombed causing considerable damage to the huts and was out of action for 30 minutes. It was able to operate on low power until the evening when full power was restored.

The raid on Ventnor was the most severe; just after mid-day a force of over 30 bombers appeared, mainly Ju88s, dive bombing the station, destroying most of the wooden buildings and causing the area to be evacuated because of the number of delayed action and unexploded bombs that had been dropped. This assault was the most concentrated on any CH station so far and, in view of the effectiveness of the raid, it is considered to be one of the major errors by the Germans in not repeating its scale on other stations.

It is very fortunate (for historians), that the raid was witnessed at first hand by a highly competent observer and printed in an RDF Bulletin (see P277):

"The attack, which occurred at noon on the 12th of August was expected for two reasons, first that shipping had been heavily attacked off the Isle of Wight on the 8th and 9th, coastal areas on the 10th and Portland on the 11th, and secondly we did not imagine that 200 plus aircraft were heading up our line of shoot on the 12th for fun. At the same time we had a warning from the Filter room that Dover, Rye, and Pevensey had all been bombed that morning. The following procedures had been agreed and put into effect – a raid at 20 miles the A.A. guns warned, the Army guard (other than those on duty) to the shelters, a raid at 15 miles the W.A.A.F. on watch in the R hut (the only commissioned channel) sent to the R block and the R hut manned by the C.O., the R.M.E., [the Resident Maintenance Engineer, a civilian,] the senior N.C.O. and two R.A.F. operators, the W.A.A.F. to run up the RF6 in the R block and pass ranges only when the R hut u/s or evacuated, and a raid at 5 miles the two RAF operators also sent to the R block. After the main raid had passed overhead, the R.M.E. was doing some visual spotting from the R hut roof and as he reported the first bombs falling on Portsmouth, at about 1205, he heard an unfamiliar sound and without waiting to identify its source tactfully descended from the roof. As he reached the ground level the sound identified itself as the roar of dive-bombers and as the whistle of bombs was by then mingled with it, he covered 100 yards in 3.5 seconds and found himself in the doorway of R block as the first bombs landed in the compound.

Meanwhile the C.O., the senior N.C.O. (a Sgt) and a W.A.A.F. operator, who had unaccountably been left in the R hut, hearing these same sounds proceeded in good order under the plotting table. The first bomb to fall bounced the clock off the wall into the middle of the hut, the second caused large pieces of the roof to fall on to the RF5 and the fusillade thereafter caused the table to run smartly about the room followed by those trying to shelter beneath it. Plotting from the R hut had been abandoned and in theory the operators in the R block should by now have been passing ranges from the RF6 but, as the mains [power supply] had failed completely the receiver was off and the block in complete darkness.

Also the ranges we were concerned with were measurable in hundreds of feet so Ventnor may by now be described as completely off the air. There is no point in further commentary from the R hut as the inmates were simply waiting for the noise to finish and spending their time in silent prayer. Those in the R block were alternatively creeping out into the traverse and rushing back again as they caught head on views of Ju87s and Ju88s flying at 300 to 400ft. Meanwhile a certain intrepid calibration nark who had been taking sights on a calibration aircraft from the top of one of the R towers decided to abandon his position.

An extremely loud 25 cycle [Hz] hum, which was now heard was attributed to the beat of his feet on the ladders and he arrived at the door of R block somewhat confused and very dirty some 30 seconds later. This calibration had been taking place on the RF6 while the RF5 was in the R hut and was doing its normal job, but the calibration autogyro had not stopped to ask questions and the flight was abandoned. When the noise of the aircraft had died down, and this took some time because the Portsmouth raiders were coming back over the site, the various bodies were emerging from their holes.

The three Bofors guns which had been furiously engaging the Huns were now silent and the only sound was a steady crackling and sizzling and this was found to be coming from the Army guard quarters, the N.A.A.F.I. and the Officers' Mess, all of which were ablaze. Two motor transports, a Dennis 3 tonner and a Fordson 15 cwt were both standing upside down and burning, their wheels were still spinning slowly with the tyres on fire giving a very beautiful but expensive Catherine Wheel effect. The next hour was spent getting the MB1 in the T hut and the RF5 in the R hut back on the air and the channel was serviceable within the hour. The rest of the staff carried out an inspection of the site and found the following: the wardens' quarters used as an orderly room practically demolished with a large crater some ten feet in front of the building; the W.A.A.F. rest room newly built blown in two by the blast, all Army accommodation and the N.A.A.F.I. completely burnt out, the water tower wrecked and the T hut and the R hut roofs and sandbags all over the place. It was still possible to climb into them and the watch was resumed but without weather protection, the T block was straddled by delayed action bombs and the Guard hut roof was damaged and the windows cracked.

There were approximately fifty bombs on the site and there had only been one casualty, an infantryman caught in an open trench – he was rapidly taken off to hospital and probably by now he shoots a terrific line about it. At about 1500 the first of the D-A [delayed action] bombs exploded outside the compound: thence at roughly three hour intervals some twenty of them went off. At 1800 one, which was embedded in the blast wall of the T block exploded, it severed the main incoming cable, wrecked the substation end of the building, blew all the panels out of line and wrecked the switchery. It also deposited the P.B.X. operator on top of her switchboard but she rang up R block to say that she was all right.

The station kept on the air using the MB1 and the RF5, with the T block definitely a write-off, until the following Friday, the 16th when there was a nasty little attack by six Ju88s which scored two lucky hits; one bomb fell near the R tower carrying the MB1 transmitting array and completely finished off the T hut, and another bomb fell near one of the other R towers and wrecked the R hut as well as blowing out all the feeders within 200ft. Replacing concentric feeder that had been slashed by flying fragments was no job for the station staff, so Ventnor passed out completely from that day and did not take the air again until two months later, when all the technical damage had been repaired. The damaged admin. buildings and the M.T. and so on were left lying about to fool the enemy into thinking that the station had been abandoned. This appeared to work for although the odd Hun stooged over the station now and then it never came in for another official beat-up."

To complete the day's offensives against the CH stations a 500Kg bomb was dropped on Dunkirk just missing the T block but the station remained on the air. The following day, the 13th, the CH stations were ignored though very heavy air raids were carried out on the south and southeast coasts and repeated the next day. Oddly, one aircraft again attacked Pevensey and a bomb fell on the newly finished R block breaking through the roof and depositing the protective shingle into the office below that would have buried anyone working there.

Most of the versions of the attack of 12 August are substantially the same having been copied from official histories. One version differs from the others in that it claimed that all the five stations were hit and silenced simultaneously but within three hours all the stations were transmitting again, but without receivers, so to give the Germans the impression that the damage was easily repaired and the chain indestructible.

15 August was the day of maximum effort by the German Air Force to crush the RAF and achieve air supremacy, a prerequisite for invasion. Five major actions were fought on a front of over 500 miles stretching from Northumberland to Dorset by over 1,000 aircraft, the first and last time that such extensive raids would be made. In the south all 22 fighter squadrons were engaged, many twice, some three times. German losses were recorded in most contemporary official papers as 182 but post war records showed that the figure was nearer 75 with RAF losses correctly stated as 34 with 17 pilots saved. On 16 August there was another but smaller bombing of Ventnor, already described, and on the 18th, the last major raid on an RDF station, at Poling, when 90 bombs, mostly of the delayed action types, were dropped causing the station to be evacuated. A mobile was sent to Poling on 16 August and one to Bembridge, near Ventnor on 23 August to provide emergency cover.

By coincidence, the Inspector-General, Air Chief Marshal Sir Edgar Ludlow-Hewitt, who had 'retired' as the AOC-in-C Bomber Command, was inspecting RDF stations along the southeast coast of England. At a meeting held on 16 August to discuss the effects of the bombing he reported that accommodation was badly protected and, as no attention had been paid to camouflage, the CH stations with their tall towers and standard pattern of layout were highly conspicuous from the air. Passive defence was also poor with women plotters and tellers without steel helmets or gas masks. He recommended that personnel should be moved out of the technical compound as soon as possible, that the CH transmitters and receivers should be placed outside the perimeter fence, with the receivers 400 yards or more away from the towers, and that at least one duplicate transmitter should be moved away; he strongly advised that the placing of CHL inside the CH perimeter should cease. He concluded:

> "I cannot close this report without referring to the amazing spirit shown by members of the W.A.A.F. at these stations. In spite of a trying ordeal that some of them have experienced, they seemed quite unmoved and were all in excellent spirits. All the officers commanding these stations referred in the very highest terms to the splendid work done by the W.A.A.F." [2]

His observations were passed to the relevant Air Ministry sections and the action taken sent to the Air Staff. There was general agreement that main and standby equipment should not be placed in the same building and for future CHLs to be outside the CH compounds, but advice was that remote operation of CH transmitters and receivers was unworkable. For Dover it had been suggested that it might be possible to place aerials in front of the cliffs at Dover and at St Margaret's Bay. This met with the approval of Watson Watt, who considered that Dover was a special case because of its vulnerability to being shelled by enemy guns across the Channel. The possibility of constructing a CH station with the aerials against the face of the cliffs and the technical and operations room in the caves below was explored. The survey report was ready by 30 August but further investigations were abandoned when attacks on Dover and other stations had ceased.

The I/G had returned to the stations after the bombing and reported on the damage to the permanent brick built transmitter and receiver blocks at Ventnor and Poling and he observed:

"They should convince anyone of the need for providing a bigger and stronger traverse to take the shock of the blast. At present the sides of the heavy roof of the buildings take the full shock of the blast, and that alone must give the building a heavy shake-up, and the blast apparently abounds into the space between the building and the traverse, breaks all the windows and blows all the doors off their hinges." [3]

(Works later bricked up the windows, and to provide ventilation, the gas filtering plant was run continuously with the filters removed.)

On the one week's closure at Poling, he commented;

"that there was too much safety first sentiment about and that everyone should be encouraged to think foremost and how to carry on at once." [2]

A widely held impression on the bombing of the CH stations along the English Channel is that the Germans were aware that they were for the location of aircraft and so had to be put out of action. But an examination of German Intelligence material after the war indicated that most of them had been photographed in late 1939 and early 1940 and classified as Radio Stations. In the short space of a month that the Germans were on the French coastline, it is doubtful if their real purpose had yet been uncovered, so the air attacks were more likely for the dislocation of what was thought to be radio communications between the British fighters and their airfields. This viewpoint ties in with an enemy report that RAF fighter planes were controlled with very little flexibility in air operations.

The North West Filter Room at Barton Hall, on the outskirts of Preston, opened at 0900 hours on 13 August with plotting lines from the CH at North Cairn and the CHLs at Glenarm, Cregneish and Prestatyn but Scarlett, Bride and Nevin CH stations were delayed until 15-30 September. Those working in the Filter Room were subject to Standing Orders:

"Articles of drink and food other than throat pastilles must not be brought into the Filter Room, smoking not allowed, no newspapers. Personnel in the Filter Room are permitted during slack periods to pass the time by reading books, knitting or indulge in other silent pastimes that do not involve the use of cumbersome paraphernalia. Personnel are not under any circumstances to discuss outside the Filter Room, either amongst themselves or with any other person, any matter connected with, or a bearing upon, the work done in the Operations or Filter Room." [4]

The scientific officer there was quick to evaluate the effectiveness of the CHL at Glenarm as there were no aircraft seen beyond 25 miles, and never above 2,000ft, and at Prestatyn there were too many permanent echoes. He concluded that with the stations in their present position and state they could be shut down and the difference on the plotting table would hardly be noticed. The scientific officer at the Western (Box) Filter Room was equally forthright in his comment on the continual neglect of known defects at Hawks Tor that had allowed it to deteriorate:

"A very dangerous state exists – the D/F is completely valueless as errors of 30%, 40% are common and to call this performance erratic would be an understatement. Immediate action is called for." [5]

On 19 August, Fighter Command were able to return to VHF for R/T communication; at first, for the original sectors in 11 and 12 Group plus Catterick in 13 Group, provided there were sufficiently trained personnel to maintain and operate both sets of equipment. An unusual aspect of this decision was to retain the HF transmissions but to use dummy messages continuously, complete with the squadrons' R/T call signs. This was a ploy to discourage the Germans from searching for and finding the VHF transmissions with the certain risk of subsequent jamming.

There were now in action every day over the country 1,400 enemy aircraft or more, sometimes in mass formations of over several hundred, and the damage to RAF aerodromes, aircraft on the ground and aircraft factories began to assume serious proportions. Many industrial areas in southwest England, South Wales and the Midlands had been attacked with the consequent loss of water, gas, electricity and telephone services. On 24 August London received its 11th, 12th and 13th warning, it being recorded officially:

"There was not a semblance of panic as cricket matches and cinema shows were continuing. In Regent's Park 'A Midsummer Night's Dream' was being performed. Very few of the audience moved, the remainder finding particularly appropriate Titania's words – to each word a warbling note." [6] (A reference to the distinctive sound of the 'air raid' siren.)

The RAF retaliated with a bombing raid on Berlin on the night of 25/26, which further increased enemy action over London the following day. As the East Chain was only on one wavelength, emergency mobiles were dispatched near to the CH stations at Dover, Rye, Pevensey and Dunkirk. Works received an order on 2 September that at each site open trenches were required to shelter 32 men plus camouflage netting for three vehicles, to be ready for 5 September; very swift action was called for. One station that is not mentioned in official histories, but which made a contribution to the RDF reporting chain from 20 July, was an Admiralty CH station at Fort Wallington, near Fareham in Hampshire. Plots were reported to Stanmore via Ventnor, later with an individual line to a separate plotter. Coupled by a Selsyn motor, the transmit and receive aerials on a wavelength of 7 metres swept continuously through 180 degrees about four times a minute.

SRS had carried out an intensive study of the plot tracings of German raiders, which showed they were proceeding to their military targets with almost mathematical accuracy. These sorties continued unabated until Saturday 7 September when between 5pm and 6pm some 320 bombers with 600 fighters flew up the Thames Estuary. Huge fires were created in the East End of London and the docks areas that were added to by further bombing raids that lasted until 0430 the next day. The capital was then bombed for 57 consecutive nights by some 200 bombers. This change in the pattern of German bombing objectives from military and industrial targets to civilians is now seen as the beginning of the end of the Battle of Britain and was much to the relief of Fighter Command.

The crucial stage was between 28 August and 5 September when damage to sector stations and ground organisations was having a serious effect on the fighting efficiency of squadrons. The absence of many essential telephone lines, use of temporary equipment in emergency operations rooms, and the general dislocation was seriously felt in the handling of squadrons to meet the enemy's mass air attacks. Had the Germans continued their massive onslaught against Biggin Hill and adjacent sectors and knocked out their operations rooms or telephone lines, the fighter defence of London would have been in a perilous state during the last critical stage when widespread air raids had been directed against the capital. AVM Park wrote:

> "On September 7, the enemy first turned to the heavy attacks on London by day... this change of bombing plans saved 11 Group Sector stations from becoming inoperative and enabled them to carry on with operations, though at a much lower standard of efficiency." [7]

Dowding's comment on the role of RDF in the Battle of Britain has been repeated many times,

> "The system operated effectively, and it is not too much to say that the warnings that it gave could have been obtained by no other means and constituted a vital factor in the Air Defence of Great Britain."

Watson Watt was certainly not satisfied with the way that the Air Ministry was administering the chain; he wrote a highly critical letter on 3 September to the Secretary of State on the manning of the CH stations concentrating mainly on the selection, training and mode of working of the personnel. He did not understand the principles of selection but was certain that the wrong people were being chosen, insisting that RDF observing was a skilled profession that demanded initiative, intelligence, conscientiousness and enthusiasm. He did not know why a carpenter or a pneumatic driller should be thought promising material for posting straight to the tube face without training, and when two latrine cleaners from No 5 Signals Wing were similarly drafted, then the supposition was that the selector thought that RDF was a contagious disease:

"I propose that we start a fresh collection of specialist W.A.A.F.s (with a school grounding of one year or more in some science such as physics, chemistry or biology), officer them with women graduates and give them a specialist commandant chosen from outstanding women physicists. I have heard and seen nothing to shake my belief that such women will be more conscientious and diligent, and more continuously accurate and reliable than men of the same initial qualification and 'a fortiori' [for a stronger reason] than the uninspired and bored louts who form a large proportion of the present teams." [8]

Training was lamentable:

"Even the better material, which is clearly available but unused, will not be made into R.D.F. Observers by a three weeks course at a school, even when the school is not in a chronic state of being about to move to an unknown destination... There is no adequate provision for the post-school instruction at operational stations which would make them quick R.D.F. operators. Even as members of a watch they would only get about one hour per day on the tube; this is barely sufficient to maintain skill, and quite insufficient to improve it.... The excuse for insufficient observing time per observer is risk of damage to eyesight; I think a vast deal of nonsense has been talked, and some 'lead-swinging' done, on this. A.M.R.E. workers do not feel undue fatigue after three hours on the tube, and the days when I was observing for two two-hour spells per day over several months produced neither temporary nor permanent discomfort....

There is an almost universal tendency, perhaps a little more marked among the W.A.A.F.s ex-Yatesbury (who are not as good as those ex-Bawdsey), to funk the more difficult parts of observing, e.g., to fail to D/F... in bad signal to noise conditions, to fail to D/F when beating with fixed echoes or echoes from other aircraft (even on formations of three aircraft), to fail to reduce pulse-width for better resolution of formations, and to fail to dissect big formations into separate sub-units for observation and reporting.... In cases where we have made good observers the 'system' is against us keeping them. Re-posting for other duties often robs us of good observers; the reward for a good observer is promotion to a non-observing post; the punishment for a bad observer is to be left as an observer!

The Resident Maintenance Engineers [civilians] are very variable in quality...
it should be made clear...that the state of their receivers is as important as that
of their transmitters; too many of them regard themselves as transmitter nurses
only. Officers in charge of Stations:- Here again review and elimination are
required. In too many cases a smattering of amateur technical knowledge,
insufficient to be useful on a station, has been given undue weight in selection.
The greatest danger in plotting comes from boredom... many of the plotters
have failed to recover the concentration and keenness with which they began
their work.... [Some plotters] become over confident and authoritative, and
select or reject, on their own responsibility, the intelligence proffered by
observers... The retention of good plotters is made difficult by the attractions
of commissions as cypher officers....

Officer filterers have been recruited mainly from such circles as
stockbroking, banking and the like. Inevitably their training course has been
inadequate, in the absence of a suitable background, to enable them to weigh
up the technical factors producing the discrepancies which they are there to
resolve... They are liable to make serious errors of judgement for lack of a
grasp of the scientific and technical background. They go into unnecessary
'flaps', they fail to get all the information the R.D.F. station can usefully give
them and they waste precious seconds in needless talk with stations. Some add
the sin of ill-founded professional pride to other defects; the advice of the
scientific observer in the Filter Room is not always cheerfully accepted even
when it is right. Arrangements should be made to recruit scientifically trained
candidates." [8]

Watson Watt instanced a number of cases to illustrate his points:

"(a) A.O.C. 60 Group is stated to have given instructions that all R.A.F.
personnel on R.D.F. stations should be instructed on observing. It is quite useless
to expect that a putatively good cook should be turned into a good observer by
sporadic local action,

(b) One tube was observed by a D.C.D. representative to have 12 echoes
between 0 and 90 miles; of these none beyond 40 miles was told. The N.C.O.
on being asked why, replied 'Anyway, I've got as many echoes as I want in the
40 miles',

(c) W.A.A.F.s are frequently observed to adopt one echo as a pet and to be
grief stricken on losing it. Initiative is not always exercised to recover it by
switching from the 240ft to the 80ft aerials,

(d) An [RAF] Observer has been seen, during his observing spell, using the
optical converter table as a foot rest,

(e) Filter room instructed a C.H.L. station to concentrate on one line of
observation. Meanwhile ten Me.110s (with one bomb each) arrived unobserved,

(f) No one in the R.D.F. network has known to be 'demoted' or thrown out for
incompetence." [8]

The hurried race to provide RDF cover along the west coast of England,
Wales and the Isle of Man was clearly shown by the reporting of the I/G
during September and October:

"At St. Twynells the C.H.L. has been on site for two months but there is no protection, not even sandbags for the C.H.L. huts which are standing in an open field, exposed to enemy fire. There are 35 Home Guard of which only three are armed and only ten Army men including an N.C.O., all billeted in stables at Stackpole House, the place perfectly filthy and in a bad state of repair. At Strumble Head C.H.L. site, the workmen went home after Saturday morning not to return until Monday morning yet German bombers were overhead. At Hayscastle Cross C.H. site only one wooden mast half erected, huts are ready, mobile gear is still in lorries and trailers, there is a shortage of labour and material and slow progress by Works. Glenarm C.H.L. has been in operation since July 15 yet there are bad permanent echoes from the Isle of Arran and the mainland of Scotland..

At Cregneish the C.O., a Pilot Officer, is very young and inexperienced and not yet fit to run an isolated station of this kind. I would suggest that he and other inexperienced boys of his age should do a period as an assistant to an older C.O. at one of the established C.H. or C.H.L. stations. Range is irregular, plots are lost as close as 30 miles. Bride C.H. station was not yet calibrated, no steel helmets or respirators or accommodation for the Army guards. No gumboots and s'westers for the guards – no proper water supply. Scarlet Point C.H. operational for only two weeks, not yet calibrated, results seen not satisfactory, a test run on 4 October not seen at all, plotting inconsistent, aircraft disappear unaccountably. At Drytree the camp is a sea of mud with standing water up to a foot in depth anywhere off the main paths... the C.H.L. is to be moved to Penolver." [9]

He had also visited Worth Matravers, suggesting that it lent itself to the possibility of a surprise attack by the enemy, but Freeman's (now VCAS) opinion was that it would not be all that easy. Swanage was heavily garrisoned by the Army, the enemy certainly could not scale the cliffs and ACAS had ruled out seaborne and airborne raids and sabotage by fifth columnists (civilian saboteurs).

On 6 September an informal meeting was held at AMRE with Watson Watt, Joubert, Lindemann and others to examine the progress of research on airborne equipment. During the discussions it was proposed that as the Research Establishment changed its ministry but not its function, that the title should be Telecommunications Research Establishment (TRE); it was agreed that the proposal would be put forward to the Controller of Telecommunications Equipment in the Ministry of Aircraft Production. As if the Air Ministry had never recognised the transfer of AMRE to the MAP, they issued a Confidential Order B376 part of which announced that with effect from 1 October 1940, the name would be changed to the Telecommunications Research Establishment.

SRS had followed closely the performance of the Filter Room during the Battle of Britain and had noticed during the mass raids in August and early

September that some of the enemy airfields were situated within range of the RDF stations in the Dover area. Consequently the relatively protracted process of the assembly of mass formations of the enemy bombers and fighters could be observed and early warning of raids imparted to groups and sectors. The presence of heavy bombers in these raids had set limits to both the speed and the heights of the formations, which were well tracked and intercepted with comparative ease, and both these factors had contributed largely to the success of the RDF reporting chain. In late September, however, the enemy changed tactics in that the heavy bombers were replaced with fast fighter-bombers and fighters in mass raids by day, with activity confined almost without exception to London, the Home Counties and southeast England with landfalls between North Foreland, Dungeness and Beachy Head. The use of fast fighter-bombers had reduced the time of warning of an impending raid and this was coupled with the greater height of the formations requiring more time for the RAF to intercept. At the CH stations the very large numbers of enemy aircraft at different heights and varying formations had made it almost impossible to extract the location information due to the merging of the echoes.

Although air attacks on RDF stations had ceased the Germans were preparing, as an option to the possible loss of aircraft and crews, to silence them by jamming. The Germans had now located and measured the frequency of the CH and CHL stations and transmitters had been installed along the French coastline in the Calais/Boulogne area and near Cherbourg. On 9 September they were simultaneously switched on just before the commencement of the mass daylight raids and after a few days remained on for most of the day and night. The jamming was reported at all CH stations from Worth to West Beckham with the maximum intensity at Dover, Dunkirk and Bawdsey, which at first slowed down the taking of bearings and plots but was not sufficiently intensive to disable the stations.

The jamming was known technically as Frequency Modulated Continuous Wave (FMCW), that caused part of the tube trace to be displaced into an inverted bell shape curve, which moved along the trace from end to end and frequently reached saturation (a technical term that indicates that the trace had touched the bottom of the screen and flattened out). Its success by slowing down plotting was very much dependent on the skill of the operators who had never before seen any form of intentional jamming.

The Stanmore Filter Room had noticed that stations like Bawdsey, Dover, Dunkirk and Canewdon were never out of action for more than a few minutes, which was not the case with Rye, Pevensey and Great Bromley. One scientific officer reported that:

"...many operators have only haziest idea of how to use an A.J. [anti-jamming] tube and no notion at all on their capabilities. Efficiency of operators is in direct proportion to the technical competence of Commanding Officers and the amount of time that they spend in the receiver room." [10]

CH receivers incorporated two rejector units that 'sucked out' a small part of bandwidth that gave some reduction in jamming, but CHL receivers at first had no such device. Dover CHL suffered severely, being completely jammed on a bearing of 130 degrees but, when the beam was off it, the effect was considerably less. Within days AMRE had designed and fitted a 'rejector' that reduced it to a level that allowed working on all but the weakest signals. The jamming was designed to severely overload a receiver to corrupt the output, but it was not completely successful with a pulse waveform.

By 29 September proposals had been prepared to set up a ground deception organisation to ensure that enemy believed that his existing procedures were such as to discourage him from devising more effective and extensive methods. Ideas put forward were switching off main CH stations and transferring to another wavelength of 6 metres from mobiles or reserves, or pulse transmissions only on a bogus 15 metre wavelength. In November jamming was reported at Strumble Head CHL on a bearing in the direction of SW Eire, which caused some concern until it was discovered a short time afterwards, that a nearby electric lamp with a birdcage filament was responsible. The jamming level began to increase during early November and then ceased altogether after 11 November much to the surprise of all concerned.

On 14 September, Dowding received a letter from the Air Council inviting him to nominate a representative to be associated with a committee, with Marshal of the Royal Air Force Sir John M.Salmond as chairman, that the Minister of Aircraft Production, Lord Beaverbrook, was setting up to undertake a thorough enquiry into the equipment and operation of night fighters. They had suggested that AVM Sir C.J.Q. Brand would be particularly suitable and on the 17th, Dowding's short reply was that he understood that Brand had already been summoned and given evidence.

There is an indication that Dowding was not at all pleased as his letter was the second one that he had written; the first one was not sent and is missing from the file. His suspicions were no doubt confirmed when he received a copy of the committee's report on 25 September from the Air Council, that had, no doubt to Dowding's astonishment, been completed by the 17th. Out of the 18 conclusions was Item 2 – 'Operation of filtering should be transferred from Fighter Command to Group Headquarters in order to reduce delay.' Dowding wrote back immediately to protest that:

"...the matter has no particular connection with night interception and the arguments that were adduced against it in January of this year still hold good. I request, therefore, that I may be spared the necessity of discussing the question afresh." [11]

Secretary of State Sinclair thought differently and Dowding was summoned, along with the CAS, Joubert and Salmond, to a meeting on 1 October when the question of filtering was re-opened. Dowding asked that it be placed on record that his belief was that the proposal to transfer filtering to groups would not improve the efficiency of night interception...the proposal would involve a considerable expenditure of money and effort which in his opinion was not justified. Joubert was openly at variance with Dowding and also asked that it be placed on record that, in his view, such delegation would improve day, as well as night, interception.

At the War Cabinet meeting on 7 October, where the Salmond report was under discussion, Dowding was instructed by Prime Minister Churchill to render a report, with a copy to the CAS and the Under Secretary of State, on the points he took issue with. In his report dated 8 October Dowding wrote that he disagreed strongly with item 2:

"I was asked whether I agreed with the practical steps which were being undertaken...I replied that I had agreed with all the proposals but in some cases unwillingly and under pressure... It was the greatest surprise that I learned that this subject had been disinterred by the Salmond committee. It is a general question having little specific connection with night interception." [11]

On 10 October Churchill approved the Salmond report with the filtering recommendation deleted but the Air Council objected and appealed to Churchill, who sent a personal minute to Dowding on the evening of 23 October, to which he replied the next day:

"Your minute reached me this evening and I note your instruction regarding its personal nature and will make no reference to it officially or otherwise. The Secretary of State's minute contains a few inaccuracies, only one of which is important and that is the statement that it is really an undoubted fact that time is saved in getting squadrons into the air by filtering at Group HQ – it is substantially untrue. Plots are told to Group HQ from my table without delay with the average lag in transmission of a plot is less than 15 seconds. I am very surprised to find that the Salmond committee had included in their recommendations a paragraph on the subject.

The metaphorical edifice what you have seen in my Filter and Operations Rooms has been built up brick by brick under my own eye during the last four years. My predecessor, Joubert, had left the Fighting Area as it was, without having made the slightest effort to tackle what had been in fact one of the greatest problems of the defence, by the differentiation between friendly and enemy aircraft. When exercises were held, all bombers available were enemy, no system for identifying enemy aircraft existed or apparently not been thought of. The system that I have devised might not be perfect but it cannot be improved by disruptive criticism on the part of people who do not understand it as a whole. I started with the idea of decentralisation of filtration and abandoned it in favour of centralisation. My greatest grievance however is the matter of expenditure of my time in arguing with the Air Staff of every intimate detail of my organisation. Surely the C-in-C should be left to manage his own affairs if the general result is satisfactory. I have expended no less than 50 hours on this controversy. As the Secretary of State says, I agreed to decentralise under strong pressure because it is not a matter that is going to lose the war and I have to fight the Air Staff over so many important issues. I raise this question only because at your meeting in the Cabinet War Room, you asked whether I agreed with the findings of the Salmond Committee. If you feel bound to support the Secretary of State in his plea, that the considered view of the Air Council should not be set aside, I shall quite understand although I feel that we shall pay £100,000 in material and labour in order to secure a slight reduction in efficiency." [12]

Duplication of equipment was standard for all essential wireless channels in the RAF to allow for maintenance and the prompt restoration of service in the event of breakdowns and the CH chain was no exception. But at the outbreak of the war the CAS had ruled that it needed further protection by a third channel. Known as a 'reserve', it was to be buried to ground level some 300 yards from the technical compound. It was intended that the separate T and R sites 100 yards apart would have an aerial on the main group of transmit and receive towers plus a 70ft standby tower at each site; the prototype would be at Stenigot. By November 1939, Works had completed the design and were anxious to arrange tendering contracts, but there was slow progress in construction and the Battle of Britain had come and gone without one reaching its completion date. TRE were now of the opinion that the original intention of providing aerials on the existing transmitter and receiver towers with long coaxial and open wire feeders was not practical; perhaps a rethink was now necessary after the effects of the bombing raids on the south coast CH stations.

Further delays arose as the proposed 105ft transportable guyed tower was considered inadequate and was replaced with a 120ft tower that was the top half of the 1940s designed 240ft tower with special footings. Half way through the 'excavation programme' the construction was changed from brick to concrete: Stoke Holy Cross had one of each. All were at the 'building completed' stage by the end of November, ready for contractors to fit the heating and ventilating plant. Asked by Signals for the completion dates, a Works officer reported that as the Air Ministry had very cleverly placed the contract for 20 installations with one firm, it was their job to decide priorities. Hart was of the opinion that the fitting by MetroVick of an MB2 and an RF6 should be deferred as all efforts should be made to install CHL and extend the West Chain.

TRE continued to send survey parties for CH and CHL sites along the west coast of England and Northern Ireland, and to Islay, the Outer Hebrides and the northwest coast of Scotland. One team had attempted to get to Cape Wrath in Sutherland but reported that it was impossible due to totally inadequate transport. The only means of access was a ferry across the Kyle of Durness and then on foot across to the Cape, a distance of 12 miles. A scientific officer reported:

> "Investigations at Durness showed that transport would be extremely difficult, a small rowing boat being used for the ferry is limited to very small loads, the road of the Cape has the same limitations and is very winding and steep. Communications are often difficult at the best of times and are often cut off entirely during the winter. Land is a peat bog with subsoil 10 to 12 ft down, weather conditions are always the worst. Gales to 100 m.p.h. are common in winter." [13]

An area for a combined CH and CHL was found on a headland one mile east of Durness village and, to avoid confusion with the Deerness CHL near Netherbutton, the station was named Sango after a nearby cove.

The search for sites was now made more onerous by the issue of a new set of guidelines. At a meeting on 30 October to discuss further expansion, DCD, Signals and others heard from Joubert that as a result of the I/G's report on the bombing of Ventnor and other CH stations, the layout of all CH stations west of Ventnor was to be changed to improve security and future CHLs were not to be erected within half a mile of the CH compound. He said:

> "A grave error had been made in the establishment of the Eastern [CH] chain...They were a most inviting target and we had given them inadequate protection...[Two] vital stations had been knocked out, one for two months [Ventnor] and one for six weeks [Poling]...Three others had been more or less seriously damaged...[There] were objections by the Army to placing their guarding troops in or close to the R.D.F. Compound...[They] said it was not fair for men to be lodged on the target. By some curious freak of providence, or some blank spot in the German mind, we have not had an attack on an R.D.F. Station for nearly two months, but we must not be lulled into a false sense of security as when it suits him to make further attacks the enemy will do so." [14]

Joubert also advised that he had carefully considered the damage done by recent enemy air action; with the main and standby equipment in the same building it would be obvious what would happen if it were bombed. There was a complete absence of camouflage. These points were to be rectified for the forthcoming West Chain installations.

Deception was paramount followed by dispersal; the four sets of guyed masts would be split into two pairs and moved to positions that were most suitable to provide the best deceptive conditions with two transmitting buildings to be sited at any place within half a mile of the aerials. The two receiving buildings were also at a distance from each wooden tower with the transmission lines following natural features. All fences were to avoid being rectilinear in shape, preferably to follow boundaries such as hedges, ditches and streams, and trees might be of use in concealing masts or buildings. The twin beam station layout was now abandoned in favour of the single Line of Shoot. On all site visits a representative of the Defence Camouflage Works Department had to be present but the overriding aspect of a technically sound site remained with TRE.

At a later date, when complaints were beginning to arise from Fighter Command over the slow rate of completion of the West Chain, the DCD claimed that in following the new guidelines each new site was different and had to be looked at as another prototype. There was now no standard layout. Works were also affected by the change as the original buildings, which were specified as unprotected and for two sets of equipment, and already constructed at seven stations, had to be modified with 9 inch brick walls, a concrete roof and a traverse blast wall. Future stations would be laid out with four earth covered semi-underground reinforced concrete blocks each containing one set.

In October reports were arriving for TRE from the British Technical Mission at Washington on the position of centimetre wavelength work in the USA; Cockcroft had visited most of the radio valve makers and taken notes on what he had seen, or perhaps, what he had been allowed to see. The Klystron valve was being developed for receivers as an oscillator of low power and tuneable, with crystals for detection, and for high power where pulse outputs had reached 30 to 40 kW at 40cm wavelength using applied voltages of 30kV. A Klystron was being dispatched to TRE but for reasons not disclosed, it was considered advisable to send the crate to a private residence and Dr Dee was the only one whose address was known by the Mission. General Electric were conducting experiments on a version of the British 10cm magnetron and were aiming for powers of around 100kW, the University of Berkeley was working on pulse transmitters at 32 to 40cm wavelength for powers around 100kW while RCA were developing receiving valves for 50cm and lower.

60 Group produced in October a survey of the technical and operational failings of the CH and CHL chains and distributed it to 'interested parties' ie, those outside Fighter Command. It stated that equipment was good but

unreliable and required a very elaborate maintenance organisation. The back to front ratio of the CH transmitting array was poor, the concentric feeders were a continual source of trouble requiring constant attention to phasing and the need for calibration was a major disadvantage. The CHL array mounting and feeders were of a poor design and in high winds had to be locked. The intensification of air warfare – the Blitz – had produced a most complicated CRT display but whose interpretation was mediocre because of the 'violent dilution of the operator grade with entirely untrained and partially trained personnel'. Plotting and telling were a bundle of trouble as the CRT operator could no longer suffer the distraction of allocating plots to track numbers and answer queries from the filter room. CHLs reported plots by phone to the nearest CH station, which greatly increased the flow of information and overloaded the single telephone line between the CH station and the filter room. It was the view of 60 Group that filter room personnel of all ranks should visit a CH station and spend at least two watches there, one of which should be at night.

Group emphasised that they were only responsible up to the telephoning of the information and, after that, the filter room was the responsibility of other authorities. Group thought that they should be responsible for interpreting the operation of the chain from the CRT display to the handing over of the tracks to the operations rooms thus ending the divided responsibility. Joubert obtained the comment of Signals:

> "The implication is that 60 Group should acquire operational responsibility to the Filter Room which, if agreed, could lead to the logical conclusion that 60 Group should train the operators instead of 26 Group. The next extension would be the suggestion that 60 Group be expanded to a Command, and taking the entire responsibility for air movement reporting, including the Observer Corps and Centres." [15]

Joubert replied to 60 Group that he generally agreed with the points mentioned and outlined the measures being adopted to improve efficiency, such as the use of lead covered sealed coaxial cable for the receiver feeders and splitting of the combined plotting lines. He also made it perfectly clear that 60 Group's responsibility ended at the station and that he fully intended to keep it that way.

Works were busy providing camouflage for the East Chain stations, a massive wire mesh net covering 9,000 square yards, weighing 20 tons, raised 20ft above the ground and covered with painted steel wool, which could not be used near the R block as it affected the height calibration. Camouflage for CHL had not been forgotten, Rowe writing:

> "We have talked a lot about enclosing the whole of the C.H.L. station in a hut so that camouflage will be easy and wind effects will not arise. The subject is

as old as the war – we ought to try the scheme here." [16]

Some work had been done at Dundee by surrounding a CHL aerial with screens and camouflage, but the results were not promising as during wet weather there was major attenuation of the signal. It was thought that a simple solution could be best effected by the expedient of erecting a wooden roof over the aerial but wind problems would remain. Rowe agreed that a non-operational CHL set nearby at Worth would enable suitable experiments to be made.

The change in tactics of the German Air Force in switching from day raids to night bombing brought to the surface the issue of night interception for Fighter Command and just how little or nothing so far had been achieved; German bombers could still fly almost anywhere at night virtually unhindered. The Biggin Hill and 'Lamb' interceptions were daytime experiments where visual range was considerable, and it was within the capability of the CH stations to provide positioning to within five miles to ensure interception.

But at night, to use AI, the fighter needed to be within 1½ miles directly behind the enemy aircraft and fitted with IFF to ensure positive identification on the display tube. CH was ruled out as it was almost impossible to obtain two accurate close sets of plots using a goniometer and CHL was unusable as the German bombers never flew lower than 5,000ft. Furthermore, both the CH and CHL chains looked seaward; the success of AI depended on high level sea and land looking RDF stations.

As early as 18 July at the ninth meeting of the Night Interception Committee, a proposal was made by Hart for a Mobile Interception Station. Rowe had tried to force the pace on AI interceptions by modifying the research CHL at Worth with power turning of the two arrays and a Plan Position Indicator (PPI) display. 604 Squadron at Middle Wallop was fitted with AI equipment but the results were totally disappointing. In one month not one enemy aircraft had been fired on, mainly due to the high failure rate of the AI and R/T in the aircraft, bad weather, aircraft not available, and lack of practice for the AI operators.

Rowe had circulated a MOST SECRET memo to Wilkins with instructions to destroy it after the contents had been seen by himself and selected staff:

> "I had a talk with Air Marshal Joubert on Sunday. He is confident regarding the war situation, provided that we can really solve the problem of night interceptions and that we can devise means of bombing important hostile targets with accuracy at night or in bad weather....The night interception problem is more difficult since it depends not only on A.I. but on the chain. In this

connection Air Marshal Joubert is convinced that we should now be obtaining much greater success at night if height were available. We may have to consider mobile stations, specially sited to provide height. I should like everyone to be considering this night interception problem in all its aspects. There may be something new which we are missing. As far as I could gather from conversation with Air Marshal Joubert and others, we have an extremely good chance of winning this war if we can solve the two problems I have referred to above." [17]

The reference to Sunday in the text refers to the growing practice of senior Air Force officers visiting TRE on that day. The meetings became known as 'Sunday Soviets', referring to the type of meeting where individuals could argue without deference to rank. Rowe issued an order at a later date:

"Because of the frequency with which Air Marshal Joubert, S.A.T. and others visit this establishment on a Sunday, I have decided that all scientific and technical staff must be here on Sundays and that rest times must be taken on other days."

Larnder's opinion was that the success of AI would be jeopardised if RDF independent of the CH and CHL chains was not provided. He wrote to Rowe on 15 August:

"Unless some rapid action is taken for the development and provision of ground equipment...we are in danger of finding ourselves possessed of a valuable piece of apparatus [AI] which we will not be able to employ effectively." [18]

A meeting on 19 August concurred that what was wanted was a receiver in a miniature operations room that would provide more efficient ground control to enable fighters equipped with AI to be successfully positioned and would be, in the first instance, a mobile located near fighter airfields and capable of sea and land looking. RAE were instructed to produce one within a month with the name Ground Control of Interception (GCI). There was one feature of the Worth CHL that did not meet favour with Hart and that was the use of scientific officers as the ground controller for speaking direct to the pilots. He wrote to Joubert that he thought that the pilots would prefer their own types and added:

"I feel that my reputation is staked almost entirely on the satisfactory performance of G.C.I., because I originally went ahead with this station some time ago and, now that it is coming, it has simply got to work." [19]

The prototype was ready by 10 October and moved to Durrington on the south coast and, after a number of changes, to a location at Palantine Road, West Worthing. The siting criteria was awkward as all the vehicles and trailers had to be arranged in file along a stretch of road some 220 yards in length to avoid screening effects. The prototype was based on the first type of CHL with separate T and R aerials that were hand turned, but with a difference that the aerial array was fixed to the side of the trailer with the centre of the array 10ft above the ground for high level cover at 5000ft and above.

The transmitter was in a trailer some 12ft behind the array and connected to it by an open wire feeder – only the aerial trailer turned. 100 yards behind was the receiver array, fixed to the side of another trailer that contained the receiver. Twelve yards away was the Operations Room which was a vehicle with range and azimuth CRT displays and space for the PPI console when it became available. The plotting line was connected to the Sector Operations Room at Tangmere. The remainder of the convoy were support vehicles for spares, the petrol/electric generator and for future VHF equipment. TRE inspected the station where a number of items had been forgotten; there were no blackout curtains in the trailers, no clocks or stopwatches, stationery or tea making equipment. Guards had not been organised so the local police force provided policemen, one during the day and three at night.

Operations took place every night but there were early failings. Aircraft range was 35 miles at 5000ft but IFF was not available and there was a blind area from 75 to 172 degrees from a total sweep of 260 degrees. Fighters fitted with AI were restricted in flight as they could not be sent more than 30 miles from Durrington, either out to sea or inland and not over the sea at all during the day. By the middle of November the height finding equipment had been installed that used the same principle as the CH chain, the evaluation of two voltages from the split receiver aerial with centres 7½ ft and 12½ ft above the ground with a clever and simple display. To observe an echo on the PPI and range tubes the two aerials were combined but when switched for height the two halves of the aerial were separated and alternatively switched to the receiver input; the echo on the range tube appeared as two vertical lines side by side. The height ratio of the two lines enabled the aircraft height to be read off a calibrated chart. The Air Staff ordered 120 sets to be made as quickly as possible with 12 to be ready by the end of the year, but Joubert had already acted. He ordered six copies of the Durrington prototype to be ready by 31 December; there was no question of waiting for the results of flight trials.

The AOC 60 Group found that the ever increasing expansion of RDF was producing an administrative nightmare; he could only deal direct with stations on the supply of technical stores and queries.General admin required correspondence with five Command HQs, 16 Group HQs, 36 parent stations and eight Radio Servicing Sections. Transport that belonged to 60 Group was held on the strength of the parent station so the Group could do nothing to effect major repairs or write-offs or conduct a Court of Inquiry if an accident occurred and a vehicle was damaged. 60 Group had no say in the matter of promotions which, again, were handled by the parent station.

At Leighton Buzzard, the HQ of 60 Group, there were a large number of civilians all with terms of service and regulations quite different from those normally serving on RAF stations. Queries on travelling claims and subsistence were made by the accountants to the parent stations, who did not know the conditions of service at 60 Group and referred queries to Command accountants, who knew even less. The AOC only had disciplinary powers over personnel at 60 Group; a person charged with a technical offence, which was beyond the powers of the junior officer commanding the station, had the case judged by an officer of a parent unit unacquainted with the technical work at the station and who was not allowed to be told because of its secret nature. These seemingly impossible anomalies were put to the Director of Signals for action.

In November SRS issued a major document that was stamped 'MOST SECRET' and titled '*THE CAPACITY OF THE R.D.F. SYSTEM.*' It conveyed the fact that much information was lost, not only at the source but in the subsequent passage through the reporting sequence. The first limitation was the CH tube display, which showed a useful range from 20 to 100 miles but as a single echo was about two miles wide then the total number of echoes that could be resolved was 40. If the echoes merged then there were difficulties in obtaining range, sensing, direction, height and counting.

The German Air Force, like the RAF, did not attempt to fly at night in large formations but crossed the coast at 10,000 to 20,000 ft in a single file moving in parallel tracks confined to a narrow belt often no more than 10 to 15 miles across. One aircraft crossed the coast approximately every four minutes giving an echo every twelve miles, ie, eight echoes per 100 miles; the resulting display quickly became known as a 'crocodile'. A 1,000 bomber raid would give 100 echoes per mile producing no recognisable pattern on the tube and it was doubtful if any information could be obtained with a 360 bomber raid. But the situation was compounded by additional echoes from aircraft behind the station and those of aircraft that were not part of the crocodile. It was concluded that the resolution of large night bombing raids was beyond the capacity of a single dimension display.

The second limitation was the CH tube operator; the three measurements of range, direction and height took all of 24 seconds per echo that required re-checking every two minutes. Even a good operator could only handle five echoes with the average being four so his capacity was much less than that of the tube. The enemy daylight raids presented a different matter as they covered a wider area with less aircraft that involved a greater number of CH stations plus additional information from the nearest CHL station.

This time it was the filter room that was overloaded rather than the CH station.

The improvement that would occur when CHL stations had their own plotting line would double the number of persons around the plotting table – not possible at Stanmore as the Filter Room there was already crowded and incapable of expansion. It was already decentralised with part of the table going to Preston (9 Group), Box (10 Group) and Kirkwall (14 Group) but the existing numbers of filterers and tellers were inadequate even for 11 Group only, yet the table was providing telling to 12 and 13 Groups. Centralised filtering that had appeared to Dowding in 1938 as the most effective and economical way to conduct air operations had been rendered almost unworkable by the sheer quantity of information coming in from the chains which had doubled in size in less than a year and were continuing to increase.

The technical aspects of CH did not escape criticism although the failings were already known and improvements being taken. The main fault was the low reliability of the receiver transmission line, which was susceptible to short circuits due to the collection of copper dust caused by friction with the internal ceramic separator, and a low internal resistance caused by moist air inside the tubes. The latter had been mitigated to some degree by filling the tubes with compressed air, but the long term solution was already under way with the cable makers under contract to supply solid cable with sealed terminations. The second major defect was the presence of responses on the tube from aircraft behind the station and Larnder had made his point in a memo to Watson Watt:

> "At Pevensey, Poling and Rye, the tube [is] cluttered by back echoes of the German Air Force on night operations when London has heavy attacks, mainly at 15,000ft. In any case we would say that something really must be done about cutting down the responses from aircraft flying behind the CH station." [20]

One method to reduce further the back responses was to decrease the leakage of radio power behind the transmitting array by increasing the number of dipoles. As the existing arrays were on a steel tower that would not allow any expansion, RAE were asked to design an array for suspension between the steel towers with priority for Pevensey, Rye, Poling, Great Bromley and Canewdon.

SRS offered a number of changes both long and short term in order to extract the maximum useful information covering every aspect of the chain. The one that was to become most effective was the introduction of a second tube fitted with a 'tracker' mechanism to match the echo on the tube with a track identification number received back from the filter room. The difficulty in matching at the station end had imposed a heavy burden on the whole reporting system, the gravity of which was never overestimated. A method had been tried with considerable success that permitted 20 tracks to be followed, whereas even the best tube operator relying on unaided memory was unable to sort out the designations of six echoes.

It was the quality of the personnel that SRS reserved its greatest condemnation, drawing attention to the fundamental importance of employing competent people throughout the two chains if full advantage was to be taken of the latest technology. They were of the opinion that the average skill and ability of the operators were far below the standard that was possible and desirable. The rapid expansion in numbers had resulted in less stringent standards of entrance, shortened and mutilated courses, with basic defects in the existing training and in the general education of the candidates. There was a defective establishment and order of promotion and a lack of appreciation of the importance of the psychological and physiological factors for efficient work.

Anxiety over training continued through to the end of the year; the supply of trained operators was doubled by the simple expedient of transferring all the instructional staff from the Bawdsey RDF School, with its limited accommodation, to Yatesbury, but the shortage of operators was acute as nearly 2,500 were urgently wanted; 'Top Secret' telegrams were sent to Australia and New Zealand for help. The supply of mechanics was equally desperate and as a result of broadcast appeals and other publicity during the year, over 1,000 radio mechanics were enlisted, which caused considerable embarrassment for a short time owing to the lack of training facilities.

It was foreseen that many more mechanics would be required, but the Ministry of Labour protested that too many men had already been taken from industry so further publicity was not allowed. Realising that the sources of recruitment for operators and mechanics were nearing exhaustion, a request by the Air Ministry was sent to the Canadian government with a proposal to open a radio school in Canada as an alternative to Yatesbury, but this was turned down and Cranwell was proposed. In November Joubert wrote to the AOC in charge of Technical Training:

"I am horrified from your letter...that we have not yet got a home for our radio school and that Cranwell is merely an interim measure. We must get on with Cranwell for the present and the thought of building a new place with all the consequential delays shakes me thoroughly. It is terrible that it is nearly six months since we started this call for a school and nothing is settled." [21]

The AOC replied:

"Difficulty in finding a site, first Northern Ireland, then Prestwick and now Cranwell..." [21]

And a final threat from Joubert on 3 December:

"Unless something is done immediately, we should be compelled to tell the Air Staff that further R.D.F. expansion is impossible." [21]

The West Chain was being rapidly extended to meet expected enemy action from as far as Brest in northern France and the possibility of a German invasion of Eire. Extra CH and CHL cover was needed for Land's End, the Isles of Scilly, St George's Channel, the Irish Sea, Liverpool Bay, the Isle of Man and Northern Ireland. To meet the danger of raiders from bases in occupied Norway extending down the Minches, additional cover was also needed in the Outer Hebrides and northern Scotland. The siting parties initially consisted of TRE and 60 Group representatives whose recommendations were usually approved by DCD and Signals. The sites were then revisited by a layout party that included a camouflage expert whose consent was foremost.

To meet criticism from Fighter Command that height information from the West Chain was inadequate, the existing 70ft guyed masts of the Advance CH stations were replaced with 105ft masts, which were erected to a height of 87ft then fitted with height aerials. As an interim measure the masts had been erected with the steel upper guy wires replaced with hemp so as to eliminate any possible spurious electrical effects. But that had made them unstable in gale force winds, which occurred in November, and resulted in the masts being blown down overnight at Nevin, Scarlett, Bride and North Cairn.

There were two separate and significant improvements to CHL that transformed the performance in terms of plotting and range. From 20 August, the prototype PPI was in operation at Foreness 2, a single site CHL with a Yagi aerial on a common axis. The PPI with five mile range rings and bearing indications every ten degrees, did not find favour with the operators until the original display broke down for several days when the superiority of the PPI was then realised. The officer in charge reported that plotting was faster and less tiring for the observer and that unskilled operators quickly reached a good standard.

The second was the aerial. RAE had almost completed the development of a power-turned double array when they were informed of a novel advance; a single aerial for transmit and receive. DCD wrote on 9 December:

"T.R.E. have developed a very successful method of using a common aerial with a single feeder system, the receiver tapping in from the down lead with a spark gap." [22]

Common Aerial Working (CAW) as it became known, unique to pulse working, is possible by a number of methods, but the favoured one is using the transmissions to act as a switch. The Admiralty and RAE were developing diode switching but there were difficulties in obtaining a special diode that would prevent damage to the receiver input valves. Spark gap switching using a gas discharge tube proved to be very effective even with the early handmade prototypes but intense development by GEC was needed before a long life was attained. Foreness 2 was chosen for the first trial and the effect of the conversion was astounding as all the echoes immediately doubled in height, the only initial drawback being that the spark gaps had to be changed weekly: the range was extended from 60 to 90 miles. The third improvement to follow, but by no means the least, was the replacement of the bright emitter output valve VT58 with a thoriated filament version, the VT98, that produced over four times the emission and, with set modifications, increased the range to 150 miles.

60 Group regarded the state of CHL with some dismay as electrical and mechanical changes were virtually non-stop with very little paper information. There were 38 stations, all hand turned, with a mixture of double and single sites and, at the latter, three different aerial systems. The next CHLs would have a common aerial that was power turned across a specific compass range. An experimental one was at Bawdsey with the single aerial suspended below the 200ft cantilever of one of the steel towers. Performances ranged from good to excellent, in most cases aircraft ranges were 25 miles at 500ft and 55 miles at 4,000ft. Tannoch (Wick), however, was singled out as having never given more than a second-rate performance. The installers knew more about CHL siting than the survey party as it was reported that:
"The installers expressed criticism of the siting which, for full appreciation, should be heard in the original." [1]

Deerness was on an exposed and isolated site which was completely waterlogged and 'knee-deep' in mud in places. The Admiralty CDUs at Saxavord, Sumburgh, Fair Isle, Dunnett Head and South Ronaldsay were performing well with average ranges of 85 to 95 miles; the broadside of the battle cruiser HMS *Hood* gave a saturated echo at 30 miles.

The CH situation facing 60 Group was equally chaotic. There were a total of 36 CH stations; the majority of the East Chain were on Final but only with one wavelength and without a buried reserve. None of the 14 West Chain stations was on Final and expansion was continuing. The ACH at Tan-y-Bwlch, a few miles south of Aberystwyth, was only 15ft above sea level and, as prone to flooding, needed a re-site to Castell Mawr, a few miles south. The CHL at Trevose Head and an ACH at Trerew replaced Carnanton. Siting signals were arriving from Tiree in the Western Isles and from the Isle of Lewis to fill the gap between Cape Wrath to cover enemy aircraft flying west of the Hebrides. In the south of England a site was found for additional heightfinding at Newchurch between Dover and Rye, at Southbourne (Dorset) to replace the Worth Matravers station, at Downderry (Cornwall) to release the ACH at Hawks Tor, at Trevescan (near Sennen) to cover the Isles of Scilly and at Northam (Devon) to cover the outer Bristol Channel. Installation work was continuing in the Shetland Islands: the Noss Hill ACH was working and further north at Skaw the T and R huts were complete with equipment but bad weather was delaying the arrival of the two 350ft steel towers.

The Air Staff felt compelled to enlist the aid of the Secretary of State to write to Lord Beaverbrook on the shortages of radio and other apparatus. He replied on 4 December:

> "Reels, Aerial, type B, production will fall behind, not due to Air Commodore Leedham, [the Air Officer responsible for supply] but due to enemy action at Siemens, Woolwich and IRGB, Silvertown. In the meantime we suggest this Ministry should be authorised to search the [RAF] Equipment depots. You have no idea what we find in these treasure houses, Sinbad the sailor and Aladdin with his wonderful lamp could get tips from our experiences with the Equipment depots. We wanted Browning guns a few days ago – Equipment records showed 1,000 – experience showed over 6,000 on hand, (God bless the E.D.s)." [23]

Sinclair replied:

> "We already have stocktaking parties operating in the Equipment depots to bring to light any equipment that may have been taken into stock without being recorded...in your mysterious case of the Browning guns it is true that you found 6,000, but they were not all disposable stock, 5,000 of these were already due out and were, rightly, not regarded as stock." [23]

Beaverbrook to Sinclair:

> "I have received your letter of 27 December in reply to mine of December 4. It is now proposed that we send search parties to look into E.D.s for any stock that might be useful to us. If you do not agree to this proposal, kindly let me know, so that I may raise it with the Cabinet. Yours sincerely, Beaverbrook." [23]

A memo from DCD to Rowe enquired if his plans for the secret destruction of equipment at TRE had been completed; Rowe replied that there were no such plans available and would unlikely to be so until a fully qualified defence officer had been appointed. The Director replied with a personal letter to the effect that some plan should be at his disposal without waiting for such an appointment. Rowe replied:

> "When we had Alert No. 3 some weeks ago, all papers were put into a mobile

van each night and a driver made available. Had the balloon gone up the van would have got away the best it could. I have said officially recently, the question of defence, fire and A.R.P. is my greatest source of anxiety at this establishment. If there were some kind of catastrophe and an enquiry followed, I should be forced to use some very bitter words about Headquarters, supported by documentary evidence. Not to put too fine a point on it, I think this establishment has been treated disgracefully in these matters." [24]

The procrastination in completing the second wavelength plan for the East Chain and the Final stage for the West Chain was now involving Watson Watt and, with direct access to the Secretary of State, he had written memos in May and June conveying his displeasure. He had proposed the formation of a high powered committee to co-ordinate the departments in the MAP and the Air Ministry. Nothing had happened. He wrote again on 21 December to convey his opinion that a more powerful organisation was needed, planning was on too small a scale and there was a dispersal of interest and effort:

"We are attempting to build a radio network larger than any other in the world, in a time several times smaller than that allowed for building earlier and smaller networks...If we proposed to set up all the stations of several B.B.C.s within a few months, would we put the contracts in the hands of a civil engineering group that was primarily engaged on other work (as is the Air Ministry Works Directorate), of a public utility company primarily engaged in the daily operation and maintenance of an existing undertaking (as is 60 Group) and of an electrical engineering drawing office with a total strength of 26, (as at RAE)? Since the answer is certainly in the negative, our task is to say how our present methods can be amended on a grand scale." [25]

He urged the formation of a single engineering enterprise to have the whole responsibility for installation embodying the general aerial principles that had long been available, and internal equipment now becoming ready for use in large quantities. His second memo followed a few days later:

"I suggest that the Ministry of Aircraft Production should be asked to undertake the provision of complete stations...[Let] the whole construction and installation contract, undivided, to a selected major civil engineering firm...A commission [would be set up] that would advise on the selection of such a firm in a week." [25]

Watson Watt's memos were circulated to members of the Secretary of State's Night Interception Committee before the next meeting on 1 January when the subject was to be discussed. Captain H.H.Balfour, the Parliamentary Private Secretary to the Secretary of State, had prepared a reply on 29 December to answer Watson Watt's criticisms. He advised that any course followed should not be arrived at impetuously and put forward a number of comments. He was doubtful if large civil firms would have the organisation and plant which could undertake a lot of small contracts all at the same time in different parts of the country. Did they have the men and the materials available for putting onto a number of stations straight away having regard to the difficult general labour situation at present existing? Costs would have to be ascertained which would require the setting up of a Works Accountant department and there was also the final responsibility to Parliament in the shape of the National Committee on Public Expenditure and the Public Accounts Committee. He concluded:

"These stations will be finally handed over for R.A.F. use. We therefore cannot divest ourselves of an interest in their design and construction at all stages. Are we prepared to hand over this interest to the M.A.P., has that Department got a Works organisation which can carry out the letting of contracts and supervision of work?...Nor have they the equivalent of a Land's branch for surveying, negotiating with landowners, serving notices and obtaining possession." [25]

Works had their own answer to Watson Watt:

"There is no firm in existence who have the organisation for taking on the work, no one in practice as a consulting engineer who could master the difficulty of the problems and overcome them in the time available. Ever since the R.D.F. programme commenced, we have had the greatest difficulty in obtaining the information as to the requirement and endeavouring to get finality in any scheme. About May 1940 Works were asked to proceed with the West coast scheme with 39 projected CH stations and to date, December, we are only told where 29 are to go with nine still waiting. Of the 29 stations only 22 have been sited, contracts let out for 13, three held up due to indecision on the layout of masts, two resited entirely and one under debate as to which of the three alternative sites is to be used. Works delays are solely due to not obtaining sufficient labour which can be attracted to, and would remain on, isolated sites." [26]

The RDF section in the Air Ministry, Signals 4, suggested that the appointment of an RDF dictator was essential, the need to create an executive body of sufficient power to function efficiently without Signals or DCD support and further proposed that 60 Group be made a command.

Night attacks on London had diminished towards the end of October but were replaced by a series of night raids on the Provinces. The first one was the 400 bomber raid on Coventry on 15 November, followed by Southampton, Birmingham, Sheffield, Liverpool and Manchester with Cardiff and Swansea as chief targets in the New Year. The six GCI sets ordered by Joubert were nearing completion and to meet the target date of 31 December were hurriedly assembled, three at RAE and three at ADRDE, with the personnel working an 18 hour day, some sleeping on the premises. Such was the urgency to combat the heavy German night raids, which were causing so much damage and civilian casualties without any loss of enemy aircraft, that the GCI sets had to be ready without the PPI or IFF, which would be added at a later date.

The on-site flight trials were successful in spite of two weaknesses, one being that the aerials had to stop turning for height readings to be taken, with the consequence loss of plots, and the other was that the PPI tube, when fitted, was too small in diameter for the controllers to work directly from it. Nevertheless, nine out of ten interceptions were declared accurate. After many experiments, the eventual method of interception was to provide the course for the fighter, the vector, from the plotting map and as the fighter approached closer to the enemy bomber to pass corrections direct from the PPI tube face. RAE were well aware of the primitive nature of the first GCI set; the major shortcoming was that as the lowest angle of elevation was between three to four degrees, the aircraft range at 5,000ft was only 35 miles that gave little time for interception. The 'Intermediate' design would incorporate all the latest CHL improvements and an aerial with a minimum angle of elevation of 1½ degrees that would extend the range to 55 miles.

The end of the year saw the approval by the Air Staff for the devolution of filtering to groups that for so long had been resisted by Dowding with one very sound reason; he did not want to see a complicated organisation that had taken years to assemble, that was ready to deal with the heavy air raids, which were expected as soon as war was declared, to be re-arranged geographically with all the consequential delays and inefficiency that would inevitably follow.

He was in charge of Fighter Command and it was his reputation that would have suffered if the devolution of filtering, if insisted upon by the Air Staff, had taken place at the wrong time, say, just before the Battle of Britain. But the issue had already slipped out of Dowding's hands as the increasing volume of information from the West Chain and the CHL stations, whose existence could not have been foreseen in 1938, all demanded space on the filter room table.

Was Dowding made aware of the approval by the War Cabinet on 14 October for the Air Raid Warning network to be decentralised from Stanmore, which to be effective, required Group Filtering? The Air Staff on 1 November agreed in principle to the provision of Filter Rooms for 9, 10, 12, and 13 Groups and being ready by February 1941 and in use by the next month. The Post Office, however, were responsible for the illuminated map in the filter room showing the air raid warning areas, together with the lighting, control and line termination equipment, so it was not until September 1941 that the Filter Room at Stanmore was used solely for 11 Group.

Air Chief Marshal Sir Hugh C.T.Dowding retired as the AOC-in-C of Fighter Command on 18 November. It should be mentioned in passing that the acrimony that arose due to the way his retirement was handled by the Air Ministry, combined with the squabble between his two senior Group Commanders, will always remain an unsatisfying aspect of contemporary top RAF and Government politics. His last message was sent to all operational units:

"My dear Fighter Boys, In sending you this my last message, I wish I could say all that is in my heart. I cannot hope to surpass the simple eloquence of the Prime Minister's words, 'Never before has so much been owed by so many to so few.' That debt remains and will increase. In saying goodbye to you all I want you to know how continually you have been in my thoughts, and that, though our direct connection may be severed, I may be able to help you in your gallant fight. Goodbye to you and God bless you all." [6]

REFERENCES

1	AVIA7/440	2	AIR33/4	3	AIR20/196	4	AIR29/141
5	AVIA15/8	6	AIR24/525	7	AIR20/1006	8	AIR20/1484
9	AIR33/4	10	AIR2/7348	11	AIR16/387	12	AIR16/277
13	AVIA7/258	14	AIR2/3272	15	AIR2/7439	16	AVIA7/1141
17	AVIA7/256	18	AVIA53/301	19	AIR20/1521	20	AVIA15/218
21	AIR2/3004	22	AIR2/7151	23	AIR20/2270	24	AVIA7/945
25	AIR20/1536	26	AIR20/2268				

Chapter 10   1941

AT the meeting of the Night Interception Committee on 1 January the various members put forward their views on Watson Watt's proposals. 60 Group submitted that it should be consulted on the design and construction of the stations, at present the sole responsibility of DCD, to ensure that Fighter Command, through the group, would have its proper share of control. The AOC-in-C Fighter Command (now Air Marshal W. Sholto Douglas) said that one delaying reason was the elaborate precautions of dispersal and camouflage, which might well be dispensed with, but Joubert, who was responsible for them, ventured to disagree.

The Secretary of State directed that a small sub-committee be formed to find the long and short term answers and to report back within a week. Its solution was the recommending of a special technical committee, subsequently known as the RDF Chain Committee, to be formed from the most senior representatives of the departments in the Air Ministry and the Ministry of Aircraft Production. Sinclair ordered it to report weekly.

On 2 January Joubert sent a memo to the Secretary of State:

" S.A.T. [Watson Watt] has put in a paper on the engineering of the Chain stations. I am afraid that I disagree with his thesis. I have now watched the development of chain stations for over a year and I am afraid that I have come to the conclusion that the main cause of failure to calibrate, to produce additional wavelengths, and to give Works a straight issue lies directly with the D.C.D.'s department....Nearly all the trouble...has been due to the changes of policy, for which the Air Staff, the Signals Directorate, Home Forces and the D.C.D.'s department, all bear a measure of responsibility. To suggest that all the troubles from which we suffer would be cured by handing over the construction of new Chain stations to a big contractor is, I think, to be wilfully blind to the complexity of the organisation which is concerned with obtaining R.D.F. information. The Air Staff requirement is usually expressed in the vaguest terms such as 'cover against air attack in a given area'....conditioned by such things as the siting of aerodromes, of Sector headquarters, of Group Headquarters and of the network of communications involved. There is the technical consideration of finding a suitable R.D.F. site. Even today the scientists are not agreed on this point. Within the last month the entire R.D.F. layout of Northern Ireland has been condemned by a scientist from T.R.E., although four months ago a brother scientist went carefully into the matter and pronounced on certain places being satisfactory. You can understand that the plans made in this department for taking up land, telephone circuits, etc., are now upset by this change of view. We have to go hat in hand to Works and apologise for the disorder that we have thus caused...[On] the question of security, many of the West coast stations are in very isolated localities and if they are damaged repair is difficult. I am therefore most anxious to use camouflage and dispersion to the largest possible extent so as to obtain protection against air attack. We have now got a good working arrangement with the Director of Works on this last point and I do not want to upset him." [1]

Joubert concluded his memo by suggesting that all the DCD (MAP) needed to do was to provide equipment and drawings; the Signals Directorate (Air Ministry) would set up a section to deal with installation queries....which was now rather unsuccessfully done by DCD....to employ a firm like Marconi to erect aerials....Works to put up the buildings and masts...with 60 Group to install the equipment....

"If the Directorate of Signals is given the facilities that I recommend, I am sure that construction of R.D.F. Stations throughout the country will go ahead as fast as is necessary." [1]

Joubert also considered that the Signals empire should be strengthened (ie, upgraded) and put his view to the CAS that it was essential that the Director of Signals, with the rank of Air Vice Marshal, was under the personal and undivided attention of an ACAS, and to split the Directorate into three sections, R/T, W/T and RDF with director ranks of Air Commodore. The Deputy Director of DCD expressed the view that:

"there would be no material improvement in efficiency until there was a well defined executive control. Signals, Works, 60 Group, DCD (with T.R.E. and R.A.E.) all played a vital part in the work of providing stations...[it] was difficult to avoid the scuffles of interested directorates and groups...[The] vital importance of the chain justified special and immediate action...[The] appointment of a chief executive officer was proposed." [2]

The RDF Chain Committee first met on 17 January with the various departments outlining their programmes; the Air Ministry was intending to raise the status of RDF in Signals to a separate Directorate, DCD in the Ministry of Aircraft Production were mobilising outside contractors such as Marconi, MetroVick, Cossor, the Post Office and STC for additional work, all of which had some knowledge of RDF except Marconi, and were also proposing to take over all the installation aspects and transfer completed stations to the Air Ministry.

At the second meeting on 21 February the main discussion centred around a suggestion that attempts should be made to standardise the layout of the 30 West Chain sites as hold-ups were being caused by alterations to plans connected with camouflage. There were no further meetings for several months until Joubert received a request from the Under Secretary of State on 17 May for a report to be submitted. A hastily arranged meeting on 22 May discussed the preparation of the report, Joubert stating that the active liaison between the branches, which had been hoped for, had not materialised.

The new Deputy Director of Signals gave his impressions that the trouble was due to defective planning, which gave a too optimistic a picture of the prospects, and set up a timetable that in practice was impossible to fulfil. Works agreed. Watson Watt said that branches should not accept work if they regarded it as impracticable. At the fourth meeting on 30 May Joubert admitted that the original schedule for the West Chain was framed without the experience of executing a programme of remote sites with full precautions for camouflage and dispersal; the obstacles were not fully appreciated.

The too ambitious workload appeared to have been unachievable on the basis of resources available even if everything had gone well. Alterations to the design and layout, desirable on operational grounds, had been introduced without the full realisation of the disruption that was caused. Works and 60 Group were seriously understaffed but it was not considered that any radical changes should be made to the present procedure.

All the committee members were of the opinion that the transfer of work to an outside body would not be a practical idea, except for Watson Watt, who submitted a blistering report to the Under Secretary of State. He opened with the observation that the committee had not met weekly as directed by Sinclair, had heard no evidence from non-members of the committee, except 60 Group, there were no detailed examinations of delays and it was proposing to report without specific recommendations. All the CH, CHL and GCI stations were requiring effort for completion to the Final stage or needed mass modifications.

The project was worth £10,000,000, an engineering enterprise of the first magnitude; he knew of no comparable undertaking that did not have an undisputed executive head authorised to give orders to all concerned including sub-contractors, one man with long experience in organising and directing large engineering organisations. He continued:

" We have adopted no simple scheme. We trust to the effective co-operation of three organisations of equal dictatorial status, viz.; D.G.W. [Works], D.C.D. and 60 Group. All have other large scale commitments. None is authorised to give instructions to the other. None is responsible, even on the individual site, for trouble finding or trouble clearing. This is pseudo democracy run mad; each contributing element is an autocracy; it is not even a chairman of Soviet. The highest grade officer in each autocracy who devotes his undivided attention to...the R.D.F. chain is:- in Works, a civil engineer who is believed to have spent all his professional life in Works, in the D.C.D. a technical officer with previous experience in gramophone electrical engineering, in R.A.E. a technical officer who is believed to have spent all his professional life in R.A.E. and T.R.E., in 60 Group H.Q. a Squadron Leader with previous experience in auto-telephony and in 2.I.U. a Wing Commander who has spent all his professional life in R.A.F. Signals. Two out of the three main executive partners each expressed his inability to carry out the proposed programme with his existing facilities. Not one of them insisted on having the facilities adequate for the programme. Each has, with gallant folly attempted the impossible; accepting responsibility without power, using junior amateurs where he might have demanded professionals of high status; knowing the War Cabinet instructions on R.D.F. priority, yet submitting to conditions which are ludicrously incompatible with the priority. Each has, less gallantly and with greater folly, assured the committee of the substantial perfection of his own contribution... and emphasised the imperfections of all the other co-equal parties." [3]

Watson Watt's solution was to recommend the appointment of an engineer of the highest calibre who would have been in charge of a major civil engineering enterprise. He would be requested to report and examine the provisions required in each of the three executive organisations and the best means available of co-ordinating them towards a speedy completion of the programme. War Cabinet endorsement had to be sought for implementing his recommendations and he would be given access to high authority. If his (Watson Watt's) solution was not approved, the sanction of the War Cabinet should be sought for a reduction in the priority of the RDF chain to accord realistically with the limited effort now being applied to its completion.

At the fifth meeting of the committee held on 12 June the Under Secretary of State was in the chair. Watson Watt added, in amplification of his report, that in his view the task set for the responsible authorities had from the first been impossible and remained so with the resources at their disposal. When the other members of the committee were asked by the chairman for their opinions on Watson Watt's memo there was general agreement with it.

At the request of Works, Watson Watt outlined what he considered to be the deficiencies of the present system, which were the lack of a single chain of executive control as would be insisted upon in the organisation of an RAF Command, and the insufficient experience and standing of the officers who were devoting their exclusive attention to the work in hand. Progress was being retarded by changes in policy and Operational Requirements but this was not thought to be one of the major considerations.

The Under Secretary of State expressed doubts whether it would be possible to have one person exercising executive authority over departments in the Air Ministry, the Ministry of Aircraft Production and the Royal Air Force. He had discussed the matter with the Secretary of State and VCAS, and they had come to the conclusion that an administrator of outside experience of a large scale organisation should be asked to exercise general supervision on behalf of the Secretary of State and to co-ordinate the departments concerned. The name of Sir Robert Renwick had been suggested; Watson Watt agreed entirely with the suggestion, which went beyond what he had proposed. At the final meeting of the committee no minutes were taken as the proceedings were largely informal with just an announcement that Sir Robert Renwick had accepted the invitation of the Secretary of State and would be the chairman of the newly formed Air Ministry RDF Chain (Executive) Committee.

Renwick was an outstanding 'behind the scenes' man, rarely mentioned in radar histories, both official and unofficial, yet he forced the pace on production and installation with complete disregard for the Civil Service bureaucracy. His success was in using civilian 'chasers' who were active in the clearing of supply and interdepartmental bottlenecks. They were qualified engineers provided and paid by the County of London Electricity Supply Company, of which he had been the Chairman, except for travel and other expenses, which were absorbed by the Air Ministry.

He soon found that the secrecy surrounding RDF was interfering with the extension of the chains and that 60 Group was seriously weakened by the lack of well qualified electrical engineers. To remedy the latter, Renwick arranged for a Mr P. de Lazlo to be made an honourary Group Captain and, with others, 'inserted' into 60 Group where they played an important part in re-organisation. His responsibility was extended to GCI and then GEE where he found supply difficulties and clashed with Sir Frank Smith and Air Commodore Leedham. No one questioned the fact that his official position did not give him full authority for many of the changes that he thought essential and implemented.

By the end of January, five additional mobile GCI stations had been sited at Sopley (near Bournemouth), Willesborough (Ashford, Kent), Waldringfield (near Ipswich), Orby (near Skegness) and Avebury (near Yatesbury) that gave overlapping cover from the northeast to the west of England. Calibrated and handed over to the RAF, they were in operation supplying vectors for fighter aircraft controlled by the nearby sector. Telephone lines to the nearest CH station, sometimes two, were essential in obtaining co-ordinating plots, especially IFF indications. At a later date the station would be able to pass the intercepting information direct to the pilot on a VHF R/T channel. The sixth GCI was reserved for siting trials.

The Operations Room was dominated by three racks of equipment each containing a cathode ray tube for range, azimuth and PPI. It was not long before it was realised that the bearings obtained on the PPI, if not equal to those on the azimuth tube, were adequate, a far reaching implication that all future CHL and GCI would dispense with the azimuth rack and tube and the complications of obtaining 'split'. There was another compelling reason in that it would allow common aerial working to be used immediately. The estimate of aircraft height required the aerials to be stopped so that echo height levels could be measured with the consequence that the existing tube tracks were lost. Sopley GCI developed a method, viewed at first with suspicion by officialdom. It was possible to 'guess' the ratio of the two halves of the echo, and make a snap height after a series of readings without stopping the aerials. Joubert was not satisfied with the progress in night fighter interception as he believed that insufficient action was being taken to find a solution; he was of the opinion that the time had come for a Night Fighter group separate from Fighter Command. His request to Sholto Douglas for control of the Fighter Interception Group was refused so he tried again, this time to Freeman, the VCAS, but without success.

By January the Air Ministry had conceded, under pressure from 60 Group, that the non-technical admin of the stations by the nearest RAF station was inefficient and announced that the Group would assume complete technical and admin control of all RDF stations and be fully self accounting. The existing eight Radio Servicing Sections were increased to ten (one for Northern Ireland) and raised to the status of Wings with the additional tasks of installation with 2.IU and calibration; aircraft and pilots would be stationed at the nearest airfield. Although all the personnel at the RDF stations were on the strength of 60 Group, through their Wing, the operation of the stations, ie, how the work was arranged and executed, remained with Fighter Command.

On 18 February the AOC of 60 Group, Air Commodore Gregory sent a personal and confidential letter to all Wing commanding officers:

> "Your reputation at the A.M.E.S. stations of your Wing will depend on what more you can give them than the old parent station. This is psychologically most important. Consequently sitting in your H.Q. is useless. You must go out to the stations, find out their deficiencies and troubles and then return and chase your staff into action." [4]

A new approach to quick and accurate heightfinding at 50 miles and over was occupying the attention of TRE. The present one was limited to site restrictions requiring a flat or gently sloping area but good sites were rare and the system could not, in principle, be further developed. Using a narrow beam on 1.5 metres in a vertical plane appeared to provide a solution with two major advantages; accuracy was unaffected by the site and required no calibration. TRE had developed experimental equipment called the Variable Elevation Beam (VEB) that gave the required accuracy and had requested a 120ft tower for trials. A demonstration was planned for early 1941; the situation was acute as at least eight West Chain stations had inferior or hopeless heightfinding.

Two principal changes were being made to the technical features of the East Chain to meet complaints from Fighter Command. The first one was to improve the back/front ratio of the transmitting aerial to reduce the effect of aircraft behind the station giving predominant echoes. The number of dipoles was increased from six to eight but the array would only be possible on the longer wavelength group if suspended between the towers. Works approval had to be obtained for the design, which incorporated a mechanical fuse, so that the stress values calculated with the array as a solid block of ice and an 80mph gale blowing did not endanger the tower stability.

2.IU had made a start at the southeast CH stations erecting the curtain arrays and the icing – up, which had been a feature of the very severe winter of the previous year, had been taken into account with the reflector curtain so designed that it could be connected to a three phase 415 volt AC supply. Early gap filling was a compromise; a dipole was connected permanently across the main transmit line taking some 35% of the power but out of phase with the main array. The opportunity was taken to provide a separate, switched, full power gap filler aerial array on one of the steel towers.

The second change was to implement the proposal made many months previously by SRS that another cathode ray tube display be provided to relieve the pressure of echo identification on the single operator during heavy air raids. Installed at Dunkirk during March, the tube was a 'repeater' of echoes seen on the receiver tube with a mechanism, at first mechanical, between the two displays, to ensure that the two operators identified the same echo. The major feature of the second tube was the RAE designed tracker mechanism, a long length of paper, marked with range scales and positioned underneath the tube horizontal time base line, that moved downwards at a slow and constant speed. When an echo appeared the position was marked on the paper and identified with a track number from the filter room.

Updated at frequent intervals the observer was able to follow at least 20 echoes whereas the tube operator, relying on an unaided memory, could scarcely sort out the designation of six; the need for continuous confirmation of track details to and from the filter room was greatly reduced. With the echo positions joined a curve was produced that related time with range and showed changes in the direction of the aircraft; whether it was crossing the station or approaching it radially. The second tube formed the basic part of the 'Operations Console', that included the plotters, teller and supervisor. With telephones and the two calculator displays added at a later date, the Mark 3 became the focal point of all the location work in the receiver room.

Although the fear of an invasion had receded, it was fully expected that with the Germans in control of the coastline from France to Norway an attempt would be made in the Spring of 1941. Watson Watt wrote to Joubert on 2 February of his concern that the East Chain, even in the southeast, was far below the standard necessary to face a renewed invasion threat, which he thought would affect stations from Worth to West Beckham. He believed that the enemy would make them the target for heavy low altitude bombing as a prelude to raids on fighter airfields and urged the rapid increase in ground defences.

He pressed for the short term installation programme of curtain arrays to be hastened, CH transmitters to be modified to increase the output to 600 kW and that the station staff should be in a position to carry out temporary repairs to aerials and feeders. For the back up of the plotting lines, he urged the provision of a 'Most Immediate' service through the station exchange line to the Group Filter Room and completion of emergency W/T links. At CHL stations, especially those nearest the enemy, there should be accelerated fitting of spark gaps for common aerial working, fitting of PPIs and replacement of VT58 valves with VT98.

The prospect of a Spring invasion was also of equal concern to the Army, who had the task of defending ports and repelling invaders approaching the beaches, and the Navy, who were defending convoys and sinking enemy shipping. The possibility arose of the three Services acting independently to provide and operate their own chain of stations. When the first group of CHLs appeared in December 1939/January 1940 along the coast for the detection of low flying aircraft, the Admiralty had asked for a watch to be kept on sea going vessels, but Dowding would not agree to the aerials being stopped so that they could be counted, although he had no objection on surface watching as a secondary role in the absence of aircraft at night.

The War Office, however, wanted independent action from the Air Ministry and began to look for sites, to design buildings, order equipment and organise a Coastal Defence (CD) chain of 135 stations that would stretch from Breckness in in the Orkney Islands, the east coast of Scotland, around the north, east, south and west coasts of England to a solitary station, Blackhead, in Northern Ireland.

To accelerate the Final installation of the West Chain, the DCD had brought in the Post Office to supply men and materials to erect transmitter feeder lines and gantries. To preserve secrecy before the war only the Air Ministry were allowed to manufacture and erect aerials. Thus, the employees of commercial firms, like Marconi, who only erected towers and masts, were not subject to security clearance, but approval was given in April when the company was contracted to design and install aerials for Bride, Scarlett, Drytree, Branscombe and West Prawle.

Marconi have their own version of events in that they claim that all the mechanical work around the British Isles after the Battle of Britain was carried out by them by an order from the Air Ministry to erect 26 Radiolocation (RDF) sets. Because of the time factor that part of the work was sub-contracted out, but the company made and erected all the aerials because they alone had the personnel, materials and the very special knowledge.

For CH and CHL cover for Merseyside, DCD had suggested that Blackpool Tower might be suitable, with transmit arrays on the north, south and west faces, and a single dipole cross at 485ft, and in September 1940 AMRE were requested to investigate the possibility. Although the Tower Company were in agreement that the top could be cut off and replaced with a CHL, that idea was vetoed by Works. By February there had been little progress on the design of the transmitting arrays as there were no accurate drawings of the tower available, but no doubt there was a sigh of relief at 2.IU when they were told that all the aerials and transmission lines would be handled by the Tower riggers. While drawings were being prepared it was discovered that the orientation of the Tower was two degrees anticlockwise of the true NSEW heading.

For the CHL an area was found on the sands of Formby, seven miles north of Liverpool, which required asking the Army to vacate an 18 room brick built house named 'Stella Maris'. Internal modifications were made so that the hand turned single broadside aerial could be on the 50ft by 30ft flat roof with the equipment inside. One station that had a short life was the MB station at Auchenbouthie Farm, Kilmacolm (near Paisley), which had been requested by the Commander-in-Chief, Rosyth, for RDF cover between the Firth of Forth and the Clyde. Diverted from Oban and quickly installed by January it closed in April after it was found that due to the impossibility of the Post office to provide telephone lines to a proper filter room, the station was not serving a useful purpose.

Joubert was alarmed at the ever increasing workload of installations and modifications as it looked as if none of the chains would ever be completed to the Final stage; the East Chain was awaiting completion to the third and fourth wavelengths, there were no West Chain stations on Final and all the CHL and GCI stations required major modifications. He wrote on 28 February to the DCAS (now Air Vice Marshal A.T.Harris):

"I am in favour of the abandonment of further buried reserves. Where no Buried Reserve is provided, the reserve will be constructed of ferro-concrete instead of brick, which should be equally effective. The original proposal to build Buried Reserves came from the C.A.S. at the beginning of the war and I should therefore be glad to have your concurrence with my decision before taking action." [5]

Harris agreed.

Most radar personnel remember with great affection their service life on remote stations but there has to be an exception, perhaps the only one, a Sergeant J. P.....in charge of Police at the newly opened CH station at Saligo Bay on the island of Islay. He had written a letter of complaint direct to the RAF Police Headquarters at Uxbridge in March, not knowing that a copy would eventually be placed in a secret Fighter Command file and be preserved for all to see after 30 years. He wrote:

"The police personnel are prevented in every way from performing their normal duties. When an airman is awarded the punishment of confinement to Camp, it merely means he is confined to his billet, and he has no extra duties to perform. The police Corporals on night guard find the position intolerable, in that they are directly responsible to the L.A.C. or Airman in charge of the Wireless watch, and must report to [him] every hour. I have had several interviews with the Commanding Officer ....to have everything reorganised, i.e.,...Village Patrols to prevent airmen from entering the Public Houses after hours...I have also reasons to believe that airmen billeted in a distillery caretaker's house are being supplied with whiskey, but I am unable to take action in my present position. I would appreciate the visit of an Assistant Provost Marshal to this station." [6]

A letter followed to all stations from the AOC of 60 Group:

"It appears that R.A.F. Service police on leaving the police school at Uxbridge are instructed that they may write reports direct to that school on any subject whatsoever. I will not permit any such procedure in this Group." [6]

The recruitment and training of WAAF operators for the filter and operations rooms had been an unqualified success and, except for stations in the Western Isles, the northwest of Scotland and the Shetland Islands, the prejudice of Fighter Command in barring the employment of WAAFs at remote sites had been overcome. In September 1940 Watson Watt had raised the desirability of employing scientifically qualified women as WAAF officers at stations to take the place of the civilian scientists who were undertaking analysis duties. But it was thought unlikely that a woman so qualified would take charge of a CH station, as it would be undesirable to place women in authority where a large number of men, technicians and otherwise, were employed.

There were two novel details to sort out; the first one was to find the qualified women but here the Ministry of Labour's Central Registry, under the eye of Dr C.P.Snow, was able to provide a list of 24 names, all with Honours Degrees. The second was to convince the Treasury to establish a technical grade in the WAAF and, far more difficult, to agree to a suitable pay scale. On 18 January the Director of Signals was made aware that no action was being taken with the recruitment of women graduates; [7] 'I was horrified to hear of the frightful delay.' A same day memo to the Deputy Director of Signals 4 (RDF) read:

> "Please see the attached [notes]. I will tolerate no further delay in this matter. The necessary training and selection arrangements are to be commenced immediately." [7]

On 23 February the DD of S wrote to the AMP:

> "It is essential to attract really first class women. I do not feel that the cheese paring policy adopted in this file is calculated to produce them. The proposed technical rates of pay compare unfavourably with the salaries they may expect to command in civil life...there is already a great loss of time... we have asked for the establishment of scientific efficiency experts, we are offered the establishment of foremen." [7]

On 30 May sanction was received for a Technical Branch in the WAAF. A course of 21 WAAF Technical Officers was held at No1 Radio School (Cranwell) from 11 August to 5 September.

The CH and CHL chains made some contribution to winning the Battle of the Atlantic and defeating the German U-boats. CH expansion was needed to detect German Focke-Wolfe Condor aircraft, which left Bordeaux in south west France at a height of 1,500 to 3,000ft, flew across Eire territory or waters, and used the remote Atlantic islands of Rockall and St. Kilda for fixes that enabled them to spot convoys and report their positions. Another route by the Condors was over the Irish Sea after passing west of Land's End penetrating as far as Mull and returning down the west coast of Ireland. CHL chain expansion was also required for the detection of aircraft over all the convoy routes in the Minches and the Western Approaches.

The Prime Minister sent the CAS a personal message from Chequers on 1 March giving him absolute priority for the chain extensions and on 21 March to Sinclair, a memo suggesting that stations be placed on Tory Island, Rockall and Loch Erne in Northern Ireland. A committee was set up to examine the Prime Minister's ideas and it recommended that a CHL be placed on St. Kilda followed by a CH with 120ft towers, and a CHL followed by a CH on Rona, but both were vetoed by Works on the grounds that the projects would exceed its capacity to construct and maintain. The latter aspect arose because very few stations in the Shetland and Orkney Islands, the Outer and Inner Hebrides and Scotland were connected to the grid electricity supply. Power was initially supplied by two, sometimes three, mobile generator sets that each needed 140 gallons of fuel a week from a never ending supply of 40 gallon drums. Final CH stations needed much larger capacity generators in brick buildings and permanent Works engineers.

Additional CHL and CH stations would be placed in the Western Approaches on the Isle of Lewis, Barra and Tiree, the northeast of Scotland and down to Northern Ireland. How the very long coast line would be covered by CH was resolved by the introduction of CHB (Chain Home Beam equipment), which was CHL fitted with heightfinding, with the plotting line connected direct to the nearest filter room. (The installations were, in the fullness of time, the Intermediate GCI, Type 8C, the name CHB being subsequently dropped.)

These proposals had in some measure already been met by surveys in the last quarter of 1940 and were now incorporated into the Final cover. The additions were a CH and CHL at Sango, a CHL at Point of Stoer (northwest Scotland and 90 miles away from the nearest railway station, and rations), on the Isle of Lewis a single channel CH at Broad Bay with two 240ft wooden towers and at Brenish with two 120ft towers, a CHB at Habost and CHL at Islivig and Eorodale.

A CHL at Rodel Park (South Harris, a day's journey by bus from Stornoway), Kendrom (North Skye), a CHB at Borve Castle,(Benbecula), a CHL at Greian Head (Barra), CH at Ard-Rudha-Mor (Barra) and CHL at Carsaig (Mull). This coverage would then meet other stations sited, in operation or under construction further south; a CH at Saligo Bay and CHL at Kilchairan on Islay, in Northern Ireland a CH at Castlerock, Kilkeel and Greystone with CHL at Downhill, Roddans Port, and Ballymartin.

Further south there were siting signals for CHLs at Hawcoat (Barrow) and St. Bees Head (near Whitehaven) to cover the Cumberland coast and, for the southern approaches to Liverpool a CHL at Great Ormes Head (Llandudno) and a CH at Rhuddlan to replace an inadequate mobile site at St. George. For North Wales a CHL at South Stack and a CH at Wylfa (Anglesey) and on the Lynn Peninsula a CH at Nevin and a CHL at Pen-y-Bryn. To strengthen the western coverage, the early CHLs at Cregneish, Prestatyn, St Twynells and Strumble Head were modified with VT98s and

CAW. The results of the modifications were reported to be almost unbelievable; at Strumble, aircraft were seen 92 miles away at 5,000ft, a hostile was seen 130 miles at 16,000ft near Liverpool, and at St Twynells, aircraft were seen over 100 miles at 10,000ft. With the need to strengthen the RDF cover along the southwest of England, the Bristol Channel and the Irish Sea, the twin beam concept station was abandoned. The stations were given a single Line of Shoot and further CH stations added, Dalby on the Isle of Man, Folly near Hayscastle Cross, Trelanvean near Drytree and Ringstead near West Prawle. Additional CHL cover at Kete, Hartland Point, Marks Castle near Lands End and Beer Head near Branscombe.

On the east side of Scotland there was also continuing expansion requested by the Admiralty to cover the Firth of Forth. At Helmsdale the CH site was now a few miles south at Loth and the CHL some miles north at Navidale, a CHL at Cocklaw (Peterhead) and in the Orkney Islands a CHL at Crustan. At Whale Head on Sanday, the ACH was operational and also nearing the Final stage. In the Shetland Islands CHLs were being installed at Clett and Wats Ness; all new CHLs were single gantry stations with a power turned aerial array, not continuous but set to sweep over a specific compass range clockwise, anticlockwise, with facilities for 'inching', with a wooden hut for the equipment. At Skaw and Noss Hill the steel towers were completed without the 200ft cantilevers and the technical buildings almost ready for the equipment.

Joubert, concerned at the ever expanding rate of installation, wrote to Signals on 9 April:

> "I have reviewed the plan for the East coast C.H. stations as regards immunity from jamming and destruction from the air. This called for four wavelengths, buried reserves, emergency alternative reserve equipment in the invasion areas, the mobile home pool and the G.C.I. stations. In view of the enormous expansion it is necessary to economise on installation effort to the greatest degree. I have, therefore, decided not to continue with the third and fourth wavelengths for the East coast C.H. stations, and to standardise both the East and the West chains to one 'long' wavelength around 10 to 12 metres, and one 'short' wavelength of 5 to 6 metres." [8]

The Megawatt amplifier that had been sent to Bawdsey was awaiting an MB2 transmitter to 'drive' it: one had been ordered in December 1940, but three months later it had still not arrived as the transmitter could not be moved until the arrival of an armed guard to escort it from the equipment depot to Bawdsey. It was not until May that air tests were completed, but the results were inconclusive as the array was without a reflector and the porcelain separators used limited the maximum aerial input to 900 kW. Rowe wrote a private letter to the Deputy Director of DCD asking if it was time to start moving towards the production of megawatt transmitters that would give double the height of the echo. The reply was that there had been no great enthusiasm by the operational people, and in view of the commitments in getting the chain in order, it appeared desirable to postpone the matter to a more suitable time. The preliminary work done, however, was to prove of great value when megawatt transmitter powers were hurriedly needed in early 1945.

There were a few CH stations that were sited to cover more than the single Line of Shoot. Kilkenneth and Skaw required two with a difference of 180 degrees and Noss Hill, Whale Head and Netherbutton required four by 90 degrees, known as 'all round looking'. Wilkins evolved a 'sandwich' of two exciter dipole curtains with a centre tuned reflector and, by suitable switching, either exciter curtain could be energised to produce a difference in the Line of Shoot of 180 degrees. Another two sets of curtains differing by 90 degrees from the first array were erected on the next steel tower that had the top cantilever turned by 90 degrees; both towers had the 200ft cantilever removed. The second pair of steel towers had one top cantilever turned by 90 degrees for 'all round looking' of the second wavelength. All the arrays had gap-fillers and the Lines of Shoot were separately switched. The prototype 'short' wavelength for the CH chain was under test at Rye on 6.25 metres but was proving to be unworkable because of large bearing errors. In what may have been an act of desperation these were finally cleared by bonding all the feeders to the lightning conductor at roughly quarter wavelength intervals down the tower, a feature that became standard for all future and existing installations.

In the filter rooms it had become crystal-clear with night bombing raids involving hundreds of aircraft that the existing plotting methods of obtaining information on individual echoes had broken down. A new practice called 'macroscopic' or area reporting was introduced that attempted to plot the front and rear edges of a formation with the mean height and estimation of numbers, or, if 'crocodiles', the breadth, direction and numbers.

German night raids had increased in intensity and extended as far as Glasgow, Sheffield, Leeds, Plymouth and Merseyside. On 7/8 April there were heavy night attacks on Clydeside, Teeside and Tyneside and in May Merseyside was bombed continuously for seven nights. On 10/11 May a London raid caused 2,000 fires including the House of Commons with over 3,000 people killed or injured; 30 enemy bombers shot down, most of them victims of GCI and night fighters. The great success of GCI is best shown by the statistics of night fighting, all the more remarkable as only five night-fighter squadrons were equipped with AI, plus a further eight

squadrons known as 'cats-eye' fighters, which were directed by GCI but
had to continue their search visually: they were very successful especially
during moonlit nights.

November 1940	NIL planes destroyed	NIL damaged
(Coventry raid over 400 aircraft)		
December 1940	2 planes destroyed	6 damaged
March 1941	24 planes destroyed	50 damaged
April 1941	52 planes destroyed	88 damaged
May 1941	88 planes destroyed	172 damaged

A composite night combat report on 11/12 April read:

"MIDDLE WALLOP 604 Squadron. Pilot F/O Chrisholme, Operator Sgt.
Ridley. Controlled GCI Sopley 0045-0120 hours. Vectored on to raid by
SOPLEY at 0050 hours at 16,000ft 160, 270, 300, 320 and 330°. Contact
obtained 7,000ft away on right and below. Pilot lost height to below enemy
aircraft's indicated position. Visual obtained 1,500ft above and 3,000ft away.
On passing through clouds visual was lost twice and position maintained on
AI. During this time 7 other blips were obtained on crossing targets and ignored.
Final visual obtained on first. Pilot crossed to slightly below e/a and above
prevailing cloud layer. Fired short burst from 50 yards. Fuselage by centre
section blew up and pieces flew back and large explosion and e/a went down
to almost vertical. Time of combat 0110 hours...." [9]

In July when the Sopley GCI receiver was changed it was recorded thus:

"[A] new R3101 for Sopley, the old one taken out of service with regret, a
magnificent total of 48 Huns inscribed on the front, the installation unique,
not off the air for a single night, installed 27.12.40, removed 15.7.41." [10]

The jamming of the stations that had suddenly ceased in November 1940,
restarted on 8/9 April and was seen from Poling to Stoke Holy Cross but it
only lasted for two hours then reappeared again at the beginning of May.
The effect on the display had not been seen before, a number of closely
spaced pulses sweeping across the tube face which were quickly dubbed
'railings'. Both the CH and the CHL receiver circuitry were unable to be
effective on this form of jamming, but the double layer tube certainly was,
as the jamming was not 'locked' and so wandered across the tube face and
was easily countered by the use of filters.

A jamming section had been set up by TRE and a mobile van had been
fitted with a transmitter plus a camera to enable the jamming on the tube to
be photographed for analysis. Of vital importance was that the operators should
have as much training as possible to enable them to identify enemy jamming
especially in the south, southeast and west of England. The van would make
a visit to a station, unknown to the operators, and the officer in charge would
visit R block on what was apparently a friendly visit. During his stay the

jamming would commence and allow him to study the reaction of the operators, observe the method that they used and when it ceased, he would instruct them on the errors that they had made, and sometimes order the jamming to come on again and to give a practical demonstration.

To speed up production of GCI sets a 'swop' was done with ADRDE, 14 CHL transmitters for one GCI set which the Army installed in the Hyde Park, London, AA gun site in July. The Army were the first with a remote PPI display; the BBC provided and laid a special cable to the Gun Operations Room at the disused Brompton Rd London Underground station, a few miles away, and the picture was reported as equal to that of Hyde Park. By June, the installation and siting of GCI stations was continuing and a further 11 were operational; Neatishead near Wroxham, Norfolk, Langtoft near Peterborough, Hack Green near Crewe, Comberton near Pershore, Hampton Hill, near Hull and Trewan Sands on Anglesey covered the Midlands and Merseyside. Exminster, Wrafton near Ilfracombe and Treleaver for the approaches to the West Country with Ripperston and Huntspill for the Bristol Channel. Further north a GCI at Northstead, near Newcastle.

Work had continued at Blackpool Tower. In June the MB2 transmitter had arrived in sections with firm instructions that it was to be taken into the tower in the early hours of the morning to prevent it from being seen when taken through public parts of the building. The station was formally opened as RAF Tower with admin and technical staff posted in. A Station Standing Order was issued :

"Airmen must not use the Artistes' door except when going on duty, they must not draw attention to themselves by standing around in groups and they must pay the 9d [4p] admission charge to the Tower like any other troops."

Towards the end of July there were indications that there were very high levels of receiver interference and large bearing errors. On 8 September TRE wrote to DCD:

"The large D/F errors are due to re-radiation from the tower, no solution can be suggested... [Doubtful] whether possible to obtain height measurements...If the complete abandonment of the station cannot be considered, [it is] suggested that no further research takes place. The site noise is five times normal." [11]

Rowe wrote a personal letter to the Director of DCD the next day:

"I wonder if you would look at T.R.E.'s official letter on the subject of Blackpool Tower. Our official letter is brim full of that well known courtesy that emanates from T.R.E... but I think you ought to know that there is a strong feeling here that any further effort on the Tower is a waste of time and money. It is very rare for us to disagree with Dixon [of DCD] but I think that he is the only one who would now defend any further work." [11]

Rowe's letter had no effect as DCD asked for the resident scientific officer to be changed immediately (a high-handed action according to TRE) and further attempts were made to improve the situation. Ignition and industrial interference, especially from the fun fairs below, was some four to five times greater than normal CH stations, as a result of which the range by day was down by 30 – 40%, with D/F errors up by 30% and likely that heightfinding was also unsatisfactory. It was not until February 1942 that DCD conceded defeat and the station closed down.

Even in moderate winds the hand operated CHL aerial arrays had to be lashed to the ground on a specific Line of Shoot. TRE had completed experimental work on a wind screen, which showed that the reduction in signal strength was very small providing that the planks were about 3 inches (75mm) wide and 1 inch apart (25mm) and were arranged vertically. Works had prepared a specification for a wind screen based on TRE work, which was estimated to cost about £1,000, for a 20ft high fence to be placed at a radius of 90ft around each array. While RAE were of the opinion that wind tunnel tests should be made by the NPL, 60 Group decided that they could do the job much cheaper and, without waiting for official approval, they decided to erect a wind screen at Bempton CHL costing £60.

RAE had visited the site in May and reported that, not for the first time, 60 Group had 'jumped the gun'. They described the design as being on the venetian blind principle made up of sections mounted on 35ft high telegraph poles embedded in 6ft of concrete surrounding the aerial array, the individual sections being made up of sixteen 2½ inch wooden scaffold poles nailed to the vertical poles and covered with Ruberoid, a trade name for wartime synthetic rubber sheeting. RAE considered that the screen was inferior because the horizontal slats supported on the telegraph poles would absorb more RF energy than vertical ones.

The mechanical structure also came in for criticism; the scaffold poles were of great length and it was possible that the normal swaying and sagging would tear the fabric even without the assistance of high winds. In addition it appeared probable that the Ruberoid itself would tear to ribbons and the poles would rip from their six inch nails and crash into the aerial array. Whatever the merits or demerits of the two systems, RAE decided to adopt neither idea and to wait for the introduction of power turning with common aerial working:

> "which will give a much quicker solution than any wind screen device and the 3½ H.P. motor is considered sufficient to deal with winds up to 80 m.p.h." [12]

The Final version of CHL was already on the Drawing Office boards at RAE: known as the '1941', it had a continuously power turned five tier single aerial array supported by a 20ft wooden gantry at one end of a single brick building 50ft by 18ft to house the transmitter, receiver/operations room, stores and other accommodation. One innovation was the 'rotating capacity coupling' that enabled pulse power to be conveyed to the aerial array.

Yet CHL was of little use to combat the next menace: German bombers were flying at heights just 50ft to 100ft above the sea, and attacking by day the convoys and shipping along the eastern coastal regions of England and Scotland. The only immediate solutions put forward by TRE were to place CHL aerials on the top of 350ft steel towers (to lower the first lobe), to give priority to VEB and to increase the power of 50cm and 150cm CHL. The aircraft were called 'wave hoppers' by Fighter Command and Sholto Douglas had written to Joubert on 6 March of his concern:

> "It is possible that some instrument built on the principle similar to those employed in the design of the apparatus which recently detected a submarine at seven miles from Worth may give the desired result. I can do no more than emphasise its importance." [13]

Joubert replied that the experimental shore station was working on a 10cm wavelength, but it was unlikely to be available within a year as there was a continual shortage of suitable research personnel, a situation that appeared to be beyond remedy.

The 10cm ground equipment designs had begun in July 1940 as soon as a production model of the cavity magnetron was available from GEC, and by the following March a set with separate 3ft T and R dishes with a half wave dipole and reflector had followed aircraft for 14 to 15 miles. The Admiralty scientific officers had also seen the ability of the 10cm set to detect submarines and, more importantly, so had naval officers who immediately saw the answer to the German U-boat menace in the Atlantic Ocean. A copy of the set was taken to HM Signal School and by March the prototype named T271 had been fitted in a corvette, HMS *Orchis*, with extensive sea trials during April when the periscope of a submerged U-boat was picked up at a range of 1100 to 1300 yards.

The War Office obtained one set from the Admiralty in April and developed an 'emergency' set that consisted of two 7ft paraboloids fixed to the side of a cabin that was manually turned, the set operating as a mobile. One was installed in July at Lydden Spout, near Dover, some 330ft above sea level with a range of 30 miles and a bearing accuracy of approximately 1 degree, which was fully adequate for the detection and tracking of shipping. One advantage for the War Office was the ability to deal direct with the manufacturer as the T271 was in full production for the Admiralty, which was not the case with CD, as the War Office was dependent on Air Ministry

CHL contracts in which they appeared to come off second best.

The shortage of skilled wireless personnel for the three Services had not only persisted but increased as the supply of civilian recruits with a wireless or television background had virtually come to an end. At the end of 1940 the War Cabinet had formed a committee under Lord Hankey to make recommendations. One of the measures proposed was the mass training of the many hundreds of 18 year old men in basic radio fundamentals at local technical colleges, who had volunteered for the RAF. By February eight colleges had begun a 17 week training course, which was later extended to 24 weeks, and by April there were 14 with a total weekly output of 120 men.

To urgently match the RAF training capacity, whose deficiency in air and ground mechanics was some 12,000, the number of colleges had by the end of June nearly doubled to 27, some of which were working double shifts giving a trainee population of 4,000: at the Glasgow Technical College (now the University of Strathclyde) over 1,200 men were working three shifts in 24 hours. Many thousands of young men would remember for all time the splendid introduction to radio that they had been given by schoolmasters and professors, many brought back from retirement.

In the House of Commons a question was asked why recruits, who were passing through a course of specialised training, were occasionally called out of classroom to do fatigue duty which could jeopardise their chances of passing the final examination. Sinclair replied that directions had been given that pupils at technical training colleges were not, except in emergencies, to perform fatigues during instructional hours and he would look into any case of non-compliance that came to his notice.

In Canada an appeal was made in May for men to join the Royal Canadian Air Force to train as radio mechanics, explaining that the source of supply of amateur and professional radio men who had been rushed overseas had dried up, and they were now ready to take 'green' men of good education who had never seen the inside of a radio set. Those men who went into the Service would be posted overseas to Britain to ground points all over the British Isles, using radio sets able to detect enemy aircraft in the air and direct anti-aircraft fire with great precision. Joubert had written earlier in the year that the position on training had been serious and, but for the fortunate arrival of Canadian operators and mechanics, there would have been the greatest difficulty in manning the chain stations.

Another possibility to alleviate the serious shortage of technical manpower, not only in the RAF but also the Army and the Navy, was the opinion of very senior American officials, who had had informal talks with members of the War Cabinet, that there would be some 30,000 volunteers who would be interested in helping the Allied war effort by coming over to Britain. To solve the difference in the rates of pay it had been agreed that they would cross the border into Canada and, after training, be enlisted into the Royal Canadian Air Force for service in the United Kingdom. This ideal arrangement fell foul of American government officials, who advised in March that in peacetime Americans living in the USA were forbidden to volunteer for the armed forces of other nations, so a legal subterfuge was adopted ; the plan was changed to the formation of the Civilian Technical Corps (CTC). The US Senate approved in April the recruitment of 21,000 skilled men in engineering and electrical trades in addition to 9,000 radio mechanics. The Canadian government, however, aired its disapproval at having a large number of Americans in civilian clothes and subject to no discipline on their soil and insisted that the induction be organised as soon as possible; the Air Ministry agreed to be responsible for the organisation. In a cable dated 9 May, the Air Attaché in Washington was less than enthusiastic:

> "It is our frank opinion that there is very little hope of obtaining more than 5% ...volunteers. Every skilled man employed has no inducement to go to Great Britain except in the case of adventurous types with no ties, of which I fear few exist." [14]

The organisation of medicals and initial interviews was the responsibility of the British Embassy in Washington, which arranged for the FBI to vet all applicants with forms to take finger printing, and for the Radio Corporation of America and the Radio Marine Corps to provide grade testing without charge. Some 200 applications were received at the British Consulate in New York by 19 June. A 15 page pamphlet on the aims and purpose of the CTC clearly showed that the volunteers did not forfeit their American citizenship and that while with the British armed forces, they were free from combatant duty and military discipline. The technical tradesmen wanted were radio mechanics and operators, airframe and engine fitters, the latter for aircraft and ships, sheet metal workers, blacksmiths and welders, instrument repairers, electricians, machine tool setters and operators.

There would be no charge for accommodation, food, clothing, medical care and travel to and from their home to the UK. Their pay, free of British income tax, was based on that of the Royal Canadian Air Force, £6 a week for tradesmen, equivalent to an Leading Aircraftman, rising to £400 a year for a Foreman of Trades, the latter comparable to that of a RAF Warrant Officer. Those who were accepted, after a local medical examination and correspondence with the British Consulate in New York, went by train to Montreal, in Canada, where the HQ of the CTC was housed in the mansion of the former president of the Canadian–Pacific Railway. There, they were enrolled and issued with a uniform and a few days later travelled to an air force barracks in Halifax, Nova Scotia, to await a ship.

There was always much speculation at BRS before the war on the possibility that the Germans also had RDF devices; published scientific papers and patent publications of the day were scrutinised. Philips were watched for the development of high power valves in the centimetric wave lengths and details of special cathode ray tubes and screen materials. Watson Watt's use of the backs of expired daily calendar leafs was well known: he had used one on 26 November 1937 to request a typist to obtain copies of the patents from Marconi on 'Electrical Oscillator Generator' and Telefunken on 'Transmitting Impulses of HF Energy'.

As the British and the Americans kept their pulse work concealed, so did the Germans until the occupation of France and the Low Countries when, in the same way that they were now able to detect and measure the wavelengths of the RDF chains, it was now practicable to detect the German transmissions although that took a little longer. In October 1940 a party of TRE technicians set up watch in the Dover area to search for pulse transmissions from across the Channel. Enemy transmissions on 80 centimetre were discovered, the German Seetakt (aid for coastal guns). By the following March the Royal Navy, TRE and the RAF listening service had found strong evidence of pulse transmissions from enemy-held occupied territory on 1.00, 1.25, 1.50 and 1.60 metre wavelengths.

A special flight of 109 Squadron was established to fly over enemy territory in order to obtain information on beam transmissions. A Wellington bomber, fitted with a GEC receiver and a conical aerial, found transmissions on 53cm, which were rechecked using a receiver with a cathode ray tube to examine the waveforms. By May, nine pulse transmissions had been found and the sources approximately recorded as the German Würzburg (aid for AA guns). By October aircraft had been fitted with a receiver covering 150-3000 MHz that located all the enemy RDF stations from Norway to the south of France.

The Inspector/General did not confine his visits to the mainland. During May he had visited Crustan CHL in the Orkney Islands that had only been operational for ten weeks and where the 47 airmen and 12 soldiers were living in Nissen huts, and further north to Skaw in the Shetland Islands that had opened on 20 November 1940 with an Advance CH and where the two 350ft steel towers were being erected. He commented that the station was still under completion by civil labour:

"which works very slowly when it feels like it, draws large wages and is given free board and lodging. A credit note from the NAAFI funds for £22 had been sent to Wing last month, but nothing yet received. In a remote station as Skaw, the most northerly of the RAF ensign, it is important that money should be available to buy footballs and sports gear. " [15]

Sites had been selected on Benbecula and Tiree in the Western Isles during November 1940 and the installations were competing for Works services also being provided for the construction of Coastal Command aerodromes there: the two RDF stations on Barra were also on the priority list. At Port Mor on Tiree the site was ready by April, but there was no sign of the ACH equipment, which had been on the mainland for weeks awaiting shipment, and rumoured to be unguarded. This situation reached the ears of Renwick, who ordered a progress report:

"It is most important that all concerned should bear in mind the fact that the Western Isles, although situated within about 100 miles off the mainland, can only be described as barren, desolate and primitive. From the point of view of the progress of major engineering works they are as remote and ill equipped with dock, pier and road and all other transport and communication facilities as the more remote parts of the world. Everything, except sand and in some cases stone, including labour, food and amenities, except in the case of Barra, has to be imported. In some cases the population of an island has been or will be increased by 50% by the importation of labour." [16]

The tiny island of Tiree found itself invaded with bureaucracy because of the additional Service and civil departments required in time of war; the Navy, the Ministry of Shipping, the RAF Embarkation officer, the Ministry of Labour and the use of special craft involving a further naval department with Army connections, the Tank Landing Craft. The absence of a port, pier and unloading facilities had introduced the Army in the shape of the Docks Operating Company, Royal Engineers and the complete lack of communications had admitted the Post Office and the Royal Signals. The report continued:

"In the main, individuals co-operated regardless of rank, but one case needed immediate action as complicated and delicately balanced arrangements for mooring, unloading and distribution had been completely wrecked by an Army visitor of superior rank demanding labour from the Docks Operating Company. Complete co-operation of the Services such as exists at Benbecula, with progress as the main objective, had involved breaches of Service regulations which tends to leave the officer responsible for fears for his future career. Tiree has the greatest problem as only one ship could be berthed at a time and an order of priority had to be evolved for mail boats that carried perishable foodstuffs and passengers, cargo coasters and requisitioned ships operated by the Ministry of War Transport. To augment this, Tank Landing Craft are used between Oban and the islands but these are under the control by authorities at Oban who insist that the TLCs shall be beached, unloaded and returned on one tide. Everything is sacrificed to this end to the extent that lorries, tractors and special plant are driven by TLC operatives, and even by the naval liaison officer himself, into the sea or at the best on to the waterlogged sand, from which position they have to be extricated by the contractors of the Royal Engineers. Transport to the island is very difficult, only one aircraft a day from Renfrew and the Air Ministry have priority bookings – sea transport by normal methods is out of the question. Many matters could be settled by telephone but few islands have telephones and secrecy forbids the use of open lines and there are no 'tie' lines. Civilian labour is the main difficulty, absenteeism occurring to an objectionable extent and a noticeable amount of unfit labour with civilian camps and canteens far from satisfactory. There are no NAAFI canteens as these are not provided until the stations are established [and] cigarettes are almost unobtainable." [16]

The ACH at Port Mor was completed in May with temporary plotting by W/T to the Filter Room at Preston. At Barrapol the chosen site for the CHB was under water and had to be moved 650 yards and a single gantry hand turned CHL was erected on the top of Ben Hough. Wing records reveal:

"...that the cooking of rations on 'B' site was critical owing to the lack of a stove, but we were lucky enough to obtain one from the galley of HMS Sturdee, a destroyer which was wrecked on the rocks and is now being broken up." [17]

When a mobile cinema arrived on the island in September it was the first time that the inhabitants had seen a 'talking picture', as the island was without electricity.

Under pressure from Renwick the West Chain was progressing sufficiently well for the reserve channels to be constructed. Hart, now the Deputy Director of Radio, wrote on 19 May to Joubert that it was time to reconsider the policy which called for reserves from Ventnor to Warren, as acceptable sites had only been found for 60% of the stations. Construction could not be started due to the heavy commitment on the main CH stations and it was unlikely that they would be completed before the end of the year. Some of the East Chain buried reserves had been completed and Hart related how he had visited one and was very forcibly impressed by the futility of the site:

"It is only just buried and therefore vulnerable to... a direct hit...I cannot see how it can ever be made dry, and....will require considerable maintenance." [5]

He added:

"R.D.F experience is showing that the C.H. type of station, with its unidirectional presentation of information, is incapable of handling large numbers of aircraft scattered some in front, some behind the station. Attempts to improve the back/front ratios [of the transmitting arrays] have failed. One is forced to the conclusion that C.H. stations under modern conditions of intense air attack are mainly useful for providing long range warning. When our fighters are airborne the tube may be so cluttered that just when we require the most accurate information, we are unable to obtain any at all. The beam station, on the other hand, can today read not only height but also considerable numbers of aircraft by the use of P.P.I.s." [5]

He recommended that GCI stations should be accepted as an economic reserve to give cover to 35 miles at 10,000ft and below that the CHL could provide the information. Joubert agreed and on 28 May he advised 60 Group that the reserves from Drytree to Northam were to be cancelled.

On 5 June Joubert wrote to the CAS of the failings of the Inter Services RDF Committee, which was established to co-ordinate the activities of the three Services; but it had no contact with the Chiefs of Staff and no authority for compliance of its decisions. Joubert highlighted the fact that the Army in an attempt to cover all the invasion beaches had initiated an installation plan of 135 Coastal Defence stations regardless of the RAF's CHL chain. The War Office was later informed that its actions were redundant as by use of the PPI tube it would be perfectly possible to fulfil the purpose of watching for aircraft, naval and approaching invasion surface vessels. Acting independently, the Army Ports Defence Committee had proposed a requirement for 630 CHL sets: 270 at home, 190 abroad and 170 sets for the Dominions, India and Burma.

Joubert's proposal was to dissolve the committee and replace it with a body of the status of the Chiefs of Staff to be called the RDF Policy Committee. On 21 August the CAS replied to Joubert's memo, agreeing to his proposal but adding:

"I think the chairmanship of the new policy committee is practically a full time job and this being the case, I can see the burden that it throws on you, as well as being appointed the A.O.C-in-C Coastal Command, must be intolerable and I do not think that it is fair to ask you to continue it." [18]

Joubert replied a few days later:

"I am disappointed that you think that I cannot combine it with my present job. I have been so closely associated with R.D.F. since it began that it would be a great grief to me to give up my present close contact with the whole concern. I realise however, that there are a number of people more or less remotely connected with R.D.F., and one at least who considers himself essential to its successful existence, who would be very glad to see me relegated to obscurity. Therefore if my continuance as chairman of the committee is going to cause you more inconvenience than you can tolerate, I shall withdraw as gracefully as possible but with a sorrowful heart." [18]

The scale of the German night bombing and the apparent lack of air defence was causing the government to be concerned about the question of public morale. In a draft memo to the Prime Minister dated 1 March from Sinclair regarding disclosure (of RDF), he added:

> "....there are strong arguments for releasing to our people all the information we can safely give them as to the countermeasures we are taking for their defence against the present scale of enemy attacks. In spite of the fortitude that these attacks have been endured, there has been as you know a great deal of public anxiety to know if we are doing all that can be done to counter these attacks as quickly as possible." [19]

The secret of RDF was revealed to the general public as 'Radiolocation' and on 17 June an 'inspired' question was arranged for the House of Commons that day:

> Q. "To ask the Minister of Defence [Churchill] whether his attention has been drawn to a recent speech by the Canadian Minister of National Defence in which he referred to a device for the detection of enemy aircraft and whether he has any statement to make on the subject."
>
> A. [given by Clement Attlee, the Lord Privy Seal]. "Yes, Sir. Thanks to the brilliant work of our scientists, great progress has been made in devising a means of helping the Armed Forces with their task of locating and destroying the enemy. This contributed in no small measure to our victory in the Battle of Britain last autumn, and there has been since devices of high promise in many directions. Our industry is now turning out increasing quantities of ingenious equipment which, for its maintenance and repair, demands large numbers of skilled men especially radio mechanics. Training in this work is being given by the Fighting Services, assisted by the Universities and technical colleges around the country. The Dominions and other parts of the Empire are also helping us, Canada in particular, is organising powerful aid. Our need for these craftsmen is increasing rapidly, and we want more and more of them. My noble Lord, the Minister of State for Air, will therefore broadcast in the Empire programme tonight a special invitation to men overseas with technical experience to come forward and help in the maintenance and repair of the new equipment which is passing into the hands of the Services and thus join their skill and knowledge with those of our scientists and technicians in the struggle we are waging in the common cause." [14]

Sinclair preferred that Lord Beaverbrook should make the broadcast, which was to be over the American Columbia and NBC radio networks, as part of a recruitment drive for the Civilian Technical Corps. He had written to him for help on 12 June:

> "Dear Max, Your voice will reach a wider public in the U.S.A. than anybody's except Winston's." [14]

Lord Beaverbrook agreed but discarded the prepared speech that had been written for Churchill, who had declined to broadcast, and wrote his own that was made in the early hours of the morning of 18 June. Sinclair wrote again:

"Dear Max, I am very sorry to hear that the Columbia and N.B.C. chains of America insist on you staying up to 2.30 in the morning to make your [live] broadcast. It is splendid of you to consent and make this sacrifice." [14]

In the House of Commons on 18 June Sinclair explained the establishment of the Civilian Technical Corps and added that hundreds of radio operators were immediately needed by the WAAF. He said:

"Young women between 17½ and 35, able to assume responsibility under active wartime conditions, mentally alert and accurate, with exceptional eyesight and sound nervous control were needed."

Joubert (now Air Chief Marshal and AOC-in-C Coastal Command) was already prepared to conduct a Press release the day following Beaverbrook's American broadcast. He said:

"It was the need of the Royal Air Force to obtain early warning of enemy air attack that brought it into being by the development of what might be called a wireless trick in the laboratory into a practical weapon of war. Briefly, it is a system whereby rays which are unaffected by fog or darkness are sent out far beyond the limits of our shores. Any aircraft or ship in the path of this ray immediately sends back a signal to the detecting station where people are on watch. These ether waves keep a 24 hour watch. They are always on duty." [19]

Carefully staged photographs and notes for guidance had been prepared by the Air Ministry for the daily papers, weekly and monthly periodicals and released on 17 June:

"Radiolocation, of which official disclosure has just been made, is one of the best kept secrets and one of the most important factors in the war. A new military science, which already has a profound influence in air, military and naval strategy has come into the world without the world being aware of its existence. It has been kept so secret that it is only referred to by three letters and even these could not be whispered outside the Services. Actually, Radiolocation was born in a rather ancient lorry at 9 o'clock on a fine March* morning in 1935. With their own hands, Mr. Watson Watt and his team made the first series of radiolocators to give warning of the approach of enemy aircraft. We want more and more men with a knowledge of radio to train them quickly so that they can look after the radiolocators that are pouring out of the country. This is not the time to talk about peacetime applications but at least I can give you an indication – in peacetime there will never be another shipwreck, never another Titanic disaster, while the many causes of accidents to aircraft will be eliminated." [20]

The Times reported on the 18 June:

"In March* 1935, one or two men sat in an old lorry on a country road near Daventry, conducting some mysterious experiments...it has now become necessary to mobilise every source of reinforcement, for scientists and manufacturers are ahead of the provision of man power and woman power...the government are appealing to the whole Empire for recruits...the combined need of the three Services immediately is for about 10,000 men and women between the ages of 18 and 60 who have radio knowledge." [20]

(* Should be February, an error, with others made by an Air Ministry writer, which clearly shows that his copy was inadequately checked.)

Although it was now public knowledge as regards the defensive aspect of RDF it was made clear to all those in RDF that on no account was AI or GCI to be mentioned.

A Wing installation party had arrived in Stornoway on 3 July for the installations in Lewis and Harris timed to meet the arrival of the technical equipment, but as shipping was not immediately available it spent most of the month with little to do. Islivig and Brenish were among the most isolated stations in Great Britain, over 45 miles from Stornoway; roads had to be reinforced and bridges built to enable equipment to reach the sites. At the Eorodale CHL site the operations hut was shown to be placed in the middle of a road, apparently obscured by snow at the time of the survey, and was resited 100 yards. On Barra at Greian Head the CHL was guarded by the local Home Guard with Compton Mackenzie, the novelist of 'Whisky Galore!' film fame, the Commanding Officer. The proposed CH station at Ard-Rudla-Mor was abandoned in June after Works had advised that there would be an eight months hold-up due to the weather.

There was a major night raid on Hull on 17/18 July but that was the last one for the remainder of 1941; the German day and night raids had declined steadily month by month due to the transfer of the majority of the German Air Force to support the invasion of Russia on 22 June. Fighter Command, unaware that the German air attacks had reached their peak and, expecting day and night bombing on the scale of the 1940s, were pressing for production and installation priority of GCI over CHL.

The VEB was coming increasingly under criticism because of the large amount of Works services required. Seven groups of eight horizontal dipoles that were 20ft across had to be assembled on to one side of a 240ft tower each spaced by 25ft. Under the tower would be a large mechanical assembly to connect to each group of dipoles which in itself would be highly complicated to install. The advantages were no special siting or preliminary calibration required, a range of 175 miles and would not be overloaded by large numbers of aircraft.

By October there were two VEB groups at TRE; one that favoured the 1.5 metre array and the other who preferred to wait for the centimetric version with only a maximum range of 30 miles, and in its present form only able to deal with one aircraft at a time, to be further developed. The official TRE line was that metric VEB met the requirements of the CH station and the centimetric version should be used for the Army GL stations and GCI but Fighter Command favoured the existing GCI heightfinding as it was easier. As Ventnor had inadequate heightfinding facilities it had been selected for the prototype installation of the metric VEB.

The Army 10cm set at Lyddon Spout was giving vastly superior results on shipping than that obtained from the Dover CHL. The AOC-in-C of Fighter Command wrote to Signals on 30 August:

> "I have heard reports, that may be exaggerated, that it is possible to observe the movement of every ship in Boulogne Harbour, a distance of over 30 miles." [11]

Such was the accuracy of gun fire that by the end of September the passage of enemy ships through the Straits of Dover by day had been halted. Further demands had followed by the Army for 10cm sets along the south coast, at Fairlight, Newhaven and Beachy Head. Air Commodore V.H.Tait, head of the Directorate of Radio, that had replaced Signals 4, was concerned about security of the new wavelength and he advised Fighter Command:

> "...that the Type 271 [10cm] should be operated at infrequent intervals so as to preclude as far as possible evolving jamming methods for the enemy." [11]

The War Cabinet were now of the opinion that the threat of an invasion had receded not only from occupied France but also by a flanking attack through Eire. Contingency plans had been prepared by December 1940 for the latter possibility by the Air Staff with a completion date of March. The requirement was for range and heightfinding up to a distance of 100 to 200 miles seaward around the entire coast, which was translated into 14 CH, 14 CHL and 8 GCI stations. Planning was a 'one-off' in that the precise siting of the stations was from maps as it was not possible to enter Eire. As there would be no Observer Corps or time to organise telephone communications, which would be liable to sabotage, all plotting and non-operational calls would have to be provided by radio links. Mobile units would be the first to move in and two were shipped over to Northern Ireland in April and sited near the Eire border. By the end of the year it was considered that the threat had disappeared so the extra equipment and personnel, including 79 Wing, were disbanded and returned to the mainland.

The battle over CHL windscreens was continued by 60 Group, which ignored the RAE preference for continuous power turning. Not for the first time did they take advantage of the slow output of information from, and the firm belief in their own technical superiority to, RAE. On 26 November, 60 Group wrote to the Director of Radio that the windshield at Bempton that had been installed in the summer had proved extremely satisfactory during the recent gales:

".. the station has for several days this month been the only station in the N.E. of England which continued sweeping during the gales; in view of the success of this experimental shield the erection of a similar shield at Marks Castle is now in hand and, if successful, it is proposed for immediate adoption." [10]

Fighter Command were urging the replacement of some existing CHLs along the east coast of England as the warning provided was inadequate for the very low level sorties made by enemy aircraft on shipping and airfields. Towards the end of the year a prototype CHL on the top of a 185ft wooden tower had been installed at Humberston, south of Grimsby. The station went on the air for the first time at 0001 hours on 10 December and gave ranges of 32 miles at 500ft, 45 miles at 1,000ft, 60 miles at 2,000ft, 77 miles at 4,000ft and 110 miles at 19,000ft, but the 3 rpm turning speed of the aerial was considered too slow. 185ft timber towers were to be constructed alongside the existing Operations blocks at Bamburgh, Cresswell, Happisburgh, Hopton and Dunwich. To extend the low cover CHL aerials were also to be placed on the 200ft cantilever platform of one of the steel towers at West Beckham and Drone Hill CH stations.

The majority of the hand turned CHLs had been modified with PPI, CAW and the Hopkins turning gear in advance of the '1941' version to be placed some 100 yards from the existing station. The opportunity was taken to replace Shotton CHL with a '1941' version at Kinley Hill and Tannoch CHL with one at Ulbster. Twenty nine were scheduled to be built in the first six months of next year including the CDUs in Fair Isle and the Shetland Islands. At Sumburgh CDU an event took place that may have given good grounds for the move to the '1941' building at Compass Head, one mile north. The lighthouse foghorn, only seven yards away from the 'T' hut blew continuously, seven seconds in every 90 seconds, from 0515 on 25 August to 2035 on 27 August – one of the longest uninterrupted 'blows' in the lighthouse records.

The Air Ministry had begun to make arrangements for the expected arrival of over 1,000 CTC men at 14 day intervals and a holiday camp at Bridlington was requisitioned, but in July cables began to arrive from Washington giving numbers of the first party of the Corps leaving New York for the training centre at Montreal as between 15 and 25. By the end of the month the total number was expected to be 150 and it appeared unlikely that the total number of recruits would exceed 800. Faced with these drastic reductions in numbers, the Air Ministry changed the reception centre to a small hotel in Bournemouth. The volunteers shared space with servicemen on overcrowded vessels ranging from large troopships to cargo vessels on a voyage that generally lasted from nine to 15 days. The long zig-zag journey across the

Atlantic was a nightmare with seasickness, poor food, queues for everything, restricted washing facilities and bunks shared on a 24 hour basis. The wartime voyages were not without danger for 19 men were lost by enemy action on the way over. The existence of the Corps had been published in *The Times* dated 18 September:

> "Their status is purely civilian and they cannot be required to undertake combatant duties. They receive civilian rates of pay and agree to serve for three years or the period of the war, whichever is the less. They have a code of discipline of their own..." [14]

The first six CTC men arrived on 19 August with numbers increasing the following months. On 4 October Joubert addressed 45 Americans. He told them that a new invention called radiolocation covered nearly every field of war activity and was particularly applicable to anti-aircraft defence and could be applied to navigation of ships and aircraft. 11 men with radio experience in operating or repair were sent to Yatesbury on 27 August and 25 men to Cranwell on 28 October. At the schools the spartan wartime conditions and especially the military discipline, which they had not expected, came as a shock to men who were used to a much higher standard of living and to being treated with respect. The more flexible of the CTC men were able to adapt to the unexpected conditions without too much difficulty, but others were traumatised. The situation was made worse when America entered the war on 7 December and some of the men were unsettled by strong patriotic feelings. A trainee wrote in his diary that the promised free accommodation was a large barrack hut with 30 single bunks. These were 'instruments of torture', the mattress was three hard thin 'biscuits', a very hard pillow, no sheets and thick woollen blankets 'made smelly by no telling how many years of use by unbathed airmen'.

During the winter the hut was so cold that the wearing of greatcoats was the only way of keeping warm. Another complaint was that they were treated as the lowest rank of airmen, whose food was terrible – no eggs, bacon or milk for breakfast. Getting meals often required standing for an extended period in freezing drizzle or snow. At the NAAFI and other canteens there were also long queues waiting to get something decent to eat. Some men had unpleasant encounters with RAF officers, who demanded that they be shown proper military respect, not knowing or perhaps not accepting that CTC members were civilians. The reason was the uniform issued in Montreal, which was standard RAF 'blue', but with black buttons instead of brass, a CTC cap insignia and a 'USA' shoulder flash. Surely nothing could be more calculated to cause confusion and irritation to an officer than the appearance of two men both wearing what looked at first glance to be identical uniforms; only the RAF man had to salute an officer and call him 'Sir'. In such situations, many of the men complied to avoid unpleasant trouble.

Coupled with the miserable climate, it is no surprise that many of the men found little incentive to buckle down and prepare for the tough technical trade tests. Some, already technically competent, became demoralised and failed the exams, which led to their return to Bournemouth and the long, dangerous return home. The failure of the Air Ministry to adequately advise those in charge of discipline of the non-combatant nature of the men before their arrival, and to ensure that it was enforced, soured the relationship with the British military and sowed the seeds of discontent that followed.

By the end of 1941 twenty nine GCI stations were in operation with five more sited. The majority were at the Intermediate stage with a power turned aerial on a wooden gantry that extended the range at 5,000ft from 35 to 55 miles. The chief disadvantage of the existing GCIs was that only one interception at a time could be controlled, at the rate of a maximum of four an hour. The Final GCI would allow a maximum of four interceptions each by two controllers at any one time with more reliable heightfinding at a longer range. Durrington was to be the experimental station with Sopley the production prototype; a total of 31 stations were to be upgraded by a new installation nearby.

A high level policy decision had been made that was to add to the ever increasing work load on 60 Group; at the request of the War Office and the Admiralty all CHL type stations were transferred to the Air Ministry for maintenance. Three reasons were put forward: (1) the admission that the RAF had been more successful in handling RDF, (2) the desire to avoid overlapping, and (3) difficulty in obtaining trained personnel. Additionally to assist ADRDE with the installation of a combined 10cm chain, known as Chain Home Extra Low (CHEL). The first station to be fitted was Ventnor with a 10cm set modified for CAW and a PPI; it gave impressive results with a range of 30 miles at heights between 50 and 200ft.

The Western Isles CH and CHL chains were plotting to the Inverness Filter Room via the Stornoway teleprinter link and the Carsaig CHL direct to the Port Mor ACH in Tiree by W/T. The West Chain stations at West Prawle, Branscombe, Drytree, Hayscastle Cross, Bride, Scarlett, Trerew, Nevin and North Cairn were now on Final with plotting ranges exceeding 170 miles, and most of the East Chain with a Buried Reserve. The slowness of calibration had earlier in the year received a typical Watson Watt broadside complaining of the use of low grade labour, the slackness and irresponsibility of some parties, the ever recurring unserviceability of aircraft and lack of supervision by Wings and 60 Group. They, in turn, blamed the calibration trouble on the design of the aerial systems, but by the end of the year the only delays being caused were those by bad weather and enemy action.

Post Office termination equipment on Air Ministry stations was maintained by staff from the nearest telephone exchange but, as the Electric Calculator was of such complexity, engineers from the Post Office were 'recruited', placed in an RAF uniform and sent to a CH station as a Calculator Maintenance Engineer. Wiring changes as a result of calibration flights sometimes involved the attendance of a scientific officer from TRE. At one station, a Mr C.E.Minnis, one of the earliest scientific officers at BRS, was making performance checks accompanied by a Mr S.H.Sheppard, who had been involved with the development of the calculator at the Post Office Circuit Laboratory, when a visiting VIP asked for a description of its functions. Mr Sheppard prefaced his explanation by asking 'Can I assume that you are aware of the principles of radiolocation?' The reply, 'Yes, you may assume that.' was spoken in a soft Scottish accent. When the VIP had left the building Minnis told him that he had been speaking to Robert Watson Watt.

REFERENCES

1	AIR20/1536	2	AIR20/4277	3	AIR20/2897	4	AIR16/879
5	AIR2/7168	6	AIR16/879	7	AIR2/7734	8	AIR2/4489
9	AIR20/1521	10	AIR26/127	11	AVIA7/318	12	AIR2/7545
13	AIR2/7151	14	AIR19/262	15	AIR33/2	16	AIR2/5336
17	AIR26/103	18	AIR8/589	19	AIR20/4222	20	AIR2/5294

THE RDF BULLETIN

The date of the first issue of the 'R.D.F Bulletin' was April 1941. Published monthly by 60 Group, it was a semi – official 'House Magazine' that was prepared by scientific officers mainly in the Filter Rooms and circulated to all RDF stations. The aim was to publicise the operational activities of all the chains so that the stations would feel that they were not isolated but part of a very compact group. Stations were now made aware of the new stations being added to the chains, those which had reported the longest single tracks, the maximum ranges achieved and any unusual plots of friendlies or foes.
(ALL EXTRACTS ARE BY COURTESY OF THE TRUSTEES OF THE RAF MUSEUM, HENDON.)

On 'Friendlies' plots, HILLHEAD set up a record for an MB1A, a total of 172 miles, NETHERBUTTON scored well at 146 miles, SOUTH RONALDSAY at 116 miles and SKAW at 106 miles. The best hard luck story comes from DUNNET HEAD who picked up a Coastal at 91 miles and plotted it out to 135 miles. Hopes of breaking S.RONALDSAY's best of 140 miles were running high when the aircraft turned back. It is understood that the language at DUNNET HEAD on this unfortunate termination to their chase reached the high standard set by Naval tradition. 9 Group tells us of enemy aircraft sneaking up inside the Eire coastline, on April 14th Raid 137 at 1220 hours was plotted from Wexford on a northerly course approximately parallel to and 30 miles inside the Eire coastline. The flight of Rudolph Hess identified as Hostile 42 at 15,000 ft was well tracked, DANBY BEACON picking it up at 96 miles, OTTERCOPS at 96 miles and DOUGLAS WOOD at 123 miles. From the north, NETHERBUTTON plotted 2 raids for some 250 miles, certain CHL stations such as DEERNESS plotted tracks 140 miles east ,DUNNETT HEAD 136 miles and many others plot regularly over 100 miles. The most noteworthy performance on 'friendlies' was a Wellington bomber that was off course plotted as X251 for a distance of 280 miles from the east of the Shetlands to the southern coast of the Moray Firth and thence inland for a further 40 miles over the Highlands. The track was of material assistance in vectoring the aircraft safely back to its base. Excellent ranges are now reported from the CHLs at PRESTATYN of 145 miles, CREGNEISH of 115 miles and GLENARM 194 miles since modification to Common Aerial Working and PPIs. In August at STENIGOT a Blenheim bomber flew between two of the steel towers at 200ft during thick fog. Full marks for aircraft recognition go to the Hurricane pilot who shot at one of our autogyros on calibration. Bright remark came from a Very High officer visiting the Filter Room. 'What time does this place close ?' he asked kindly.

Chapter 11   1942

ON 1 January 1942 Watson Watt became Sir Robert Watson-Watt in the King's New Year's Honours List and he changed his name slightly by adding a hyphen between the two family names. In Scotland it is commonplace, irrespective of class, for children to be given the mother's and father's surnames. Usually the mother's name is restricted to an initial but, if both names are used, they are not hyphenated; when knighted, Watson-Watt adopted the English middle class tradition of hyphenation.

There was another change of name at the same time that affected many hundreds of RAF and WAAF because of the secrecy that surrounded RDF; the word 'radio'. When applied to grade descriptions in the RAF such as radio mechanic and radio operator it signified RDF, but the Canadian and American military were interpreting the words 'radio' and 'wireless' as identical in meaning, ie, the transmission and reception of messages by electromagnetic waves without connecting wires. The CAS authorised the name change of all grades from Radio to RDF.

The early part of the year saw completion of most of the CH and CHL chain installations around the west coast of Scotland and the Outer Hebrides but not the filter rooms. Without a telephone line plotting was by W/T, which was regarded as a security risk if not encoded. A method was in force using a fictitious grid that required transposing the information at both ends of the communication link, which was both cumbersome and time consuming. The CHLs were of the Final type with a 150 mile range and CHs with a range in excess of 200 miles; at that distance the Kilkenneth CH station on Tiree was tracking Liberator aircraft from America. One of the frequent plots was the 'Atlantic Special', an enemy met. plane that flew daily from east to west through the Fair Isle channel between Orkney and Scotland. The Filter Room at Lerwick was at ground level and the first reported sightings of enemy aircraft were often obtained by the simple expedient of looking out of the window.

By March there were 25 East Chain CH stations calibrated but four not completed to the Final stage and only nine out of the 20 CH stations on the West Chain on Final. Netherbutton had also during 1941 reached the Final stage with four Lines of Shoot with ranges in excess of 180 miles, but the buried reserves had a measure of success of a different kind; there was five feet of water in the R block and the T block was also waterlogged. At Scarlett Point, a CH station on the Isle of Man, the transfer to the Final stage was marked by severe receiver interference which was eventually traced to the 33rd floor of the State building in Albany, New York, USA. At Ventnor ranges of 230 miles were being obtained.

A frequently postponed project was the placing of a CHL aerial array on the 200ft cantilever of one of the 350ft transmitting towers at West Beckham and Drone Hill CH stations. The Humberston CHL was approved in January but the installation of the wooden 185ft towers at the other five stations was delayed by priority for the GEE ground installations. There were also objections by the Aerodromes Board to their use on the grounds that they would constitute a hazard to aircraft using local airfields, so an appeal was made in February by the Director of RDF to the DCAS:

> "Along two stretches of the coast from Northumberland to East Anglia the height of the coastline is only of the order of 50ft, which means that using C.H.L. only at present to detect low flying aircraft, it can provide with its existing aerial system on a 20ft gantry a mere 20 miles warning at 200ft. On very low flying aircraft and on surface craft no useful warning whatsoever is obtainable. The increasing number of enemy attacks on the east coast convoys and aerodromes is due to this lack of C.H.L. warnings. Considering the moderate height and the stations few in number, I feel that the operational aspects outweigh the gravity of the flying obstruction aspect." [1]

He concurred but it was not until August that 60 Group began installation.

In the few official photographs that were taken of CHL sites the one of Hopton is the most likely to have been seen, which has been assumed by some researchers that all CHLs around the coast were on 185ft wooden towers, but this was not the case. The lateness in the completion of these tower CHLs made them obsolescent even before they became operational as Fighter Command were patiently waiting for the introduction of 10cm sets. The experimental one at Ventnor was producing consistently fine results; on 23 May 20 aircraft were detected flying 50ft at a range of 34 miles, that were identified one minute later as hostile.

The one great success of the German jamming organisation was on 12 February when the German battlecruisers *Scharnhorst* and *Gneisenau* with the *Prinz Eugen* were able to escape from Brest in occupied northern France to Germany. Daringly, the ships departed at night and travelled through the English Channel in daylight as it was thought that the British would consider such an audacious move unlikely. Jamming was to ensure that the CH and

CHL coastal stations would be unable to plot the course of the ships and their air cover; Dover CH was singled out for extra attention. The first plots of the day came from Beachy Head at 0824 when hostile aircraft were plotted off the French coast seemingly not moving but circling; the significance was not recognised as they had been observed for several days, a specific manoeuvre by the Germans to fool the plotters that they were air exercises. By 0930 the overall jamming became noticeably more severe and by 1030 the Dover CHL and the Army GLs were completely blotted out, as was Newchurch CH station, which had a specific transmitter allocated. Other stations from Foreness to Beachy Head could not plot along the French coast to within 15 miles of Cap Gris Nez.

Ironically, the performance of the 10cm sets, which were unaffected by the jamming, was let down by other factors. Ventnor was out of action that very morning due to a fire outbreak the night before. Fairlight, east of Hastings, obtained the first definite detection of the ships at 1050, but there was no direct line to the Dover Naval Plotting Room or the Coastal Artillery Operations Room, so the message was delayed until 1131. The Army set at Lydden Spout (Dover) was next to provide plots from 1130 to 1245 followed by the set at Fan Hole (St Margaret's Bay), but by this time the ships were out of gun range and in the North Sea, surviving a determined attack by the RAF and the Navy but damaged by mines before they reached Germany.

There were urgently arranged meetings to discuss the involvement of various stations and, in particular, one that was convened on 23 February to discuss the jamming, which had begun at a very intermittent level and then had gradually increased in intensity until it ceased at 1930. Affecting CH, CHL and GL but not 50cm or 10cm, the assumption was made that these wavelengths had not yet been detected. The conclusions drawn by meeting were:

"That the enemy had clearly shown that it is possible to deny to us all our R.D.F. and V.H.F. communications over an area south of Severn to the Wash, without an excessive expenditure of effort and yet retain all his own facilities...[The] enemy is now geared to using jamming operationally and an enemy R.D.F. countermeasures organisation must now exist and would no doubt be developed. There is as yet no such R.D.F. countermeasures organisation here and it is possible that the weight and extent of a properly organised attack on this country had been underestimated. Investigations have shown that the amount of effort required by enemy to produce an 80% wipe-out of our R.D.F. and V.H.F. frequencies... and to maintain attack over 14 days would be no means excessive... as all four C.H. wavelengths could be jammed by 1Kw transmitters on the French and Belgian coasts." [2]

The 'escape' was a severe blow to British pride as masters of the English Channel so an enquiry was ordered by the government, conducted by Lord

Justice Buckhill. When the report was ready, a copy was requested by General H.H.A. Arnold, Commanding General of the U.S. Army Air Forces, to which the Air Ministry and the Admiralty agreed. A copy was dispatched on 30 March in the Diplomatic Bag, with a covering note from the CAS, Portal:

> "I am sure that you will not take it amiss if I emphasise the extremely confidential nature of this document. The Prime Minister has refused to table a copy for the information of the House of Commons, and there would be a great deal of criticism if it were discovered that one had been given to you. I would therefore ask you to restrict the circulation to one or two of the most senior Army Air Corps officers, and to ensure that no quotations from it are allowed to appear either in official or unofficial papers and that no part of it to be copied." [3]

On 5 May the Air Staff were treated to a showing of an eight minute film of the breakout, a copy of a German UFA newsreel.

TRE had evolved a 50cm CHL with a range of 60 miles from experimental work in 1940. In the interval higher power transmitting valves had been developed for the Admiralty, together with improved receiver techniques, to make an alternative replacement for the 1.5 metre CHL, plus the fact that TRE knew that it was one of the enemy wavelengths and hence would be less likely to be jammed. By April there were three 50cm mobiles under construction at TRE for installation at Fairlight, North Foreland and Beachy Head to act as standby for the 1.5 metre CHL, with a second batch of three required as soon as possible.

There were very strict rules in force to ensure that the enemy remained unaware of their existence: the aerials had to be pointed north during testing, maintenance was limited to ten minutes a day with radiation restricted to short bursts. An order from the filter room had to be received before they could be switched on and the 1.5 metre CHL had to remain on during the period of jamming. By July there was a 50cm CHL at Dover and a mobile one at Ventnor but, due to extreme urgency, it had not been possible for security reasons to test their performances either at TRE or on site. One day it was found that contrary to instructions, the 50cm CHL at Dover had been in operation for 1½ hours due to an error by the filter room; this lapse resulted in an order being made that 50cm CHLs 'must not be operated without the personal permission of the AOC-in-C or his Deputy.' It was also discovered that a Works instruction leaflet had been distributed showing the wavelength so all copies were withdrawn.

The existence of two CHLs, and possibly more, with different wavelengths was eventually solved by the introduction of a Type numbering system, the 1.5 metre CHL became Type 2 and the 50cm CHL Type 11. It was not at first a popular change, one person commenting 'that he could not remember what Type 2 was but could always remember what CHL did'.

By early 1942 Bomber Command were beginning to send larger and larger numbers of aircraft on night-time operations and the need for accurate navigation for precision bombing and to prevent collisions in the air became imperative. During 1940 the question of such bombing accuracy had arisen and Watson-Watt had remembered that a young scientific officer, R.J.Dippy, had submitted in late 1937 a proposal for a hyperbolic grid pattern using pulse techniques as a fighter beacon system, which had been 'put on ice' because of the demands of the CH chain. He suggested to Dippy that he should resubmit his scheme, with the additional advantage of target finding by grid reference, as an aid to Bomber Command.

During September 1940 in the greatest secrecy (MOST SECRET), TRE were conducting flight trials with a single receiver and two ground stations, one at Worth and the other at Christchurch which developed into the GEE (G for grid) system and into a series of chains both fixed and mobile. Although not strictly a radar device it made use of pulsed transmitters with a cathode ray tube presentation in the aircraft and was another instrument to be fitted into many hundreds of aircraft and maintained by RDF mechanics. It was also an additional workload for 60 Group and Wings to find sites and install transmitters which was the ubiquitous MetroVick MB2 on a 6.15 metre wavelength.

GEE was used for the first time on March 8/9 when 350 night bombers raided the Ruhr followed by raids on 9/10 and 11/12 March when Essen was the main target. Without GEE, the 1,000 bomber raid on Cologne on the night of 30/31 May could not have been attempted. GEE is mentioned here because of the urgent need for 350ft steel towers; two were taken down from Schoolhill and Douglas Wood and replaced with 325ft guyed masts. Towers were also dismantled without replacement from Ottercops Moss and Worth Matravers. Such was the top secrecy of GEE, that even when sharing a common site with CH, the working groups of operators and mechanics remained apart and at all times were forbidden to discuss technical and operational matters.

From the beginning of the war the filter rooms had provided plots for outgoing RAF bombing missions, with a constant watch for any enemy fighters coming out to intercept them and, with the advent of the thousand bomber raids, the effect on the CH tube presentation was reported simply as 'dripping with echoes'. The returning bomber plots were, however, far more scattered and a special watch was kept for aircraft returning by unexpected routes or returning late due to loss of speed or in distress. The enemy had taken advantage of the returning bomber 'streams' by flying in their own aircraft, which often escaped detection until they were over the home airfield, then revealing themselves by bombing and firing machine guns. But identification was difficult when the enemy tracks and heights were the same as the friendly bombers, many of whose crews did not use IFF on the return home and when they did it was often impossible to relate the response to a specific aircraft during mass raids.

IFF was now at the Mark 3 stage with a separate specific allocated wavelength and a slightly changed name, 'Interrogate Friend or Foe'. The IFF return could now be seen on all types of RDF ground systems irrespective of their operating wavelength plus the advantage that the operator could de-select the transmitter-interrogator if the display became cluttered with returns caused by aircraft IFF sets not being switched off when requested.

Although the might of the German Air Force was on the Russian front, the experts' opinion were that there still remained some 500 enemy aircraft capable of making a sudden attack in the West. The year had opened with sporadic night raids plus a new form of day attack in the form of 'tip and run' raids by single or several fighters or fighter-bombers mainly on coastal towns. The tactics adopted, however, were much more effective and accurate with the avoidance of RDF by approaching the coast at a very low level. The Shetland Islands, Sunderland, Belfast and Dover all experienced reconnaissance, machine-gunning or the dispatch of a few bombs.

From April night attacks began to increase in intensity, in what became known as 'Baedeker' raids, a reference to the name of the pre-war German guide book on the United Kingdom, which was outstanding for its reference to cathedrals and other cultural places. Cities of no military significance that were without adequate defence such as Exeter, Bath, Norwich, York, Canterbury and others were each being subject to an onslaught of bombs of exceptional weight and a great number of incendiaries causing immense damage and loss of life. These raids ended in June but the daylight 'tip and run' tactics continued mainly on the south of England coastal towns.

At Under-Secretary level in the Air Ministry the fate of the Civilian Technical Corps was being considered as a report suggested that it could not continue as it was not giving good value and should be disbanded. Seven months of recruitment had cost £341,500 and had been suspended in February. The RAF reception centre at Bournemouth was administered by a wing commander but the Americans were under the control of a commandant, also an American, Mr D.L.Gill, who had previously worked with the Red Cross. In his report dated 30 June he detailed the causes of the problems, the major one being the variable standard of enlistment in the USA that had permitted a noticeable number of men with low intelligence –in Gill's words 'chronic drunks, half wits and heels'– those chronically unhealthy and men with an inadequate trade knowledge, to enlist. Secondly, CTC volunteers had expected living standards would be reasonable and were assured of their exclusion from military duties and discipline. They got neither. Conflict in the RAF was unavoidable between officers and the men who were wearing uniforms almost indistinguishable from other ranks. Unable to place the men on 'charges' for the more serious breaches of anti-social behaviour, commanding officers were forced to go to the local courts to maintain discipline. By July 264 men had been repatriated for various reasons back to the USA from a total of just 900.

Due to a change in the manning requirements there was not enough work available for the non-technical grades that formed the majority of the CTC. Numbers of them who had been considered unsuitable for the RAF, Army or the Navy were at Bournemouth awaiting a decision on civilian employment. The Air Staff had attempted to transfer all the CTC members by asking the Secretary of State to write to the Minister of Labour, Ernest Bevin:

"When the Corps was first formed we were very short of skilled technicians, but our need is less now and it is proving embarrassing to have associated with the R.A.F., a civilian corps of American origin who amongst other things are not liable to combatant duty in respect of aerodrome defence and so a transfer to industry is requested." [4]

Bevin's reply was short and to the point:

"I fear not a practical course, as the many principles employed by the CTC would cause serious trouble in Industry." [4]

But the Air Ministry was not keen to let the best men go and it was thought that some 500 would stay on for the duration of the war and there was no reason to expect serious trouble from those who remained. Towards the end of the year the American Embassy agreed that members of the CTC could volunteer to be transferred to the Lockheed Overseas Corporation, whose personnel were being transferred to the US Army. For the signing of 150 completion certificates the Secretary of State was asked if he would be prepared to sign the certificates in the original, which would add immensely to their value; he agreed, provided there were not more than 15 a day.

(In February 1944 proposals were put forward to an Assistant Under Secretary for Mr D.L.Gill to receive the Order of the British Empire (OBE) and for a CTC man, Mr W.H. Manning, to receive the British Empire Medal

(BEM). In recommending the proposal, he added:

> 'Although the Civilian Technical Corps was not the success we hoped it would be, owing to indiscriminate enrolment in the United States and partly due to the entry of the United States into the war, the 140 members or so who remain in the Corps have done good work and have lived down the undesirable reputation which at one time seemed likely to attach to the Corps.') [5]

The successful night raid on the French coast near Bruneval on 27/28 February to remove the vital components of a Würzburg 62A system, prompted a suggestion that a similar type of retaliatory exercise might be undertaken by the enemy, the object being TRE at Swanage. The security worried Rowe since there was virtually none; between 7pm and 9am there was no one on duty, and in the event of a sudden attack by parachutists how could they cope with the destruction of over 2,000 files and documents? Who was going to destroy the secret equipment which would then make it impossible for TRE to continue. What arrangements could be made for the evacuation of the 364 members of TRE, over 500 including families, at a moment's notice?

Churchill had decided that TRE must move, its capture even for a short time could not even be contemplated and a suitable place was eventually found at the College for Boys at Malvern in Worcestershire. In early May the building adaptation was nearing completion, the MAP supplying over 1,000 packing cases and contracting Pickfords to arrange the transfer. In deciding the date, Rowe said:

> "The personnel are quite willing to put up with an inconvenience as a temporary measure...they would be prepared to sleep on a clothes line for a month." [6]

On 26 May the move to Malvern took place to the astonishment of the civilian population at Swanage - 'they were there one day and gone the next'. There was one very important part of Swanage that went to Malvern, the name TRE. An attempt had been made to alter it but the idea was firmly overruled by Rowe who said that the initials were too well known to be changed. He was certainly right about the latter as the following humorous extract from an RDF Bulletin informs:

> "There has to be a place for all the original ideas to start from and this is T.R.E. (They're Really Erudite). It started at Bawdsey, moved off north when the supply of beer fell off at Felixstowe, swung south to Swanage after the attempted invasion of Scotland and then moved off to Malvern after the dreadful result of a quarterly overhaul at Worth Matravers. Lots of people at T.R.E. are inventors who walk about with sinister packages under their arms and a wild gleam in their eyes. Now and then one of these inventors is let loose on the chain which is (a) near the sea, (b) near a good pub or (c) a long way from 60 Group. Boffins-some unkind people say these have a connection with T.R.E. but this is totally untrue.

Boffins are the radar form of gremlin. The usual disguise is a long beard and a pair of corduroy trousers. Their secret weapon is a special form of soldering iron for making dry joints. This is used in conjunction with chewing gum and string."

ADRDE at Christchurch was also in a similar position to the possibility of an enemy ground foray and was transferred to the nearby Malvern area, with the opportunity taken to omit the tenuous link to air defence – now re-named the Radar Research and Development Establishment (RRDE).

The War Office had complained of a severe shortage of radio mechanics as too many young men had volunteered for the RAF, so a decision was made on 17 April to transfer 2,000 from the RAF to the Army. In an action that would cause widespread grief, 1,000 men, who were undergoing ab-initio training at technical colleges, would be told at the end of their courses that they were to be posted to Army units. A further 500 were anticipated from a near future intake, plus a further 500 from those who had yet to volunteer.

Arising from the possibility of an invasion attempt by Germany in 1941, some moves had been made to combine the activities of the three Services to form a common watching coastal chain, but with little success. Not until it was shown that a single CHL station could provide two PPI displays, one for the RAF and one for the Army or the Navy with their own plotting lines, did the Triple Service Watch Stations, as they were called, begin to be assembled. With the agreement last year for the Air Ministry to take over all the CD and CDU maintenance, it was a short and corresponding step for these stations to form part of the original CHL chain, so from the Army CD chain of over 60 stations, which was far from complete, 12 were chosen.

New names began to appear for the Wing mechanics to visit; Bard Hill (North Norfolk), The Needles and Boniface Down (Isle of Wight), Goldsborough (near Whitby), Crannoch Hill (Elgin), The Law (Carnoustie, Angus), Westburn (Aberdeen), Bolt Tail (Salcombe), Jacka (near Falmouth), Oxwich Bay (Gower Peninsula), Marsden (South Shields), Blackhead (Co. Antrim) and Westcliff (Portland) with more to follow in the future. All would be upgraded to continuous turning with other modifications and form part of the reporting chain or made redundant. The CD building differed from CHL in that there was no wooden tower for the aerial as the Army had favoured placing it on the roof.

There was 'tweaking' of the CH chain. The Director of RDF had approved an increase of the CH transmitter output to 750kW with the design, production and erection of a suitable aerial, known as the Megawatt array, contracted out to Marconi. June had seen the remainder of the West Chain transferred to Final, and also at Skaw, after 26 months of continuous effort.

On Tiree the CHB at Barrapol was now operational and the transfer from the ACH at Port Mor to the Final station at Kilkenneth had only been completed by moving the two transmitters a distance of 1½ miles, which took ten hours. The Westburn and The Law CD stations after upgrading to CHL were producing plots off the plotting table, 163 and 178 miles respectively. The Admiralty had asked for a longer detection range in the Orkney Islands and Whale Head was chosen to take the 1 Megawatt amplifier from Bawdsey, which was unused and required an overhaul before it could be moved. A signal was sent in July from DCD to RAE to do the work but they found it impossible to nominate an officer and suggested TRE. There was little enthusiasm there but on 1 September, 60 Group agreed to undertake the work and on 5 November they requested the services of Mr D.H. Preist, who was the designer, from TRE for a few days to line up the transmitter, but that proposal had to be abandoned due to pressure of work. The task fell on 70 Wing.

The Germans continued to use their massive jamming power that had been set up along the French, Belgian and Dutch coasts. During their bombing raids the CHL stations from Hopton to Ringstead suffered greatly from 'railings' jamming as some of the cathode ray tubes were not yet of the long persistence type and were blotted out when the aerials were looking across to the Calais/Boulogne area. The jamming continued during the year, heavy on some occasions and only ceased in November when the wintry weather brought a sharp reduction in the number of raids.

The British countermeasure was the development of 'Window' by TRE, the code name given to thin metallised strips of paper which, when dropped in front of RDF stations, caused multiple reflections on the tube displays that made accurate plotting difficult and sometimes impossible. Although the concept of 'Window' was a elementary physical fact, the reflective effect of a dipole cut to the required frequency, much work was required to decide on the minimum amount to be dropped. The policy on when it was to be used was far from easy or agreeable. Sholto Douglas of Fighter Command wrote to the CAS on 15 July:

> "I beg you to abandon the idea [of dropping Window]...against the enemy as I feel that the repercussions which we might suffer will completely nullify all the work that has been put into the complicated machine which had brought night interception to the peak of efficiency which exists today." [7]

Bomber Command was obviously wanting and waiting to use it as soon as possible to reduce losses on its bombing operations so the final decision was placed with Churchill and not given in its favour until July 1943. Such was the great concern that the existence of 'Window' should not be compromised after tests on the effect of it on the GCI at Neatishead, that all the correspondence, records and results were destroyed by fire.

Development on the magnetron had continued slowly; the original output power of 7kW had reached a maximum of 70kW but above that the magnetron suffered from 'frequency jumping' which prevented further increases. There was a general opinion that the maximum output power had been reached and as this was the limiting factor in the range of any radar set, it was considered by TRE that 50cm was the ultimate lowest wavelength that could be used for long range location. The problem was referred back to Birmingham University by the Admiralty with no specific time scale for the solution, perhaps in years rather than months, but during September 1941 the university conveyed the news of a 'startling development' in magnetron design. By the strapping together of alternate cavities, as a result of suggestions made by Professor J. Sayers and Dr H.A.H. Boot, the efficiency of the existing magnetron was instantly raised from just over 10 per cent to nearly 50 per cent, which allowed an output power of 350kW to be immediately realised on existing set designs.

This was one of the factors that led to the abandonment of the 1.5 metre VEB. The main one was the appearance of serious design faults appearing on the Ventnor prototype caused by permanent echoes appearing not only from 0 to 4 degrees but also in a second band 9½ degrees to 13½ degrees at right angles to the Line of Shoot: a large proportion of the available coverage was not available for the detection of aircraft, a disadvantage that was not immediately recognised. TRE would not admit defeat; a very original and remarkable idea was suggested that by using a delay line to cancel out the permanent echoes, only moving targets would be seen on the tube display. But the complexity of the dipole turning mechanics and the need for a wooden tower were also compelling reasons to favour a 10cm version.

Recognising that even higher pulse powers would be available in the near future, it was clear to TRE that the 10cm wavelength, which produced very sharp horizontal and vertical beams, was the answer to heightfinding and plan position from 30,000ft down to almost zero feet without gap filling. The earliest 10cm sets for the RAF were mobile, the Type 13 Mark 1 or CMH (centimetric height finder); a remote hand turned aerial system consisting of two 6ft 8in paraboloids that could be swung in elevation from -5 to 95 degrees and rotated 360 degrees in elevation, the equipment contained in a GL cabin some 100 yards distant together with the CRT displays. Height accuracy using 'split' was 0.2 of a degree at a range of 40 miles.

Experience, however, was to show that it was very exacting to use operationally and indicated the necessity for a completely new format for the Mark 2. The CMHs were found, nevertheless, to be excellent in the location of very low flying aircraft and, surprisingly, for technical equipment, two appeared as 'Susie' and 'Mary' in Operations Record Books (ORBs). It is highly likely that the WAAF was responsible as they were always a civilising influence on the laddish RAF.

The War Office had decided that there was no need to undertake a complete redesign of the Admiralty T271; all that was required was the assembly of the units into something simple that was completely self-contained and suitable for easy and rapid installation both at home and overseas. ADRDE produced a 'transportable' known as the 'Gibson Box', which was a large furniture removal van, that in transit contained all the components including spares and the aerial, now a single 7ft paraboloid for transmission and reception; on site it was fixed on the outside and the van, which was hand turned, became the plotting office.

During September one was installed at the Rosehearty CHL station and, initially, operated by the Royal Artillery with the plotting line to the Naval Filter Room in Aberdeen. Many hundreds of these 'boxes' were made eventually replacing the existing earlier 'crash' double aerial models; they were capable of easy conversion to the higher power magnetron and power turning and became one of the Army's most successful group of sets.

They appeared on Army CD or RAF CHL sites from Breckness in the Orkney Islands, around the coasts of Scotland, England and Wales to Eorodale on the Isle of Lewis in the Outer Hebrides. At many permanent sites appeared the universal Nissen hut, a wartime expedient that avoided the delay in providing brick and concrete buildings, and across which was a wooden gantry to support the aerial. Where the need arose to obtain a greater range, the set with the operators was placed on the top of a 200ft steel tower and here the Army were considerate as a lift was provided. The RAF adopted a different approach in that the sets were installed on existing wooden towers and at Bawdsey on one of the steel towers' 200ft cantilevers.

The Admiralty 10cm coverage had taken place at the same time that the original CDUs were updated to CHL. At Compass Head, Fair Isle and Dunnet Head, the medium power 10cm set, the NT273, was installed in the CHL '1941' building with the aerial and its Perspex cover on the roof and the equipment below. At Saxavord and South Ronaldsay the 10cm set was installed in the CHL T hut made vacant by the introduction of Common Aerial Working.

GCI installations had continued throughout the year to a maximum of 39. There were additional mobiles at Cricklade near Cheltenham, replacing

Avebury, Trimley Heath at Felixstowe, for Waldringfield, Patrington for Hampton Hill, Seaton Snook near Hartlepool, Long Load, in Somerset, Hope Cove near Salcombe, Devon, St Annes near Blackpool, Staythorpe near Newark-on-Trent and Roecliffe near Ripon. There were emergency mobiles at Allen's Hill near Gravesend, Doctor's Corner near Kenley, in Surrey, Knight's Farm at Burghfield, Reading and at Aberleri, near Aberystwyth in Cardigan Bay. None yet had transferred operations to the Final form, the Type 7, which had been developed from the comparatively simple prototype that appeared at Durrington in October 1940, into an elaborate continuously rotating aerial with an underground chamber immediately below for the turning and electronic equipment. A short distance away was the technical and operations building, which was 140ft long, 40ft wide and 16ft high.

Thirty one stations were earmarked for conversion by the end of the year but there were many difficulties, mainly mechanical, and Renwick had called in Mertz and McLellan, and Grubb Parsons who were civil consulting engineers. To add to the delay, the Mark 5 receiver was not approved until September and some components were not available because of higher priorities elsewhere. Thirteen stations were promised for 1 November but the number fell to six, then two by the end of the year. At a meeting in December, there was agreement that the programme was beyond the resources that could be devoted to it and, coupled with the expectation that it was unlikely that there would be any more large scale night raids in the immediate future, the number was reduced to 21. Five of the existing 39 stations, Balldonaghy, Lisnaskea, Dunragit, King Garth and Foulness would be placed on Care and Maintenance, with 13 to remain at the Intermediate or Mobile stage.

October and November saw the remaining buried reserves for the east chain in operation. Along the south coast a CH station had been built at Hengistbury Head, Southbourne, Bournemouth to replace Worth Matravers but a remote reserve site could not be found on the mainland. Surprisingly, it was built at St. Lawrence, on the Isle of Wight and as the site was only 50ft above sea level it was permanently manned to provide height for Ventnor, a few miles east.

The growing reduction in the attentions of the German Air Force was immediately recognised by the lack of activity in the filter rooms. The first casualties were in the Inner Hebrides with the closure of the CHB and CH stations on Tiree that had been in service for only a few months and the dismantling of the Carsaig CHL on the Isle of Skye. These stations would be joined by many others to ensure that men and equipment would be available for the overseas theatres of war. A policy was in force that replaced the men with women, indeed, some CHL stations were already commanded by a WAAF officer. Although only in the post for 14 days, the Formby CHL was commanded by an American Army Signal Corps Officer, 2nd Lieutenant H.B. Wood and a 2nd Lieutenant Pittman took over the command of High Street.

The operational history of the Royal Air Force is contained in monthly summaries in the Operations Record Books of commands, groups, wings, squadrons, stations and miscellaneous units. Because of secrecy, the parent stations were not allowed to mention the existence of the AMES stations that had diaries and log books for recording the day by day events. When 60 Group was formed in February 1940, ORBs were opened for the maintenance sections, but due to an almost complete absence of effort there are no references to the operations of any RDF stations until early 1941, a very serious omission. The accuracy and content of the entries are very elastic and are completely dependent on the attitude of the commanding officer. The first example is a mini sermon from 71 Wing:

> "The 'students' stoop' brought about by much poring over cathode ray tubes
> and plotting tables has been counteracted by open air daily parades, refreshers
> in march discipline, saluting and, for the R.A.F., arms drill. Backs are
> straightened and complexions are more appealing in natural freshness as a
> result." [8]

The second example is much more interesting as 77 Wing recorded an unfulfilled dream of a posting for many RAF radio mechanics at the naval T273 station at Gwespyr, near Prestatyn, which had recently opened:

> "The personnel, including the O.C. are W.R.N.S. Ratings with the exception
> of one male radio mechanic, who it is understood will be replaced with W.R.N.S.
> Mechanics in the near future. The station will then be manned entirely by
> women, an experiment that will be watched with interest." [9]

The Wing record failed to record what it was that would be watched with interest. Was the chauvinist RAF expecting the station to fall apart after a few weeks?

The introduction of the electric calculator had shown the possibility of the automatic transmission of plots using a teleprinter circuit, so the Post Office was given the task of developing the system which was known as the Message Recorder. Only the East Chain was fitted during 1942/43 as the Air Ministry had decided that as enemy air activity over the West Chain was declining, its provision rated a lower priority than the installation of telephone equipment by Post Office engineers at the increasing number of Final GCI, Type 7 stations nearing completion.

The installation of the five CHLs on a 185ft tower had been seriously delayed; the prototype at Humberston was operational at the beginning of the year but Cresswell was not in service until November followed by Hopton and Happisburgh in December with Bamburgh and Dunwich not until April 1943. The longest range was 140 miles, at 500ft 32 miles, at 10,000ft 110 miles, but by this time it was becoming essential to move away from 1.5 metres because of the effectiveness of enemy jamming. Work had also ceased on the placing of a CHL set on the 200ft cantilever of a steel tower at West Beckham and Drone Hill.

Portal, the CAS and Freeman, the VCAS, had invited Renwick to accept the appointment of Director-General of Signals in the Air Ministry, but although prepared to accept the responsibilities of the post he did not want to become an RAF officer. He accepted the civil position in October of Controller of Communications directly responsible to the CAS for all aspects of communications in the RAF. He made a condition that Air Marshal Nutting (the Director of Signals) and Air Commodore Gregory (60 Group) be relieved of their posts and suggested that Air Commodore Tait should be the new Director-General of Signals as his own lieutenant in the Air Ministry. Tait was somewhat junior to receive the rank (of Air Vice Marshal) immediately but it was understood that he would be given it in due course.

By the end of 1942, the United Kingdom was covered by nearly 200 stations consisting of 62 CH, 62 CHL, 3 CHB, 19 Army CD/CHL and 39 GCI stations, but not including the many mobiles that were providing emergency cover for a number of CH stations.

REFERENCES

1 AIR2/7181   2 AIR20/1523   3 AIR20/3061   4 AIR19/262
5 AIR2/8991   6 AVIA7/603   7 AIR2/7707   8 AIR26/100
9 AIR26/128

EXTRACTS FROM 14 GROUP BULLETIN.

During the last few months (March and April), enemy activity in 14 Group has consisted almost entirely of the usual high flying reconnaissance – Weather Willie, the Atlantic special and a few particularly precocious ones flying over Scapa Flow. Weather Willie has been intercepted and damaged once again. More strenuous efforts are being made to intercept the Orkney reccos but a considerable length of warning track is necessary to give fighters time to take off and climb to about 30,000 ft. KILKENNETH CHL (Tiree) has just been renamed BEN HOUGH (rhyming with loch, we think). Sassenachs all around us call it BEN HAOW and we think that a spot of business in the best Glencoe tradition is almost inevitable. STENIGOT seems to hold the long distance record still – 340 miles (yes, we mean 340 miles) on a photo Freddie. He was actually over Wilhemshaven when he faded, (and) they picked him up again on the return at 204 miles. A few days previous they had been quite cocky about another little effort at 275 miles but now they scarcely like to be reminded of such a poor show. Things are quiet in the North. So quiet that several of the Western Isles stations are being closed down to care and maintenance and their crews made available for more active spheres.

A new and nervous Filter Officer is responsible for two new Spoonerisms. Doing his best in the 10 Group Filter Room recently he eagerly called out an identification as 'three Beaufires and a Spitfighter'. BEN HOUGH CHL has been congratulated for accuracy and long range, (and) they have been instrumental in saving one or two lost aircraft. One was a Sunderland short of petrol which was watched constantly for over 50 miles until it came down in the sea quite close to the station. Not to be robbed of the last word, BEN HOUGH then went out with an Aldis and passed backchat with the crew until the rescue boys took over. On another occasion they saved an aircraft, which no other station could see, by extending their sweep by ten degrees. WHALE HEAD CH, joyfully and disrespectfully, plotted the AOC 60 Group in a flight from Sumburgh as Learner 48. GRUTNESS and WATSNESS CHLs plotted him as Learner 2. Having flown with the Air Vice Marshal we hasten personally and in great indignation to remove the shadow of calumny from our chief. His flying may be unorthodox but it is full of interest – and he gets you there. Even the Royal Observer Corps have not been exempt from spurious echoes. On 9 April a Post reported a Monster at QJ0549 (Loch Ness) travelling North East at one minus. This was accepted by Centre as a Master and passed to 14 Group Filter Room where it was made into a learner. It is possible the someone was pulling someone's leg, but the suggestion is freely offered that the R.O.C. and inland R.D.F. experts might develop as a hobby the investigation of the numerous Scottish lochs inhabited by mysterious and (as yet) unidentified raiders.

Chapter 12   1943

THE past year had seen the start of a continuous programme by 60 Group to replace most of the earlier types of CHL with the '1941' version; power turning of a five tier common aerial, VT98 valves, a PPI and range display with a 150 mile range. The procedure was identical at most sites, the installation of the Final system some distance from the existing hand turned CHL, which then remained as the standby or removed for installation overseas. By the end of this year some 60 CHLs would be power turned with just three remaining permanently hand turned. Many GCI stations with the Type 8C, the 'Intermediate Transportable', were waiting for the completion of the Final version on an adjacent site. On Final were Durrington, Sopley, Neatishead and Trewan Sands.

By sheer coincidence, as soon as CHL and GCI came into their Final versions, enemy jamming became much more effectual and they were all near the same wavelength, 200 MHz for CHL and 209 MHz for GCI. One victim of the enemy jamming was the prototype Fighter Direction (FD) station at Appledore, in Kent, which was providing cover for offensive operations by Fighter Command that forced German fighters into battle over occupied Europe. A GCI provided plan position at a maximum range of 115 miles at 10,000ft with height provided from a nearby VEB on a 120ft tower that had been transferred from Worth ex-TRE.

For the next four FD stations the wavelength was changed to 50cm, now with sufficient pulse power and freedom from jamming. Of a completely new design, it incorporated PPI and heightfinding; a 30ft paraboloid rotated horizontally with a dipole in the focal plane moving vertically ten times a second to provide height, which was shown directly on a CRT display. With a range between 150 and 200 miles, a single fighter aircraft could be detected anywhere between Le Havre (France) and the Dutch Islands. Known as the Type 16, the first one was installed at Grey Friars, near the Dunwich CHL, followed by Hythe, Ventnor and Beachy Head.

60 Group was now not only responsible for the maintenance but also for the staffing and operation of all the Army CD/CHL stations into the RAF at the same time as emphasis was placed on the rapid consolidation of the

10cm coastal chain; a programme for the installation of medium and high power gantry and tower stations was under way at many existing CHL sites. At Doonies Hill CHL station a concrete plinth had been laid down without an explanation until one morning a 10cm mobile appeared on it without any of the station staff aware of its impending arrival. To back up the increasing burden on 60 Group the numbers of personnel had greatly expanded of whom over 70% were technical; Officers including Polish, Royal Canadian Air Force, Royal New Zealand Air Force and the United States Signal Corps 1,168, WAAF Officers 352, Other Ranks 12,412 and WAAF 7,468.

Like CHL and GCI, the 10cm sets were all required as a matter of great urgency that needed, and received, support not only from TRE, RAE and ADRDE but also from the many private firms on contract. For the equipment manufacturers vast quantities of components were supplied from an industry that pre-war was initially made up of a large number of small firms with virtually no research facilities. Commercial products had to be modified to meet extremes of temperature, operation at high altitudes, miniaturisation and tropicalisation. Such was the shortage of paper capacitors that in January 1943 orders for a total of 26 million had been placed in the USA.

The supply of radio valves was the main limiting factor in the production of equipment and, until December 1940, the pre-war total of 12 million a year was considered adequate. A policy was favoured of placing large orders for valves that would certainly be required even when it was not known exactly what they would be used for. The estimated quantity for 1941 had increased to 23 million and for 1942 to over 32 million and in the autumn of 1943 it was suggested that 60 million would be the target. In 1944 rationalisation of the many types kept production at 37.5 million plus 17.5 million imports from the USA, of which over 3 million were EF50s.

On 1 April the 25th anniversary of the formation of the Royal Air Force was celebrated with congratulatory words to the Secretary of State for Air, Sir Archibald Sinclair, from the King and many others including Field Marshal Smuts. His message included a reference to his minute to the War Cabinet in October 1917 which predicted the rise of air power and was directly responsible for the creation of the Air Ministry and later the Royal Air Force. Sinclair's reply was:

"Like your memorable minute of October 1917, your message will be cherished in the annals of the R.A.F." [1]

Sinclair had expected that on 1 April he would announce that Smuts would be the recipient of a major tribute. He had written on the 26 February to Churchill that Smuts, now Prime Minister of South Africa, should be asked to accept an honorary commission in the rank of Marshal of the RAF. Churchill's reply on 27 February, was a personal minute:

> "Yes, I will gladly do so, [but] there is no need to make out he was the parent of the RAF." [1]

On 9 March a draft message was sketched out by the Permanent Secretary, Sir Arthur Street, for transmission to Field Marshal Smuts:

> "Mr W.S.Churchill is to propose to the King your appointment as a Marshal of the Royal Air Force on this auspicious occasion." [1]

Sinclair wrote to Churchill on 12 March:

> "I am very glad that you approve of my proposal that Field Marshal Smuts should be asked to accept an honourary commission in the rank of Marshal of the Royal Air Force." [1]

On 13 March another personal minute from Churchill was delivered to Sinclair:

> "The King mentioned this subject to me when he came to Chequers last week, and we both felt very cool about the proposal. Smuts has never been identified with the Air in any marked manner except in the way you mention as a member of the 1918 War Cabinet. He was made a Field Marshal because he had commanded armies and campaigns. It would be just as natural for the Navy to make him an Admiral of the Fleet [insertion here by Churchill] as Air Chief Marshal. On the whole, therefore, I prefer not to go forward with the plan." [1]

A telegram to South Africa summed up the situation in a few diplomatic words:

> "Our proposal that Field Marshal Smuts should be made an M.R.A.F. has come to grief..." [1]

(Author's note: The papers referring to the proposal were closed for 50 years in the Public Record Office.)

During April sufficient military intelligence had been received for the Prime Minister to be informed that the Germans were developing a long range rocket. Two committees were set up, one to evaluate its size and warhead potential, and the other to devise countermeasures, which was chaired by Watson-Watt. This occasion was probably the only one where neutralising actions were being prepared to meet the threat of an enemy weapon that had not been positively identified or even thought to exist.

Proof of existence was the task of the first committee, which itself had divided into two camps: those who were sure that it did although at the time there was no tangible reasons to support them; the other, who were equally convinced that the technical advances of the day were not yet sufficient to send up a rocket with a 10 ton warhead with a range calculated to be around 125 miles. The seriousness of the situation was the estimate that one rocket would cause 600 casualties, 150 of them fatal and even at the rate of one rocket per hour on London the casualty rate per month would be over 300,000 with 100,000 fatalities. The evacuation of London and the transfer of Government offices to a safer area were considered likely possibilities. Watson-Watt's committee reported that the CH stations as they were could not provide any information relating to the range of the rocket or its bearing until fitted with cathode ray direction finding (CRDF) based on Watson-Watt's work when he was at the NPL and installed experimentally during 1942 at Dunkirk. During July, unsure of when the apparatus would be ready and when the rocket offensive would begin, a special 'watch' was set up known as 'Bodyline' from Branscombe to Dover that was in addition to normal station operations. The tube of the standby RF8 was closely watched for intermittent echos that all appeared to have an identical range and coincided within seconds at other CH stations.

The changes to the standby receiver to provide the additional CRDF display, codenamed 'Willie', was a major modification. The four radio stages were disconnected from the aerials and a single channel twin receiver connected to a set of north-south and east-west dipoles. The discrete outputs were connected to the X and Y plates of a second CRT, further amplified, added and detected for connection to the existing CRT to show the normal echo range and IFF. The operator was instructed to watch for echoes over a 30 miles range and, if though to be a rocket, to make it appear on the CRDF tube, which was normally blanked out, and lock the position of the trace which would be of a very short duration with a line that provided range and bearing. The display was filmed with a G45 camera-gun at seven frames per second when rockets were suspected.

At a later date a CRT console called 'Oswald' connected to a CRHF receiver was installed. To ensure that the rocket trace was seen for the longest possible time the afterglow was activated by the horizontal base range line moving from top to bottom of the tube and repeated every 40 seconds. The display was viewed by the operator without blinking for no more than 15 minutes and filmed continuously by another G45 camera-gun at the rate of four frames a minute to record the timing signals. On seeing the rocket trace the operator shouted 'Big Ben' and switched on the 'Willie' camera. When requested by Stanmore both films were developed on site and sent there for analysis.

It had been correctly surmised that the speed of the rocket was such that very little warning could be given to the public as to where it was likely to fall. Plots from the CH stations would be used, along with other data, to project the tracks back to France in an attempt to locate the firing points with a follow up operation by Bomber Command. Additionally, the RAF Radio Monitoring Station at Kingsdown Hall, near Farningham, Kent, was listening for any unusual signals in the HF band that might reveal the existence of a guidance system.

As a precaution against jamming of the CH stations, a number of CHL sets were modified for 'floodlighting' and installed at Ramsgate, Hythe, Highdown Hill, Bexhill and Whitehawk (CD/CHL sites). The War Cabinet concluded that on the evidence before them, there would be no attempts by rockets or unmanned aircraft until the following year, part of the evidence being photographs of the destruction inflicted on the secret German experimental base at Peenemünde by 580 bombers on the night of 17/18 August.

The CMHs were on the move again. In January, 'Susie' went from Pen Olver to Kingswear and, according to 78 Wing ORB, the first operational day was most spectacular. On the air at 10.45, a track of two aircraft was picked up at 10.51, some 29 miles southeast and plotted until it faded into wave clutter at 8.97 miles. Guns opened fire at 3,000 yards and the hostiles turned back before reaching the coast. Later that day another track was picked up at 23 miles. Typhoons were vectored with the result that one aircraft was shot down and the rest made off for France also without crossing the coast. 'Mary' had been moved from the Jacka to Beer Head and during a raid on Torquay on 30 May had plotted 16 'Hostiles' flying at sea level. Three were shot down by guns and one by fighters. By June 'Susie' and 'Mary' had arrived at Hopton to give low cover at close range for the increase in bombing attacks in East Anglia and specially for Great Yarmouth; one was situated north of the CHL and the other south. When they were removed in July 1944, 'Susie' had a wreath laid on her and 'Mary' a notice 'No flowers by request'; 100 rounds of ammunition was fired to complete the ceremony.

During June, plotting by the East Chain was mainly of the heavy RAF bombing raids on enemy territory. On 11 June, at West Beckham, there was an indication by 2340 that bombers were starting to go east, by 0004 the numbers had increased to 250+, by 0028 increasing to 800 at a range of 180 miles. Returning bombers began to appear at 0253 and by 0420 the activity was over.

The German Air Force continued to use the technique of 'intruder' aircraft during night raids by sneaking them in over the coast with British bombers returning from France. In such a raid, 23 enemy long range bombers followed the residue of 600 returning friendly bombers together with 40 friendly ones going out at the same time. These attacks were mainly confined to the region of airfields along East Anglia. The CAS called for the quickest action but Watson-Watt advised him that:

> "...no solution offered nor is one in sight for the problem of the infallible identification of one enemy aircraft mingling in a stream of friendlies." [2]

In 1940/41, the tube saw masses of German aircraft with few British but now the situation was reversed.

On 14 July an order was issued by the Director-General of Signals that the letters RDF and the word 'radiolocation' were to be superseded by the word 'RADAR', an acronym for RAdio aid for Detection And Ranging. The word had been suggested by two Lieutenant Commanders of the United States Navy and approved by Admiral Stark in 1940. Watson-Watt claims to have brought the word back from the USA on one of his visits in 1943 when he was Deputy Chairman of the Radio Board of the War Cabinet and suggested its adoption as part of the standardisation between the two countries. He pronounced the word not as 'raydar' but as 'raddar'. His book *Three Steps to Victory* gives the date as 1944, an obvious misprint. The American Army Signal Corps had, at that time, a more appropriate word, DERAX, an acronym for Detection, Elevation, Range, Azimuth and EXperimental.

What is of interest is that in Volume 4 of the Air Ministry Signals Series titled *Radar in Raid Reporting*, that is copious with official file references, there is not one that refers to the change of RDF to RADAR. It is certainly curious that a change that surely merited much discussion and comment, and needed the approval of the CAS, could not be found in a file by the Air Historical Branch and was only mentioned in three lines with an incorrect date of September.

The Admiralty 500kW 10cm set was in production as the NT277 and the Army was quickly arranging for modification of six CD sets on top of 200ft steel towers at Trimingham, Hopton, Winterton, Benacre, Bard Hill and Thorpeness. A combined Army/Air Force exercise had ADRDE outside the Nissen hut with the wave guide, aerial and equipment, and 60 Group inside, with the display and control equipment.

The first such 10cm set on the ground developed by ADRDE, was cabin mounted with a horizontal 'cheese' aerial, nicknamed 'Gorgonzola', and when used for the RAF appeared in many guises with a double or triple 'cheese'. As a mobile with a vertical aerial, it became the Type 13 Mark 2 specifically designed as a nodding height finder, the set giving direct reading of height at a range of 70 miles without the need for further calculations. With a horizontal aerial and two PPI tubes it was known as the Type 14 and gave 20 miles of extra warning at low levels and an increase in height to 30,000ft.

The effectiveness of 10cm equipment was shown by two enemy raids on 25 May, the first at Folkestone; the Capel T14 first detected aircraft at 18 miles that were immediately identified as Hostile 197 and broadcast the information to the AA guns half a minute later. Seven Spitfires on patrol sighted the formation of 12 FW190s before they had crossed the coast and shot down five. The second was at Beachy Head where aircraft were detected at 22 miles and AA guns given a 3½ minute warning; five enemy aircraft were destroyed by guns and two by fighters. On 30 May, the T14 at Beer Head detected aircraft at 26 miles but the nearby Kingswear CHL only saw them at nine miles. On 6 June 14 FW190s crossed the coast at Pevensey at zero feet and were detected 29 miles away.

In early 1943 the use of 'Window' had remained in deadlock as the arguments for and against were unresolved, plus another factor, that of the quantity to be dropped which varied according to the calculations of the experts. Fighter Command had suggested 100 tons but the opinion of R.V.Jones of the Air Ministry Scientific Intelligence Group was that;

> "...only 10 tons would be necessary on the grounds that although the Germans were in a better position than we were on account of their narrow beams, they appear to be seriously behind in transmitter power and in presentation devices. When these factors are considered it is very possible that their system is nothing like as 100 times as immune as ours and may prove to be equally vulnerable." [3]

In June, Churchill gave the decision to drop 'Window' on hearing that Fighter Command's objection on the grounds that retaliatory action by the Germans would jam the night fighter interception system had been met by the use of 10cm equipment in the air and on the ground. It was estimated that it would take the Germans three months to organise such action and this time could be used to organise the installation of mobile Type 13 and 14 at GCI stations along the south coast of England.

The first target for Bomber Command was the city of Hamburg on the night of 24/25 July when 20 tons of 'Window' were dropped, roughly 2 million strips and the results exceeded expectations as bomber losses were reduced from 5% to 1%. Two thousand strips of 30cm length and width 1.5cm constituted a bundle weighing 2lb which was 'unwrapped' when thrown into the slipstream of the aircraft. The descending strips represented an aircraft echo that persisted for 15 minutes: the German GL and GCI Würzburg radars saw the equivalent of 12,000 aircraft.

The Germans were soon to use their own form of 'Window' called 'Düppel'. On the night of 7/8 October, 20 enemy aircraft crossed the coast and were counted as 80 by West Beckham and plus 200 by Dunwich CHL. There was a second attempt on the night of 23 October when 20 raiders over Yarmouth were reported as plus 300 by Dunwich. An attack on Plymouth on the night of November 15 had all the hallmarks of the dropping of 'Düppel' as only 15 aircraft took part but CHL stations reported from 60 to 350 and the filter room over 40. The only but surprisingly successful antidote to the jamming was by the operators, who were able to detect the use of 'Düppel' by the slow moving pattern across the tube display.

CHL, GCI and GL were seriously affected, CH only moderately so but, as expected, the 10cm ground and airborne radars remained completely free of interference. There was no immediate technical advance that could defeat the chaos that resulted from the equivalent of thousands of simple dipoles dropped in front of radar stations but its effectiveness was dependent on the skill of how it was identified by the operators. It was to remain a most serious menace whenever it was used by both sides for the remainder of the war; the most stringent precautions to ensure that a new working wavelength was not discovered by the enemy was the only way to ensure freedom from all forms of jamming.

The end of the 1.5 metre VEB was in sight. RAE were informed that they were to stop all development work and cease the field trials at Ventnor. For record purposes a lab. report summarising the present state of the work and the major difficulties that had been encountered should suffice. The report concluded that it was impossible to read height to within 10 miles of Ventnor due to the existence of a block of echoes, which were permanently shown at saturation. Works were advised that as the operational requirement for VEB had been cancelled, the installation programme was to be abandoned. In the future height measurements would be obtained using 10cm equipment, the Type 13 Mark 2.

By the end of the year all the CH transmitters had been modified for 750Kw output and coupled to the megawatt aerial; with the RF7 or RF8 receiver the ranges achieved were incredible compared to the early days at Bawdsey. At Douglas Wood the range at 24,000ft was 190 miles and the station had made a record plot of 245 miles, Dover had plotted 750 Flying Fortresses for 186 miles, right to the end of the trace, Bawdsey had reported + 850 aircraft that gave a continuous 100 mile trace down to the bottom of the tube only fading after 180 miles. The remaining Final GCIs were now operational, mainly at night but if the weather was bad or the visibility poor then daytime control was taken over from the Sector Operations Rooms.

REFERENCES

1   AIR2/7842   2   AIR2/7818   3   AIR20/1709

EXTRACTS FROM RDF/ RADAR BULLETINS

On March 24 a Messerschmitt 210 was destroyed by a Sumburgh Spitfire piloted by Sgt. Lane. It was first picked up by DEERNESS CMH at 17.36 hours at a range of 20 miles east of Orkney ; it was subsequently plotted by the CHL stations in this area. The enemy aircraft flew south for 10 miles then turned NNE, flew 14 miles west of Fair Isle where it was intercepted at a height less than 1,000 feet. It was shot down into the sea 10 miles NW of Sumburgh Head 18 minutes after its first appearance. On 21st March a track was picked up in the Shetland area at a height of 3,000 feet and was identified as hostile. This aircraft was tracked on the Filter Room table for 300 miles apart from a gap of 48 miles due to one CHL station being lashed and kept at a constant height of 3,000 ft. Later it was found that this was a bomber which was 500 miles off course.

Enemy activity during May has been on a reduced scale only 21 tracks being reported. 13 of these were our old friend the 'Atlantic Special' which continues to appear usually about sixty miles north of the Shetland Isles. The only one tracked for a long time was X22 which was picked up at 120 miles NE of Kinnairds Head. It made landfall near Helmsdale, turned North flying parallel to the coast and went out to sea due east from Wick. This hostile aircraft was plotted for over 300 miles. Plotting at ranges greater than 180 miles seems to be a regular occurrence on the CHL stations in 14 Group. Several ranges greater than 200 miles have been recorded; 203 miles from ULBSTER, 205 miles from EURODALE and 208 miles from DEERNESS.

Our RDF life saving association continued to do good work. The most outstanding occasion was at 0540 hours on June 4 when Bomber 404 showing broad IFF entered 14 Group area 60 miles east of Montrose. Two Spitfires were sent out from Dyce and intercepted the aircraft at about 100 miles east of Rattray Head and brought it safely back to Peterhead. The aircraft was a Wellington from Cranwell on a training flight and owing to a breakdown of W/T was completely lost. The crew were under the impression that they were over the English Channel and on landing there was only ten minutes of petrol left.

On 16 May there was a parade of the Barra Home Guard, who were guarding the GREIAN HEAD CHL. Captain Compton Mackenzie, O.B.E., sent a telegram to the King and received the following reply :
"I sincerely thank all the ranks of the most westerly Home Guard in Britain for their loyal message that I appreciate. George R.I. Colonel in Chief."

At BAWDSEY on December 17, in a returning bomber force from Berlin, a Halifax collided with the only serviceable R tower wrecking the top dipole array, the station now only operational on the Buried Reserves pending the commissioning of Mk 3 feeders. A scientific officer, possibly a schoolmaster, made a literary comment on the Buried Reserves quoting from Shakespeare's *The Taming of the Shrew* "Neither art thou the worse for this poor furniture and mean array."

Chapter 13 1944 to 1945

THE first three months of 1944 brought heavy night raids with some on London, the heaviest since May 1941. On 21/22 January there was a 30 minute warning of an enemy raid and 'Düppel' was dropped when German aircraft left the French coast and by the time they were mid-Channel the Foreness CHL and GCI and Wartling GCI were almost unusable with Durrington and Trimley Heath less so. During enemy raids in February it became clear that under jamming conditions the 10cm ground stations were not affected by 'Düppel' so airborne interceptions continued without difficulty. On 5 May, some 25 airborne jammers were operating; CH was only slightly affected but all the south coast CHLs were completely out of action, the Type 7 GCIs badly affected and IFF Mark 3 also heavily jammed; a serious situation for night fighting but for the 10cm sets now in operation on the ground, the Type 13 Mark 2 and the Type 14 Mark 3 and in the air, AI Mark X.

The attacks on London and other cities, which was called the 'Baby Blitz', were not expected to last for long as intelligence was trickling through that the Germans were almost ready to launch the first V for Vengeance weapon, the V1, a flying bomb. The word 'Bodyline' had been replaced with 'Crossbow' in November 1943 to indicate all V-weapons but in February the code word 'Diver' was adopted for all V1 activities. Estimation of its air speed varied between 250 to 420mph flying at a height of 7,000ft and expected to be easily recognised by radar stations and the Royal Observer Corps (renamed in 1941) because of its straight track and constant speed.

The wartime history of radar up to this point had been the rush of resources to meet the aggressive actions of the German Air Force whenever and wherever they occurred but, in the areas where air raids were now absent and the realisation that they would never return, stations began to be assessed for their usefulness. Fighter Command and the Director of Radar were pressing for a policy ruling for the reduction in cover for air operations only, not coastal watching, to release the personnel to man the mobile radars and GEE chains for the intended D-Day operations and the invasion of Europe. Radar stations for closure, which had begun in late 1943, were placed in one of a number of categories of which (F) was for the station to be dismantled, with aerials and equipment removed, (E) reduction to Care and Maintenance (C and M), which ensured that the station could be returned to full operational status within 14 days, and C and M Caretaking, which delayed the return of full operational status for six months.

As month followed month so the list of closed stations began to grow, Rodel Park, Habost, Point of Stoer, Navidale, Kendrom, Loth, Roddans Port, Kilkeel, and Ballymartin. To add to the closures the GCI station at Trewan Sands on the west coast, which was in an area remote from enemy air activity, was connected to the nearest filter room and the surrounding CH and CHL stations of Nevin, Castell Mawr, Wylfa and Pen-y-Brn placed on Care and Maintenance followed by Prestatyn, Dalby, and Scarlett. With GCIs at Northstead and Seaton Snook also in the reporting chain it was possible to close Ottercops CH station. By June a total of 24 had been closed.

By April and May the personnel at the CH and CHL stations along the English Channel were aware that 'something was in the wind'; the stations had accumulated large increases in stores, rations and petrol and all incoming and outgoing mail was censored. Nine mobile GCIs were dispersed at suitable places to act as an emergency backup for CHL and GCI stations. A great number of American troops had appeared, many roads were blocked and guarded and movement restricted; two WAAFs had been injured when they were knocked down by a runaway American Army truck.

In preparation for the D-Day landings, all installation and modification efforts were concentrated on upgrading to 500kW the medium power 10cm sets along the east, south and southwest English coastline, which were then able to pinpoint crashed aircraft and survivors with sufficient accuracy for successful rescue attempts to be made.

At the beginning of June the stations began to be aware of a great number of friendly air activities that culminated in the invasion of the Continent on D-Day, 6 June. CH operators watched with amazement the CRT displays with echoes that reached right down to the bottom of the tube, slowly drifting off the end of the trace reaching over 180 miles; the filter room told them that they were not interested in receiving plots.

While it was believed in Scotland and the north of England that there was now little possibility of air raids, this was certainly not the case in southern England where it appeared to the ordinary citizen that the war was far from over. At 0400 on 13 June 1944 the first V1, the flying bomb, from northern France appeared over the North Downs and fell with a loud explosion at Swanscombe, near Gravesend, Kent, followed during the next hour by three more and then another ten and that was all for the day. The next day there was a short respite until the15th, when the attacks began again with an increasing intensity with over a hundred crossing the coast towards London and, at first, more than half reaching the capital. It was quickly assessed that the majority were flying at an altitude between 2,000ft to 3,000ft with speeds constant between 230 and 430mph. To facilitate identification between aircraft and flying bombs, a circuit for detecting propeller modulation was fitted in the CHL receiver.

From fixed launching sites there was no great change in the spread of tracks with the majority of the bombs crossing the south coast between Cuckmere Haven (East Sussex) and St. Margaret's Bay (Kent). Ventnor saw only a few tracks but Beachy Head CHL recorded that not only were they plotting the incoming 'Divers' but also the huge bomber forces going over to raid the sites. Sometimes the tracks were being plotted coming in with the returning bombers. During one month 2,140 'Diver' tracks had been recorded at Fairlight CHL, where off-centre PPIs were in use so that long range echoes could be read direct instead of from the linear time base, and one watch period of eight hours at North Foreland CHL had plotted 110 'Diver' tracks.

For civilians the flying bomb, or buzz bomb as it was called by Londoners, had held no immediate terror for as soon as the characteristic 'phut-phut' sound was heard, the skies would be scanned and when sighted to watch its progress with a mixture of alarm and relief. The alarm factor was in the listening for at any moment and without any warning the noise would suddenly cease. The bomb was put into an almost vertical dive by the action of tail detonators that caused the fuel in the tank to fall and uncover the outlet pipe stopping the engine. In those seconds of silence it was essential to find cover as the warhead was designed for maximum blast as it hit the ground. The relief factor came into play when the bomb was seen to pass overhead and drop elsewhere. Housing was the biggest casualty; 20,000 damaged each day, over 200,000 in the first fortnight with over 1,600 lives lost.

For the next four weeks nearly 100 flying bombs a day were being dispatched of which half were still reaching the London area. To improve on that figure the ground defences were massively re-organised in mid-July by moving all the AA guns, stores and ammunition from the North Downs to the coast in under five days. The American radar type SCR584 that had an electrical predictor and automatically followed an echo was used with the Army 10cm GL Mark 3. (Of interest is the difference in the number of personnel used for research and development of the two similar radars; for the SCR584 over 1,500 people covering three years, for the GL

Mark 3 a team of 20 at ADRDE in 1941/42 tapering to 16 in 1944 and 25 at BTH/EMI.) Another important factor in the defeat of the flying bomb was the use of AA shells fitted with a proximity fuse, a British invention that met with severe manufacturing difficulties and had to be sent to America for further development and quantity production. In the air were Thunderbolts, Mustang Mk 3s, Tempest Mk Vs, Spitfire Mark XIVs, Mosquito fighters and the very first British jet fighter, the Meteor Mk 1s of 616 Squadron. When the guns of Meteor aircraft EE216 jammed, it had the distinction of causing a flying bomb to crash by the dangerous tactic of the pilot in tipping its wing. The numbers of flying bombs that failed to reach their target began to rise considerably.

On 28 August, of 94 flying bombs approaching the coast only four reached London, 23 being shot down by fighters and 65 by AA guns; balloon collisions added two. In the early stages of the flying bomb offensive a fairly large number of radio signals were detected in the range of 340 to 450 Kc/s (KHz) – a long dash of about 20 seconds followed by one Morse number. These transmissions were 'meaconed', ie, retransmitted from a distant source to confuse the navigational information for the listener. The number of bombs fitted with a radio transmitter never exceeded 5% of the total number and gradually declined until they ceased altogether. RAE were able to examine a perfect specimen transmitter which consisted of a single triode valve with two batteries, 1,000 volts 100ma, and 15 volts 1Amp, both of 30 minutes' duration.

As the Allied armies advanced in Europe the launching sites were abandoned and a new threat to London arose with flying bombs appearing from the east and at night being launched by specially equipped Heinkel 111 aircraft from bases in Holland. With the capture of the launching sites in the Pas-de-Calais area and Holland the 'Diver' operations appeared to have ceased with the last bomb falling on 5 September.

On 6 September the Vice–Chiefs of Staff reported to the War Cabinet that all areas from which flying bombs and rockets might be launched against London had been, or were about to be, occupied by Allied troops. On the strength of these reports a public announcement was made on 7 September that the Battle of London was over apart from a few test shots. As if the enemy were listening, the first rocket, the V2, fell the next day at Chiswick, in London, followed almost immediately by another at Epping (in Essex), then two a day for the next ten days.

The arrival of the 13½ ton rocket was completely different to that of the flying bomb as the first indication that it had fallen was the sound of a double thunderclap, which was the explosion of the one ton warhead, followed almost immediately by the delayed sound of the rocket in flight. Reaching a height of 50 to 60 miles, the rocket had a velocity on the downward track of speeds up to 3,000 miles per hour and only took six or seven minutes to reach its destination; air raid warnings could not be sounded because of insufficient time for detection. Of a greater penetrating power than the flying bomb, there was more destruction at the point of impact and public utility services suffered accordingly. The rocket, code name 'Big Ben', posed the biggest dilemma for the authorities as many of the investigations undertaken were based on guesswork and one of the possibilities to be countered was that the rocket had a guidance system and, if it had, then it could be jammed. TRE had suggested that 6 metres would be likely and although jamming from the ground was nearly prohibitive in terms of radiated power, immediate arrangements were made to obtain a number of transmitters of powers ranging from 5kW to 100kW with fourteen 15 kW transmitters ordered from the USA.

Jamming from the air had not been overlooked as six American B17 Fortress aircraft were carrying transmitters and were standing by in East Anglia, and B24 Liberators were being fitted out at the American air base at Burtonwood, near Warrington, now in Cheshire. Bomber Command were asked to plan a 24 hour patrol with aircraft carrying four transmitters and a squadron to listen out for signal transmissions. On 9 September a telegram was sent to Washington that two rockets had landed in London the previous night and the matter was being kept dark 'until we see how things develop.'

By 13 September the ground radio countermeasures were complete; at Hope Cove there were 20 Marconi SWB11s of 8 kW each and 20 Naval 1 kW transmitters, at Brighton there were two jammers 5 kW each and at Crowborough there were two 50kW transmitters from the BBC. In the air were 214 Squadron (Fortresses) operating two patrols of four hours duration over the suspected launching area with 192 Squadron listening out for radio transmissions. Within a short period of time these nullifying actions were found to be unnecessary when it was confirmed that the control of the rocket was entirely internal and automatic.

The CH stations from Stoke Holy Cross to Rye, which were fitted with CRHF, had the power increased to 1 Megawatt except for Bawdsey, which was 2 Megawatt plus the CHL radiating on a fixed bearing of 85 degrees true. Four Megawatt transmitters were nearing completion but one negative aspect of increasing the pulse power was the knowledge that the Germans had developed a system called 'Heidelburg', which used the CH transmissions to provide early warning of raids by Bomber Command. Direct evidence had come from the interrogation of a prisoner and according to his story the apparatus known as Wassermann was equipped with a receiver only, no transmitter. Plots were obtained by locking onto the pulses from Dover CH, which gave a known fixed range, and detecting the pulses scattered by the incoming bomber force. The path length from the bomber force to the Wassermann would lie on an ellipse whose foci were the CH station and the Wassermann, the position determined by the taking of a bearing; a maximum range of nearly 300 miles was expected. TRE quickly agreed that the method was possible but thought that there might be some difficulty in using the system. Nevertheless counteraction was suggested, which included the obvious one to switch off the CH transmitter, or destroy the enemy aerial system which was a very large array of some 30 metres in height and 22 metres across.

The increase in CH power to 1 Megawatt was expected to identify what was expected to be just a small part of the rocket trace, which was recorded on film, and gave the rocket range to within $\frac{1}{2}$ mile and the time to half a second. By range cuts at the Stanmore Filter Room taken from a number of films, the upward path of the rocket could be plotted and, by projection, its estimated firing point. This information was mainly used as a corroborative element for details derived from detection equipment that was nearer to the suspected base; indications were that the first two rockets had been fired from southwest Holland.

I am indebted to Mrs Gwen Reading for permission to publish an extract from her account of Service life as an 'Oswald' operator:

"When the V2 rockets came along, special equipment was installed in the R block. Known as 'Oswald', the screen showed a faint but distinctive thread like track when a V2 scorched through the atmosphere. The operator then yelled 'Big Ben at Bawdsey' down the line to the Filter Room... The screen of 'Oswald' had to be watched very intently. The tracks were so small and appeared so briefly, that they could be missed altogether if the operator blinked. The watcher had to be changed every 15 minutes, whereas the ordinary operational screen could be watched for an hour. A few minutes after the 'Big Ben at Bawdsey' call, Stanmore sent instructions to 'change Oswald'; this was our cue to remove the film which ran within 'Oswald' and develop it. Stanmore staggered the times for changing 'Oswald' so that no two stations would be off the air at the same time. The supervisors were trained to analyse the filmed trace, and from the information gathered by a group of stations, the location of the launching pads could be ascertained. Members of the watch were required to develop the films in an improvised darkroom – a shed in the CH block compound. It was more than a little eerie walking through the pitch blackness of the night and then by the light of a tiny red bulb, develop the precious film. To speed up the drying operation the film was wound round a frame and spun over an electric heater. I recall an occasion when I neglected to secure a frame properly, then as soon as the spinning operation started, the whole thing fell onto the heater with disastrous results."

On 16 September, the rockets having temporarily ceased, flying bombs were again directed against London, this time launched from aircraft with bases in western Germany. A short-lived success, due to the absence of AA guns, was an attack on Christmas Eve 1944 when thirty flying bombs were launched from a position off the east coast between Skegness and Bridlington. They all crossed the coast, were reported by the radar stations and estimated to be flying in the direction of Manchester where only one reached the city, the remainder falling within 15 miles. Three weeks later all air launchings ceased the last one coming down at Hornsey, London, on 14 Jan 1945; but it was not the end of the flying bomb campaign.

There had been a six week lull but now they were being launched from ramps in Holland, the first on 5 March 1945, but the air and ground defences were in place and, coupled with the retreat of the German army, the last one fell at Datchet on 29 March 1945. The effectiveness of all the countermeasures can be judged from the statistics that with over 10,000 flying bombs dispatched only 2,419 reached the London area.

Rockets began falling again on 25 September 1944 but this time they were landing in the Norwich area and continued into October, with suspicions of launching sites in northern Holland. London was again the target from the beginning of October with rockets coming from The Hague, Holland, area and continuing at the rate of three a day, sometimes four that increased to ten a day during February 1945. The only possible and practical defence that could be made against them were attacks on the ground, mainly the stores, back up sites and buildings, railway and road communications. The last rocket, the 1115th, fell at Orpington, Kent on 27 March 1945, the majority of which had been aimed at London.

At a meeting on 19 September the CAS agreed to the abolition of the radar chain and air raid reporting organisation from Cape Wrath to St David's Head including Northern Ireland but, under pressure for the consideration of air safety he acceded to retaining cover in the Outer Hebrides, Downhill and St. David's Head to assist aircraft crossing the Atlantic.

The argument put forward to the Air Staff, who wanted the radar stations closed, was that between January and June, 1944, as a direct result of distress information provided by radar plotters, a total of 141 aircraft had been provided with assistance, 72 of which were in the Western Approaches, nine being reported in one day. Radar stations not only plotted enemy but friendly aircraft when in trouble or distress; what would have happened if there was no radar available? The question asked was what was the comparison of radar man hours to those necessary to replace aircraft and training the crews. Advice was to follow that the retention of radar cover for aircraft safety in wartime 'is an expenditure of man hours and equipment, which has been found that we cannot afford, and in peacetime this will be even more accelerated.'

A month before the end of the war with Germany, the Air Staff began preparations for the long awaited stand down on air defence. The 24 hours watch keeping would end at all radar stations, and operations and filter rooms would be reduced to eight hours a day with five hours at night. All surplus personnel would be withdrawn as soon as possible except at the coastal and surface watching stations, which would retain continuous watch so that the Admiralty could proceed with the recovery of mines. Many CH and CHL stations had already ceased operations as the Allied armies began to move into Germany and by May 1945 some 44 were under 'caretaking'. Operations before VE day were mainly Lancaster bombers dropping food into Holland and afterwards, the plotting of aircraft bringing back prisoners-of-war.

The 8th May 1945 was VE day, the cessation of hostilities in Europe, and the ORB of 2.IU recorded that by mid-day all except essential persons were on their way to various forms of celebration. The last known hostile track on 9 May 'A370' was plotted in across the coast in the Middlesborough area flying in the region of 2,000ft. The track of this aircraft coincided with one which had been plotted overland across to Northern Ireland where it landed bringing passengers of Nazi origin from Norway. At 1200 on Saturday 12 May after almost six years of continuous manning, plotters were overheard to say 'Cheerio, 'til Monday at 9' to their station, the procedure reversed on the morning of the 14th at 0900.

From the 19 stations that were barely operational at the beginning of the war, the radar stations by VE day had reached a peak of over 200, which virtually covered the whole of the United Kingdom, with approximately 60 each of CH, CHL and 10cm stations plus 25 GCI stations. By the end of 1945, at many deserted CH stations the curtain arrays had been dismantled and stored, with only the red warning lights atop the hundreds of towers a reminder that the first and the most inventive decade of British radar was over.

EXTRACTS FROM RADAR BULLETINS.

Activity across the chains was summed up by one station 'there has been every variety of activity between slight and nil', and comments from some of the Shetland stations where most of the airfields had been closed. CLETT CHL reported 24 watches of nil activity and WATSNESS CHL recorded 33 such watches adding that on their busiest day they plotted 23 tracks. The Hebridean chain had been busy with the reporting of all the American aircraft that were returning to the USA, over 2500, some flights having been cancelled because the airfields in Iceland were already full of aircraft awaiting return to the USA. There was the usual valuable aid to aircraft in distress. A Halifax bound for Eire which developed engine trouble was diverted to Stornaway and landed safely, a Liberator flying north with a u/s engine was also directed to Stornoway. Not all the American aircraft got home without mishap. The vital importance of recognising aircraft responses as distinct from 'spurious' was unhappily emphasised when, on July 23, Stornoway had two faded plots which could not be associated with a track and were therefore dubbed 'spurious'. Later it was reported from Portree that a plane had been seen to circle with bits falling off before it crashed into the mist covered hills. An eye witness was convinced that it had hit a high point on Rhum before attempting to make a forced landing on Skye. Fourteen Americans did not return home.

We prophesy that the career of the radar specialist will be worth following, a job into which many of you will be proud to place your sons and daughters. And the time will come when all you little Waafies in mob caps and ringlets or whatever the recognised dress of dear old ladies will be in the nineteen nineties, will gather your grandchildren round you chiding them for the easy life they lead on consoles that 'count every ship upon the sea, fill in the log book and make the tea' and rambling on tiresomely, as old ladies will, about how you tried to estimate six plus on a beating pulse long, long ago when radar was called RDF and there were real enemy planes to shoot down.

Chapter 14   Radar Awards

AFTER World Wars One and Two, a Royal Commission was set up to decide on financial awards to the holders of patents whose inventions had been used. There were strict rules of procedure; the claimant had in the first instance to present his claim to the government department which he alleged had made use of his invention. Many of the applications arising from patents used in wartime were sifted by an investigating committee to ensure that only bona fide claims were dealt with by the Commission.

Most of the internal government work fell on the patents section of the Ministry of Supply, which had the onerous task of discovering the whereabouts of the relevant files, of searching for and copying documents, tracing and obtaining evidence of persons conversant with the development of the invention in question. In many cases the department and the claimant would reach agreement as to the payment to be made but where the department rejected the claims outright, they were referred to the Commission.

Procedures and principles were based on those adopted by the Commission after the end of World War One but there were changes, one being that an inventor or an owner of a patent could also be a servant of the Crown. As government employees were by regulations compelled to assign any invention to the Crown, it was only possible for an inventor to request that in his case he be considered for an ex-gratia payment.

It did not follow, however, that such an award, if recommended, would result in payment for as a civil servant a 100% discount would be liable, but there were special conditions that could apply, such as an invention of exceptional brilliance and utility, foresight and resourcefulness, dogged perseverance even in the face of official discouragement.

There were two examples; the first of Sir Frank Whittle, the inventor of the British jet engine, who was not a claimant, but had his case put forward by the Ministry of Supply, which had asked the Commission to assist the government by undertaking an investigation and making a recommendation, which was an ex-gratia payment of £100,000. The second was the claim of Sir Donald Bailey, the inventor and designer of the Bailey Bridge, who had been a junior officer at the War Office Bridging Establishment at Christchurch. During periods between 1936 and 1940 he had worked on his invention largely in his leisure time but nevertheless informing his Superintendent, who had indicated to him that the War Office favoured tubular construction and could not undertake additional investigations. By January 1941 the bridging problem was becoming acute and when the first production model of the bridge was received at Christchurch for testing it failed. Orders were at once given for a full scale trial of the Bailey Bridge, which reached the troops in production form by November 1941. The Commission thought that this remarkable achievement reflected praise on all concerned but the main credit was with Bailey for bringing his design to an advanced state of completion. The award recommended was £12,000.

Other claims had been dealt with by the investigating committee such as those raised by EMI for the use of cathode ray tubes and Klystron patents for which they received £65,000. The Philips Company made a claim for the use of over 1,000 patents and were asking for a payment of £150,000 subject to tax, which after discussion, was reduced to £50,000 free of tax to cover three patents, negative feedback, magnets and all-glass radio valves.

The Treasury were told that the Ministry of Aircraft Production wanted Mullard (Philips owned) to pass the all-glass technique to GEC, Marconi/Osram, Cosmos and Cossor and to allow copies of the plant associated with exhaust machines to be supplied to these contractors. Mullard appealed against this request on the grounds that it meant passing over all the knowledge that had enabled Philips to make better and cheaper valves than its competitors. As a result of further discussions, agreement was reached to limit the information to Marconi/Osram and to the USA to meet contracts to be placed in America for additional quantities of radio valves.

The Treasury were advised that it was doubtful in peacetime if any firm would have agreed to reveal all the details for a payment of less than some hundreds of thousands of pounds, a capital payment tax free and, if considered by the Commission, the award might well be greater than £100,000. The Treasury took notice and offered the Philips company £50,000 mainly for the transfer of plant and know-how to America and Canada for all-glass valve manufacture.

There was also the question of an award to Professor F.C.Williams, MSc, PhD, AMIRE, who was responsible for fundamental inventions in every type of airborne radar used by the RAF. He had joined BRS on 6 March 1939 and received a broad direction to extend the wavelength of IFF and by December had designed the Mark 2 to cover two CH wavebands and one GL. He was regarded as the most prolific inventor in the field of electronics at TRE, his post enabling him to be employed as the expert in general circuit design for the whole station. A letter was sent to Rowe, who by this time, July 1947, had left England for Australia where he had taken up the appointment as Vice Chancellor of Adelaide University. His reply took four months as the letter had been sent by sea mail and wrongly addressed to him at the University of Sydney. He wrote that he was strongly opposed to the giving of financial awards to government scientists for any work that they had done within the proper spheres of effort. He added:

"I note that you have some difficulty in deciding the limits of Dr. Williams' responsibilities and that does not surprise me. The difficulty arises from my belief that the work of a man so brilliant as Dr. Williams should not be closely defined. He was never instructed to write a report and I doubt if he was instructed to do anything. He was a brilliant designer of circuits and I suppose it is true to say that during the whole history of radar no man brought as much novelty to circuit design as did Dr. Williams. If, unhappily, it is the intention of the Department to give financial awards in connection with radar, then I know no man more worthy of consideration than Dr. Williams." [1]

TRE had been asked to nominate individual items of exceptional brilliance and utility in respect of some 17 main items of Dr Williams' work but preliminary inquiries had shown that the investigation of any one of these would be equivalent on its own to that required for a major award case. TRE hesitated to do so on the grounds that his work was at a consistently high level and that the body of his inventive work considered as a whole had to be regarded as far and away beyond what could be normally expected of an officer of similar status. Others were to write:

"An astonishing series of masterpieces which he produced were of such exceptional value [and of] unique brilliance and painstaking endeavour." [1]

The committee awarded a payment of £10,000. Further payments were £5,000 to Mr R.J.Dippy for his invention of the hyperbolic navigational aid GEE, £2,000 to Professor T. Merton for the double layer cathode ray tube screen and £12,000 each to Professors J.T. Randall and J.Sayers and Dr. H.A.H.Boot for the cavity magnetron of which over a million were made.

As early as January 1946, Watson-Watt had enquired of the Ministry of Supply, which had absorbed the Ministry of Aircraft Production, if he might be eligible for an award for the invention and development of radar but he was advised that the department could not move without a recommendation from the Royal Commission; a second request in October produced a similar reply. In April 1949 he again visited the Ministry to enquire what awards had been made in the radar field and he was informed of those that had been made to Professor F.C.Williams, R.Dippy and others. The situation as understood by Watson-Watt was that a number of persons had been given awards arising solely from the invention of radar, for which he held the patent and, so far, had received nothing. On 10 August he submitted a rough draft of his claim with a request for co-operation in the description and identification of the inventions; there was a negative response but a clear message that any further action would only be dependent on his submission of a claim for consideration of an ex-gratia payment. In a further letter dated 20 August, Watson-Watt's view was that his case was one of the few in which it would be appropriate for the Ministry to take the initiative in preparing for an award without making a claim (as for Whittle). A reply on 24 September from the Permanent Secretary was that the Minister did not feel able to accede to his request and that the matter must be dealt with by the submission of his claim to the Departmental Awards Committee, which would conduct an investigation and advise on facts and principles.

The Committee Chairman's report to the Deputy Secretary was dated 15 June 1950, and he made an early statement:

> "There is no question of this principle [of echo reflection] having been discovered by the claimant and he has been at pains to make this clear." [2]

The committee recorded the view that a distinction should be drawn between the two periods of time (1) from 1 August 1936, when Watson-Watt became the Superintendent at Bawdsey under the Air Ministry and (2) from January 1935 while he was on the strength of the National Physical Laboratory. The committee decided that notwithstanding the difficult question of collaboration there was no contribution so outstanding as to offset his status liability:

> "It cannot be said that the claimant himself showed in this period [1] such outstanding initiative, foresight and resourcefulness in making his inventions (such as they were) to offset the presumption of 100% discount....If principles mean anything, then the committee consider that 100% discount ought to apply to this period. The pre-Bawdsey period [2] began in January 1935 when Mr.Wimperis...consulted the claimant about the possibility of disabling aircraft by some form of "death ray". The claimant found this not feasible, but added that he was examining the possibilities of detecting aircraft as distinct from ...disabling them.... and he has stressed the argument that his response was outside his [official] duty....It is considered to have been entirely in the course of duty for him to suggest the investigation of radio detection of aircraft and also for him, with the aid of his staff, to investigate its feasibility. But it would seem ungenerous to suggest that it was within his duties to put forward a practical scheme for a station capable of aircraft location.

> The invention, though a combination of certain known or attempted expedients, was a novel combination and not an obvious one. In particular it was not obvious to use pulse technique. There was no exceptional scientific brilliancy as with

the inventions of Professor Williams and other workers in the field, but it was a pioneer effort which went beyond the pointing of a goal, or indicating a promising line of development, and it comprised a specification of the actual apparatus subsequently manufactured. The claimant was knighted for his services in connection with radar...it is possible to feel – and the committee realise that the Department may decide – that such an honour needs no monetary supplement for the same services. There are precedents for giving both forms of recognition and the committee have never been under instruction to take honours into account.

A long discussion on the Committee led in the end, without influential leading by any member, to the emergence of a practically unanimous view. Omitting the Chairman and Treasury representative, whose votes in the circumstances were not required, eight out of the nine members voted in principle for an award....It is only right to say that the dissenting member knows more about radar and its history than any one else on the Committee and that he bases his dissent on the absence of sufficient invention. [The person referred to had held a very senior post in Watson-Watt's original department, the DCD.]

The question of the amount then arose....they have in mind an outside figure of £20,000...The committee think that they should draw special attention to the award of £12,000 given to Sir Donald Bailey ..there has been no question of "radar versus a bridge" as the dissimilarity of the two cases will at once be seen [apparent]....A few other claimants in the field have been rewarded for work of outstanding brilliance, such as Professor Williams, and if others arise- very few are anticipated – they will have to rely on their intrinsic merit and conformity with principles. The committee do, however, wish to suggest that Mr.Wilkins, who helped the claimant at the earliest stages not only with the calculations but with helpful suggestions, should be accorded recognition...Mr. Wilkins speaks generously of his chief's work and the committee think themselves fortunate that they have not had to consider the suggestion of piracy or other forms of bad faith...." [2]

It was the duty of one of the Deputy Secretaries to convey to the Permanent Secretary the findings of the committee and make recommendations. He summarised the report that from the period of 1 August 1936 when Watson-Watt joined the Air Ministry the committee concluded that he must be regarded as status barred and it was thought that there was no doubt of the rightness of the decision. The pre-Bawdsey period presented a difficulty as regards discount by reason of Watson-Watt's duties. He combined inventions of his own to which the committee attached no great weight with existing knowledge in the electronic field producing the new conception of radiolocation and that conception or invention was rightly judged to be of exceptional utility and considerable merit.

There was no objection to the award but there was a question with the assessment; if it were done by the Department and Watson-Watt was dissatisfied with the amount then, as the patent holder, he could appeal to the Commission. There was another and perhaps overriding consideration and that was that the Treasury would not approve any payment except under 'compulsion' from the Commission. It was suggested that any letter sent to Watson-Watt should make no admission that there ought to be some reward of which only the amount was in question. The procedure should be that Watson-Watt should be asked to reproduce his claims and the Department would neither advocate nor strenuously oppose them. On 23 June 1950, Watson-Watt received a letter from the Permanent Secretary which stated that:

"...much doubt is felt whether it would be justifiable to recommend that you receive a money award.... In these circumstances, it is proposed to ask the Royal Commission to consider whether an award is justified." [2]

Watson-Watt lodged his claim on 14 August 1950. The Department's view was that they should use every argument that legitimately could be used to bring the inventions into perspective:

"Watson-Watt has claimed that his inventions were of a higher calibre than the cavity magnetron and at least as high as the work of Whittle ... we are influenced by the fact that the Department patented the inventions in his sole name and that the patents have been appraised by the Radio Patents Pool at maximum value. We should be very vulnerable to devastating comment if we pleaded no invention at all, and had to admit we had made a great fuss about protecting the invention in the USA, but we can still contend no outstanding brilliancy of status." [2]

The Patents Office was warned that his claim would traverse a long and lengthy path as it would be required to search all the old BRS files and interview all members of the early BRS staff. Letters were sent to Bowen and Rowe, who were in Australia, Bainbridge-Bell, Larnder and other BRS ex-staff with a copy of Watson-Watt's claim and asking for their comments. Rowe replied that he found it most difficult and certainly unpalatable to comment:

"Indeed I find it a little sad that Sir Robert Watson Watt is claiming financial recognition for his work." [2]

Rowe doubted very much whether radar was a basic invention; the early BRS team did not consist of exceptionally gifted men and the early work in connection with ground radar was rather of a simple character and was more of a question of engineering than science.

"I do exclude the work of Dr. Bowen and some of the work done by Mr. Bainbridge Bell. Dr. Bowen was certainly exceptionally gifted but the records show that one of the first steps I took when the University people became available was to put them over the heads of the pre-war people ...What I am trying to say is that there was nothing particularly brilliant about the early work of ground radar...In general, I would not put Watson Watt in the first two dozen radar inventors. In my opinion, however, he did a splendid job in the early days of radar in arousing enthusiasm, getting in touch with the Service people and in rapidly absorbing the nature of the problems...his influence declined during the war but there is no doubt that it was great before the war, although less in the role of inventor than as a 'seller' of a new field of applied effort. I think he did this splendidly. I should had thought that Watson Watt's efforts had been well rewarded by a Knighthood... if [he] were to receive any reward I would think that you would need to consider a very considerable number of others.

Rowe's letter ended with a PS

1. In the early days there was no invention at all comparable to the cavity magnetron.
2. This hastily dictated letter is a miserable affair but then so is the whole of the subject you raise.

and a PPS

I have just told Prof. Huxley (ex-TRE) of your letter. He considers some of the claims to be 'impudent.' " [2]

Professor Appleton's reply was that he was not concerned with defence matters until he was made a member of the Tizard Committee in 1936 and, not being in official circles:

"I do not think that I received the famous Post Office report. I imagine that Watson-Watt marshalled his proposals with powerful advocacy and convinced the Tizard Committee of their great value; he was in my opinion unrivalled in writing memorandum of this kind. When I came in touch with the practical radar work I found Bowen and Wilkins hard at work on the technical side ... but the biggest effort of all was being made by Watson-Watt in pleading, advocating, getting stores, masts and buildings. It was above all due to his drive and powerful advocacy that we had radar stations around our coast when the war broke out ...I must turn again to the supreme effort of Watson-Watt, he had the vision of what it all implied, he just burned with it. It is true to say that he had the backing of the Tizard Committee but I am sure that it was Watson-Watt's leadership of his team and his powerful and eloquent advocacy that won the day with the Air Staff and the Treasury. To sum up I think that Watson-Watt deserves a very substantial award for his work in turning scientific radar into practical radar but I would like to see others especially Bowen and Wilkins rewarded as well ...I have often said that in the development of both scientific and practical radar there is enough credit to go round." [2]

Dowding had been written to and he replied:

"I have retained no documents...[and my] memories are dim....but I am quite clear in my recollections, however, that Watson-Watt was not only the first in this country to notice and appreciate the military significance of radiated echoes reflected from aircraft, but also personally responsible for all the early development of the new techniques." [2]

Sir F.E.Smith wrote to the Secretary of the Commission asking why he had not been approached as at the time he was the Secretary of the DSIR. (He had seen the newspaper article and was now Head of Anglo-American Oil)

"I must state very definitely that the techniques and knowledge which was available was such that if none of the claimants had been available at the Air Ministry, radar would nevertheless had been developed by other personnel at the DSIR and radar devices would have been effected in the war. I was, however,definite that an echo trial should be made and had Appleton been a civil servant at the time I would have suggested his association with the work." [2]

Although all the early members of BRS had been sent copies of Watson-Watt's correspondence and were asked for comments, they finally decided amongst themselves that they would not comment adversely but would file parallel claims for the items for which they were responsible.

In January 1951 a London daily newspaper had an exclusive scoop with headlines – BIGGEST WAR AWARD MAY GO TO RADAR MAN – Royal Commission to hear in April claims by Sir Robert Watson-Watt and others. The Royal Commission sittings began on 12 April 1951 and concluded on 14 December with a total of 44 hearing days and during that time they visited Bawdsey to see demonstrations of CH, CHL, IFF, examples of AI, ASV, H^2S and their use, operation of the goniometer and interpretation of echoes. On 19 December the awards free of income tax were made public: R.A.Watson-Watt £50,000, A.F.Wilkins £12,000, E.G.Bowen £12,000, L.H.Bainbridge-Bell £2,400, H.Larnder £2,400, G.A.Roberts £2,400, W.A.S.Butement £1,200, P.E. Pollard £1,200, R.H.A.Carter £750, S.Jefferson £750, H.Dewhurst £750, J.H.Mitchell £750 and R.V.Whelpton £750.

The Commission remarked on the nature of the awards:

"It cannot be too often or too strongly emphasized that an award ... is simply a gratuity, a gift, the bestowing or withholding within the discretion of the Crown and the amount which is similarly discretionary." [2]

And finally a comment by one of the departmental under-secretaries; the recommendation by Lord Cohen of Sir Robert Watson-Watt's initiation of radar should cause no heart burning anywhere in the scientific world.

REFERENCES

1 AVIA53/630   2 AVIA53/300-302

Chapter 15   Site Locations

This list shows all operational stations from 1942 onwards but excludes CH mobiles that were positioned to cover some main CH stations. CD indicates an original War Office (Army) site.

ABERLERI	GCI-m	Nr Borth, Ceredigion
ANSTRUTHER	CHL	Fife
APPLEDORE	GCI-m, VEB	Kent
BALLINDERRY	GCI-m	Co. Tyrone N.I.
BALLYDONAGHY	GCI-m	Co. Tyrone N.I.
BALLYMARTIN	CHL	Co. Down N.I.
BALLYWOODAN	GCI	Co. Down N.I.
BAMBURGH	CHL	Northumberland
BARD HILL - CD	CHL,10cm	Holt, Norfolk
BARRAPOL	CHB	Tiree, Argyll and Bute
BAWDSEY	CH, CHL,10cm	Suffolk
BEACHY HEAD - CD	CHL,10cm	West Sussex
BEER HEAD	CHL,10cm	Devon
BEMBRIDGE	CHL, 10cm	Isle of Wight
BEMPTON	CHL,10cm	East Riding of Yorkshire
BEN HOUGH	CHL	Tiree, Argyll and Bute
BENACRE - CD	10cm	Suffolk
BEXHILL - CD	CHL	East Sussex
BLACKGANG	GCI-m, 10cm	Isle of Wight
BLACKHEAD - CD	CHL	Co. Antrim N.I.
BLANKETS FARM	GCI-m	Bulphan, Essex
BOLT TAIL - CD	CHL, 10cm	Devon
BONIFACE DOWN - CD	CHL	Isle of Wight
BORVE CASTLE	CHB	Benbecula, Western Isles
BRANSCOMBE	CH	Devon
BRECKNESS - CD	10cm	Stromness, Orkney Islands
BRENISH	CH	Western Isles
BRIDE	CH	Isle of Man

BROAD BAY	CH	Western Isles
CANEWDON	CH	Essex
CARN BRAE - CD	10cm	Cornwall
CARSAIG	CHL	Isle of Mull
CASTELL MAWR	CH	Nr Llanrhystud, Cegdn
CASTLEROCK	CH	Co. Derry N.I.
CLEADON - CD	CHL, 10cm	Tyne and Wear
CLETT	CHL	Shetland Islands
COCKBURNSPATH	CHL, 10cm	Borders
COCKLAW	CHL	Peterhead, Aberdeenshire
COMBERTON	GCI	Pershore, Herefordshire
CRANNOCH HILL - CD	CHL	Banff, Aberdeenshire
CRASTER - CD	10cm	Northumberland
CREGNEISH	CHL,10cm	Isle of Man
CRESSWELL	CHL,10cm	Northumberland
CRICKLADE	GCI-Int	Wiltshire
CROMARTY	CHL	Highland
CROSSMAGLEN	MRU	Co. Armagh N.I.
CRUSTAN	CHL,10cm	Orkney Islands
DALBY	CH	Isle of Man
DANBY BEACON	CH	Lealholm, North Yorkshire
DEERNESS	CHL,10cm	Orkney Islands
DENGIE	10cm	Essex
DIMLINGTON	10cm	Easington, E R Yorkshire
DIRLETON	GCI, 10cm	East Lothian
DOCTORS CORNER	GCI-m	Kenley, Surrey
DOONIES HILL	CHL,10cm	Gregness, Aberdeen City
DOUGLAS WOOD	CH,10cm	Monikie, Angus
DOVER (Swingate)	CH, CHL, 50cm	Kent
DOWNDERRY	CH,10cm	Cornwall
DOWNHILL	CHL,10cm	Co. Derry N.I.
DRONE HILL	CH	Nr Coldingham, Borders
DRYTREE	CH	Goonhilly Downs,Cornwall
DUNDERHOLE PT - CD	CHL, 10cm	Nr Tintagel, Cornwall
DUNKIRK	CH, 10cm	Kent
DUNNET HEAD	CHL,10cm	Nr Thurso, Highland
DUNRAGIT	GCI-m	Dumfries and Galloway
DUNWICH	CHL	Suffolk
DURRINGTON	GCI, 10cm	West Sussex
EASINGTON	CHL	East Riding of Yorkshire
EAST HILL	GCI-m,10cm	Dunstable, Bedfordshire
EORODALE	CHL,10cm	Butt of Lewis, W. Isles

EXMINSTER	GCI,10cm	Devon
FAIR ISLE	CHL, 10cm	Fair Isle
FAIRLIGHT	CHL,10cm	East Sussex
FLAT POINT - CD	10cm	Ilfracombe
FOLLY	CH	Nolton, Pembrokeshire
FORENESS POINT	CHL, 10cm	Kent
FORMBY	CHL	Merseyside
FOULNESS	GCI-Int	Essex
FULLARTON	GCI-Int	N. Ayrshire
GLENARM	CHL,10cm	Co. Antrim N.I.
GOLDSBOROUGH - CD	CHL,10cm	Whitby, N. Yorkshire
GREAT BROMLEY	CH,10cm	Essex
GREIAN HEAD	CHL	Barra, Western Isles
GREAT ORMES HEAD	CHL,10cm	Conwy
GREY FRIARS	50cm, 10cm	Suffolk
GREYSTONE	CH,10cm	Co. Down N.I.
GRUTNESS	CHL,10cm	Sumburgh,Shetland Islands
HABOST	CHB	Isle of Lewis
HACK GREEN	GCI	Nantwich, Cheshire
HAPPISBURGH	CHL,10cm	Norfolk
HARTLAND POINT	CHL,10cm	Devon
HAWCOAT	CHL	Barrow, Cumberland
HAWKS TOR	CH	Plymouth, Devon
HAYSCASTLE CROSS	CH	Pembrokeshire
HESTA GEO	GCI-m,10cm	Orkney Islands
HIGH STREET	CH	Darsham, Suffolk
HIGHDOWN HILL - CD	CHL	Angmering, W. Sussex
HILLHEAD	CH	Memsie, Aberdeenshire
HOPE COVE	GCI, 10cm	Malborough, Devon
HOPTON	CHL,10cm	Norfolk
HUMBERSTON	CHL	Lincolnshire
HYTHE - CD	CHL 10,50cm	Kent
ISLE OF MAY	10cm	Firth of Forth
ISLIVICK	CHL	Western Isles
JACKA - CD	CHL,10cm	Portloe, Cornwall
KENDROM	CHL,10cm	Kilmaluag, Isle of Skye
KETE	CHL,10cm	Dale, Pembrokeshire
KILCHIARAN	CHL,10cm	Islay, Argyll and Bute
KILKEEL	CH	Co. Down N.I.
KILKENNETH	CH	Tiree, Argyll and Bute
KING GARTH	GCI-m	Carlisle, Cumberland
KINGSWEAR	CHL,10cm	Devon

KINLEY HILL	CHL	Seaham, Durham
KNIGHTS FARM	GCI-m	Reading, Berkshire
LAMBERTON MOOR	10cm	Borders
LANGTOFT	GCI	Cambridgeshire
LAW (The) - CD	CHL, 10cm	Carnoustie, Angus
LISNASKEA	GCI-m	Enniskillen N.I.
LONG LOAD	GCI	Somerset
LOTH	CH	Helmsdale, Highland
MARKS CASTLE	CHL	Land's End, Cornwall
MINEHEAD - CD	CHL	Somerset
MOSSY BOTTOM - CD	CHL	Shoreham, West Sussex
NAVIDALE	CHL	Highland
NEATISHEAD	GCI, 10cm	Wroxham, Norfolk
NEEDLES - CD	CHL,10cm	Isle of Wight
NETHERBUTTON	CH	Holm, Orkney Islands
NEVIN (Nefyn)	CH	Gwynedd
NEWCHURCH	CH	Kent
NEWFORD	GCI-m	Isles of Scilly
NEWTOWNBUTLER	MRU	Co. Fermanagh N.I.
NORTH CAIRN	CH	Nr Stranraer, Dumfries
N. FORELAND - CD	CHL,10cm	Kent
NORTHAM	CH	Devon
NORTHSTEAD	GCI, 10cm	Acklington, Northumb.
NOSS HILL	CH	Shetland Islands
ORBY	GCI, 10cm	Lincolnshire
OTTERCOPS MOSS	CH	Otterburn, Northumb.
OXWICH - CD	CHL	Swansea
PATRINGTON	GCI, 10cm	East Riding of Yorkshire
PEN OLVER	CHL,10cm	Lizard, Cornwall
PEN-Y-BRYN	CHL,10cm	Gwynedd
PEVENSEY	CH	East Sussex
POINT OF STOER	CHL	Highland
POLING	CH	West Sussex
PRESTATYN	CHL,10cm	Denbighshire
RAME CHAPEL - CD	10cm	Cornwall
RAME HEAD	CHL	Cornwall
RAMSGATE-CD	CHL	Kent
RAVENSCAR	CHL	North Yorkshire
RHOSSILI BAY- CD	10cm	Swansea
RHUDDLAN	CH	Denbighshire
RINGSTEAD	CH	Ringstead Bay, Dorset
RIPPERSTON	GCI,10cm	Nr Kete Pembrokeshire

RODDANS PORT	CHL	Co. Down N.I.
RODEL PARK	CHL	Rodel, Western Isles
ROECLIFFE	GCI-m	North Yorkshire
ROSEHEARTY	CHL,10cm	Aberdeenshire
RUSSLAND	GCI-m	Orkney Islands
RYE	CH	East Sussex
ST AGNES BEACON - CD	10cm	Nr Perranporth, Cornwall
ST ANNES	GCI-m	Lancashire
ST ANN'S HEAD - CD	10cm	Pembrokeshire
ST BEES HEAD	CHL	Cumberland
ST CYRUS	CHL,10cm	Aberdeenshire
ST DAVID'S HEAD	10cm	Pembrokeshire
ST LAWRENCE	CH	Isle of Wight
ST MARGARET'S BAY	10cm	Kent
ST TWYNELLS	CHL, 10cm	Pembrokeshire
SALIGO BAY	CH	Islay, Argyll and Bute
SALTBURN - CD	10cm	North Yorkshire
SANGO	CH, CHL	Lairg, Highland
SANDWICH	GCI,10cm	Kent
SAXAVORD	CHL,10cm	Unst, Shetland Islands
SCARLETT	CH	Isle of Man
SCHOOLHILL	CH	Portlethen, Aberdeenshire
SEATON SNOOK	GCI,10cm	Nr Hartlepool, Durham
SENNEN	CH	Cornwall
SHOTTON	CHL	Durham
SKAW	CH	Unst, Shetland Islands
SKENDLEBY	CHL,10cm	Lincolnshire
SOPLEY	GCI,10cm	Hampshire
SOUTHBOURNE	CH,10cm	Dorset
SOUTH RONALDSAY	CHL, 10cm	Orkney Islands
SOUTH STACK	CHL, 10cm	Isle of Anglesy
START POINT - CD	10cm	Devon
STAXTON WOLD	CH	North Yorkshire
STAYTHORPE	GCI-m	Nottinghamshire
STENIGOT	CH	Louth, Lincolnshire
STOKE HOLY CROSS	CH	Norfolk
STRUMBLE HEAD	CHL	Pembrokeshire
SWANSEA BAY - CD	CHL	Vale of Glamorgan
TANNACH	CH	Wick, Highland
THE LAW - CD	CHL,10cm	Carnoustie, Angus
THORPENESS - CD	10cm	Suffolk
TRELANVEAN	CH	GoonhillyDowns,Cornwall

TRELEAVER	GCI,10cm	Cornwall
TREREW	CH	Newquay, Cornwall
TREVESCAN	MRU	Cornwall
TREVOSE HEAD	CHL	Cornwall
TREWAN SANDS	GCI,10cm	Isle of Anglesey
TRIMLEY HEATH	GCI	Felixstowe, Suffolk
TRIMINGHAM - CD	10cm	Norfolk
TRULEIGH HILL	CHL,10cm	Bramber, West Sussex
ULBSTER	CHL,10cm	Nr Wick, Highland
VENTNOR	CH, CHL, 50, 10cm	Isle of Wight
VERNE - CD	10cm	Portland, Dorset
WALTON-ON--NAZE	CHL,10cm	Essex
WARDEN POINT - CD	10cm	Isle of Sheppey, Kent
WARREN	CH	Pembrokeshire
WARTLING	GCI,10cm	East Sussex
WATSNESS	CHL	Nr Walls, Shetland Islands
WEST BECKHAM	CH, 10cm	Norfolk
WEST PRAWLE	CH	Devon
WESTBURN - CD	CHL	Aberdeen
WESTCLIFF - CD	CHL	Portland, Dorset
WHALE HEAD	CH	Sanday, Orkney Islands
WHITEHAWK - CD	CHL,10cm	Brighton, East Sussex
WHITSTABLE	CHL,10cm	Kent
WILLESBOROUGH	GCI-Int	Kent
WINTERTON - CD	10cm	Norfolk
WORTH MATRAVERS	CH, CHL 10cm	Swanage, Dorset
WRAFTON	GCI	Devon
WYLFA	CH	Isle of Anglesy

Chapter 16   Postscript

WITH the end of the European war many of the stations were closed by simply locking the compound gates. Newly formed 90 Group began the huge task of dismantling the chains; first to go were the curtain arrays at the CH stations that would be a hazard to low flying aircraft. CHL and 10cm sites that were considered to be redundant, mainly those on the west coasts of England, Scotland and Wales, and in Northern Ireland, had their equipment removed and stored in the nearest unheated CH station. Masts were lowered but towers and permanent buildings remained; land was restored to the original owner unless the Air Ministry wanted it for future use. Many farmers retained outbuildings to store hay and machinery or to shelter cattle after a suitably sized hole had been made in one of the walls: others, after modifications, were used for the feeding of pigs and turkeys.

The east coast CH stations presented the biggest problem because of the massive construction of the transmitter and receiver blocks, which were found almost impossible to demolish, as were the footings for the wooden towers. The wardens' quarters, if not all, exist to this day and were eagerly bought by private citizens who wanted houses far away from civilisation. Drone Hill eventually became a caravan park with the T building altered into a community centre and pub by removing all the internal walls, and using the protective traverse as storage space. At Netherbutton a house was built on top of the T building and the R building converted to a bungalow.

The East Chain remained almost intact but unused for a number of years with a number of stations upgraded during the 1950s as part of the 'Cold War' defences. But the ultimate fate of most of them was to be declared as 'Surplus to Requirements' and placed into the cold hands of auctioneers for disposal. Overleaf is the public announcement of the two day sale at the technical sites of the former radar stations at Rye and Pevensey on 12th and 13 November 1958, with details of the latter.

Equipment suffered a graver destiny....A newspaper reported on 20 January 1954 that a Labour MP intended to question the Minister of Supply about 1,000 cases of government radar equipment which were lying in a scrap yard in his constituency. A director of the company said that they had put in a tender for government surplus which had been described as radar equipment packed in cases and containing between 400 and 500 tons of brass, aluminium and steel.

PEVENSEY SITE

(On the Pevensey Marshes, to the West of the Boreham Street—Wartling
—Pevensey Road)

Thursday, 13th November, 1958

LOT
52   All the smaller buildings on the site comprising
6 brick or rendered buildings with tiled,
asbestos or concrete roofs, 3 three stage open
brick towers and 9in. brick and rendered
open fronted fuel bay together with the
contents :

Ledged and braced and other doors,
metal and wooden casement windows,
benching, 9 sets of tread steps, boarded
flooring, linoleum as laid, lavatory basin,
pan, cistern and piping, and all electrical
fittings.

53   The earth covered air raid shelters comprising
4 of brick and concrete and 1 of brick and
corrugated iron sheets with timber shoring
and metal doors.

54   A 6 bay compound adjoining guard room, 60ft.
x 20ft., formed of angle iron and enclosed
by chain link fencing and wire netting with
6 iron framed gates.

55   Handcraft building, 37ft. x 19ft., together with
the following contents :

2 ledged and braced doors, 4 metal case
ment windows and all electrical fittings.

56   Similar building adjacent, together with
contents as above.

57   Handcraft building, converted into pig sty
containing 4 concrete block fatting pens,
feeding troughs and pivoted sheet metal
feed guards, together with the following
contents :

3 ledged and braced doors, 6 metal
casement windows and all electrical fittings.

£30

53 Handcraft building adjacent, together with the following contents:
2 ledged and braced doors, 6 metal casement windows, quantity of tongued and grooved concrete blocks and all electrical fittings.

£7.10
Popled

59 Two brick and asbestos pig sties and runs, adjoining water tower, with feeding troughs and interior block or boarded partitions.

X

60 Elevated iron water tower with 1,000 gallon enclosed tank on 3in. angle iron supports, with iron ladder and piping.

£12

61 Handcraft building, with interior brick partition, together with the following contents:
1 ledged and braced and 2 panelled doors, 7 metal windows, Ideal Boiler, galvanised hot and cold water storage tanks and piping, enamelled bath, 2 lavatory pans and cisterns and all electrical fittings.

£10

62 Handcraft building adjacent, together with the following contents:
2 ledged and braced doors, 4 metal windows and electrical fittings.

£144

63 Range of 5 pig sties and runs, built of concrete block with corrugated asbestos roof and 5 11ft. 6-bar tubular gates, lined internally and fitted with glazed feeding troughs and tubular bar fronts, together with the following contents:
2 ledged and braced doors, 5 metal windows and electrical fittings.

£30

64 Building of 13½in. brick with beach filled concrete roof, 28ft. x 22ft., and leanto boarded shed adjoining and the surrounding concrete blast wall, together with the following contents:
Double ledged and braced door and casement window.

LOT

The following equipment in or attached to the above building will be sold as separate lots:

65 **Mirrlees – Ricardo** 60 k.w., 102 h.p. 3-cylinder diesel engine with alternator, D.C. generator, 50 gallon surface fuel tank, low tension switch board with 3 oil circuit breakers and travelling gantry and all electrical fittings in the building.

£115

66 Six cylindrical galvanised water tanks (approximately 500 gallons each).

£19

67 Underground diesel fuel tank containing approximately 625 gallons of oil, and the concrete slab covering.

£21

68 Three part drums of 6 strand wire cable.

15/-

69 Building of rendered brick, 41ft. x 20ft., with boarded, felt and trussed roof, and interior brick partitions, and surrounding brick blast walls, together with the following contents :
8 doors, 7 wooden casement windows, deep glazed sink, lavatory pan, cistern and piping.

£15
Hutchins

70 The sewage pump chamber housing two Hayward Tyler 3 inch centrifugal pumps, 4in. iron piping, iron ladder, pressure gauges, electrical switch gear and fittings and manhole covers to chamber.
(Note : The sewage pump chamber and equipment near the two cottages is not for sale).

£6

71 Rendered brick building, 27ft. x 19ft., with corrugated asbestos roof, iron guttering and down pipe, and interior brick partitions and lined roof together with the following contents :
6 panelled doors, 6 wooden casement windows with iron bars, lavatory basin and piping and electrical fittings.

£9

LOT

72 A large quantity of miscellaneous electrical equipment, spares and cable lying in the above building.

£5-10

73 Building of 18in. brick, 60ft. x 30ft., with beach filled concrete roof and asbestos down pipe and the surrounding concrete blast walls together with the following contents :

£3

Pair of 7ft. heavy steel doors and frame, 10 doors, 2 pairs of 8ft. partition doors, 5 wooden windows aud quantity of 6in. x 2in. planks.

The following equipment in or attached to the above building will be sold as separate lots:

74 The whole of the electrical equipment in the building comprising :

Ferguson Pailin 3-panel M.V. Switch Board complete with 3 ammeters, volt meter, oil circuit breaker and bus bar chambers, 3 constant voltage transformers and Ferranti 20 KVA 3 phase transformer together with all wiring in conduit, switch and fuse boxes, etc., and the remaining ventilation plant comprising inlet, gas filter and galvanised trunking throughout the building.

£26

75 **A 350ft. Transmitting Tower** of sheradised steel girders, complete with ladders, struts, bracing and boarded platforms.

£100

£100 **76** A similar lot.

£100 **77** A ditto.

£14 **78** Twenty 5in. x 4½in. R.S.J.s and pulleys as erected between towers.

£10 10 **79** Thirty-six telephone poles as erected on the site.

LOT

80 The Power Cable as laid on the site, lead covered and pipes insulated, comprising approximately :

768 yards 3 core cable, .06 x .04
800 yards 4 core cable, .0225
430 yards 4 core cable, .007
830 yards 2 core cable, .007
700 yards 10 core cable, .0045

(Note : The purchaser, before removal, must contact the Station Engineer, R.A.F. Domestic Site, Barnhorn Road, Little Common (Bexhill 3660) as there is a live 11,000 volt cable on the site. The 10 core cable must be hand dug).

81 Six stoves as fitted in Guard Room and Lots Nos. 58, 61, and 69, comprising 2 Esse Dura No. 1, 4 Rumesse barrel stoves and piping, together with sundry iron, tanks, piping, scrap and crates as lying on the site excluding any attachment to buildings or the drainage system.

EX – RAF AND WAAF NARRATIVES

GEORGE BAGRIE

On April, 1942 I joined the RAF and began eight weeks training at Great Yarmouth which was suddenly cut to three, a great mercy, due to immediate vacancies in technical training. The intensive radio course at the Royal Technical College, Duke Street, Glasgow (now the University of Strathclyde), was for eight months and we were very fortunate as my entry was the first one to go on a non-shift basis. Prior to that it had been a shorter course working in shifts including during the night but the casualty rate of those screaming down the streets caused them to revert to day time working. The unit was based at RAF Bishopbriggs, which was a balloon centre, for Admin. Lectures took place during the day at the college and in the evenings we attended a Project Centre in a private house in Kelvinbridge where some very kind ladies, wives of some of the college staff, prepared supper for us which was a welcome piece of civilisation as conditions were, otherwise, very bad.

We were billeted in filthy warehouses made vacant by the war. I was in 19 John Street and others were in Cathedral Street, Ingham Street and the infamous Telford's warehouse in Miller Street where smallpox actually broke out. There was no heat in the winter; we were packed in tight, possibly for warmth, with the only warm place being the college by day. Lectures commenced at 0800 hours prompt then around 1000 hours a short romp on the roof above sooty Duke Street laughingly called PE. Lunch was 45 minutes at our cookhouse, which was Glens warehouse in Ingram Street, then straight into the afternoon sessions, which were either the lab or workshop practice, a short break again in the soot, then on until 1800 hours. In the evenings, despite being tired, were the projects and those who failed to keep up with their practical work were obliged to go back to the college for additional instructions.

We were very well treated by the college staff; a Dr. Howie took us for Maths and Physics and we learned a lot of valuable radio theory from Professor Jamieson, who had been brought back from retirement and had been an Admiralty scientist in the first world war. Saturday was a working day and Sunday was known as the RAF's Revenge Day. It was a rather hard eight months but despite this horror story most people enjoyed it though some did not survive. For my part I received a life long benefit from it.

No. 19 John Street contained three classes of 50, plus all casualties awaiting postings and the SP (station police) who kept the whole outfit in order, a total of nearly 200. There was one full floor, a filthy floor at that, provided with a few GS tables and forms which was labelled a recreation and study centre, three 60 watt bulbs and a tiny but broken gas fire to give the necessary touch of luxury. The classes were designated from A to G which gave the total number under training of 350 at any one time. New classes took the next available letter and appeared to begin at two monthly intervals. Also at the college were some Army artificers of various cap badges training to be assimilated into the newly formed REME. This led to quite a scare amongst the RAF personnel as shortly before we arrived a complete RAF class was transferred en bloc to the new REME on completion of their course. A latrine rumour at the time had it that a further class was due for transfer but thankfully this turned out to be false.

Further to the congestion at the college during my period, we carried out overnight fire patrols for which we were actually paid and given a free supper, otherwise the college staff would have been obliged to do them under wartime regulations. There were further billets in Cathedral Street, said to be particularly filthy, and at the Bellgrave Hotel in Gallowgate, which were in the process of being run down and were only used for the temporary transit of arrivals and departures. The question of movement to and from the college was something of a sod's opera. We were paraded at 0730 in John Street and after a lot of shuffling about we proceeded via Cochrane Street, crossing Duke Street and then climbing the steep hill of Montrose Street coming to a breathless halt outside the maternity hospital. Here we came under much banter from the ladies in waiting who appeared on the balconies.

Classes from other locations arrived and together with these groups there was some attempt at drilling and shuffling, rather difficult on a 45 degree slope. The untidy throng then filtered slowly through a small side door of the college to traverse a considerable mileage of corridors and avenues to reach the various work places. It took a lot of time and was all due to a rule that we common Service students could not use the main entrance on Duke Street. On dark foggy winter Glasgow mornings each class carried a hurricane lamp front and rear, the rear one being red with a roster in force for this privilege.

The only people allowed to meander were those excused marching for medical reasons and those still wearing civilian clothes due to being awkward in size who in some cases may not have received their uniform in full by the end of the course! A point that rankled with most of us was that in addition to the privilege they had in being allowed to wander free, they also received a cash allowance for wearing their own civilian clothes and were also allowed to use the sacred main entrance of the college.

Sundays were always a lottery; there was sometimes a church parade held in the college chapel and I was unable to escape being registered Church of Scotland. Occasionally we would march to Glasgow Green to the Episcopal Cathedral and this was always an amusing thing marching through the Bridgeton area, which drew a lot of odd comments from the natives. Always on Sundays was a stringent billet inspection, although it was very difficult to keep anything clean in these warehouses. Dependent on the availability of suitable permanent staff, we received non technical training, playing about with a Swift training rifle, some anti gas and First Aid lectures, survival, and, unless you were very crafty and kept out of the way, always cookhouse fatigues.

I had an unfair advantage here having relations in East Kilbride and Newton Mearns and arranged for them sometimes to claim me on a Sunday morning so I usually managed to get out of them. Also we were claimed by various Church people and in particular the very, very kind ladies of St Johns, Church of Scotland, which was opposite the main door. These ladies were wonderful and in addition to looking after the chaps on Sunday they ran a mending and tea making facility in the church hall most evenings, which was very much appreciated, believe me.

A considerable amount of theory was taught and in the labs we played about with multi-vibrators and time bases, that we made up on bread boards in addition to making up basic radio sets. The rare occasions when we had no lectures or lab. work was called 'free time' and if you stayed around in the billet you were grabbed for something unpleasant so the technique was to get out but avoid the town patrols. Now, the worthy Glasgow Corporation had made it a rule that Service men and women travelled on the Glasgow trams for a penny, any distance, and in Glasgow this 'any distance' was quite something. We took our books, boarded a tram, probably travelled to Milngavie then right back on a car which went through to Govan, Paisley and Renfrew Ferry. We used to position ourselves upstairs near one end and have a question and answer sessions- a great deal of our revision was done travelling around Glasgow on a tram.

Glens warehouse usually held one class but the main purpose of the warehouse was the cookhouse on the ground floor. This was in the form of a big shop with the windows painted over. It was a giant dining hall and the cookhouse staff appeared to live in the building somewhere and when caught for fatigues that is where one went. It had a filthy rat ridden yard at the back and one of the great sports when playing with the spud peeling machine was to flush out rats with a hose pipe and attempt to flush them into it – all good clean fun and very hygienic! The other place that the RAF had taken over was a hotel near Charing Cross and the two non technical officers, who managed the disciplinary affairs, lived in this hotel as did the single Education Officer, who was the RAF's liaison with the college. He was a RAF Flight Lieutenant and the only intelligent person on the permanent staff, who were by and large a fairly rough crowd, mainly local people with long service, probably re-engaged regulars and most of them appeared to us, being young, of enormous age.

Reporting sick was not considered very advisable as the central sick headquarters were in St Vincent Street for the whole of Balloon Command and was on the top floor of the Cunard building – with the lift being out of bounds! The principle was that if you were fit enough to climb the stairs you were not very sick! For dental treatment at Bishopbriggs there used to be a ceremony of handing out two pennies to take the tram as far as it went near the camp and it was an unpleasant sight seeing people clutching their mouth walking back from Bishopbriggs to the tram. Baths meant a march to Townhead (Injun country!) – in our own time! My course ended Christmas, 1942, and after a few weeks leave I was posted to No 6 Radio School, Bolton, where some 5000 trainees were there at any one time. After passing out I was posted to RAF Woodvale for a few weeks course under operational conditions and left Blackpool for India in August 1943.

PHILIP BAILEY

After my six months 'ab initio' course at Bradford I was posted to Cranwell for my basic radar course and the first thing we were told by the admin. Warrant officer was that it was a great honour to be at the 'Sandhurst of the RAF'; the fact that we were not allowed anywhere near the famous college making no difference. The basic radar course included the principles of radar, the Chain Home (CH) receiver, aerial systems, Chain Home Low (CHL) transmitter, receiver and aerial system, spark gap switching (ie switching the aerials from the transmitter to the receiver between pulses) and aerial turning gear. After this course we were posted to stations on the CH or the CHL chain anywhere in the country.

Those on my course were all sent to the north of Scotland and I ended up at Rosehearty near Fraserburgh. My first posting was to the CHL at

Rosehearty where everyone lived in civilian billets and it was easy to get a bus into Fraserburgh, which was only four miles away. Once or twice a week there was a dance in the village when the English were forced to learn the Eightsome Reel, etc, and were whirled around until they were dizzy. I had never been to Scotland before and my lasting impression of the people was their kindness; it really is a joke about the Aberdonians being mean.

As well as the CHL at Rosehearty there was a 10cm Naval type 271 equipment installed in a rotatable, by hand, cabin with two parabolic reflectors on the front, one for transmitting and the other for receiving there being no automatic transmit/receive switching on this early equipment. On watch at night the radar mechanic used to help out with operating the 271 which was used to plot shipping movements in the mine swept channel that ran north/south off Fraserburgh the plots being passed every half hour to the naval plotting room in Aberdeen. The system helped to keep ships in the swept channel and reported any enemy E boat activity. Mention of the Naval Plotting room reminds me of an incident involving myself and two friends when we were in Aberdeen on our day off. On the spur of the moment we decided to find out if we could have a look around the secret plotting room, which we knew was located in a requisitioned hotel. We presented ourselves to the Marine guard at the door, told him where we were from and asked if we could have permission to enter. I think that he thought we were officers as he called me 'Sir' and after showing our identity cards and some delay we were admitted.

The officer in charge seemed a bit put out but he got the WRNS to show us around, and, as we were used to talking to them on the tie line, all went well. However the rot set in the next day when our C.O. had us in and demanded an explanation as to why we had gate crashed the naval plotting room without his consent; the navy had of course phoned him to check on our identities before letting us in. Somehow we avoided being placed on a charge – perhaps he thought we had shown a bit of initiative! There was once an unfortunate event at Rosehearty when a RAF officer arrived on some sort of inspection and insisted on testing the twin Browning machine guns, which were the usual air defence at small stations. So he got into position on the seat, pointed the guns out to sea and pressed the triggers. For some reason the guns swivelled round and most of the bullets went through the CHL aerial array damaging some of the dipoles. I think he left without further delay.

Initially, airmen were graded as radio/wireless mechanic and the first six months ab initio training was common to both, after the final exams the group was split with the top six or eight people being sent for training as radio mechanics, later (1943) called radar mechanics. The people selected for training as radar mechanics were sent to one of the two radar training schools at Yatesbury or Cranwell for a four and a half months basic radar course. The ab initio courses were provided at various technical colleges around the country such as Bradford, where I went, Leicester, one or two in the London area and several others. At Bradford we lived in various empty houses near the college, the cookhouse being a church hall, where the food was awful.

Fortunately the college was excellent, the instructors all being civilians and a great deal was compressed into six months, the syllabus comprised DC theory, AC theory, basic wireless theory and circuits, workshop practice and maths, a full and comprehensive course, which on looking back seems incredible in wartime. The living conditions were very poor at Bradford and compared unfavourably to some of the other locations where the airmen lived in civilian billets. However, it was quite a pleasant town and it was very easy to get into the country for walks and it suited me very well as it was only 60 miles from home. In June 1943 after four months at Rosehearty, I and three others, with whom I had been at Cranwell, were posted to the fighter aerodrome at Manston, Kent, where nobody knew what to do with us as we were not trained on any aerodrome or aircraft radio equipment so we were mis-employed for some time helping out where we could on the radio section. Eventually however we became involved with the testing and installation of IFF sets in Typhoons and Hurricanes, this at least had something to do with radar as IFF sets (Identification Friend or Foe) were transponders which transmitted extra pulses when they were 'interrogated' by the main radar chains. Thus the operators could distinguish between normal radar echoes and the ones with the extra pulses, which were friendly.

The six months spent at Manston was interesting and at times exciting, and gave an insight into life and work on a front line fighter airfield. My next posting in November 1943 was to Navidale in Sutherland, another CHL and 271 station, there was very little operational activity there and in fact the station was closed down in December. The nearest village to Navidale was Helmsdale, which did not have much to recommend it except that we could play badminton in the village hall. The only place to get a haircut was at the blacksmith's near the harbour where one had to sit on the anvil, which was made tolerable by the blacksmith, a kindly man, placing a sack on it.

After a basic 10cm course at Yatesbury in Jan 1944 I had a couple of months on a miserable station at Dengie on the Essex marshes, which was a 277 site using a 240ft steel tower with a lift. This high power 10cm radar was used to detect low flying aircraft off the Thames Estuary. About April 1944 I was posted to Yatesbury for a Type 9000 (Oboe) course and after this to the Oboe station at Winterton, Norfolk in June. On my first day on watch I was given a cup of tea by a WAAF who I subsequently married and she says she has been making tea for me ever since!

PHYLLIS BAILEY

I volunteered for the WAAF in August 1942 and was sent to Morecambe for square-bashing; I had applied for Clerk S.D. but before leaving Morecambe I realised that I was to be trained as an RDF operator and as we were there longer than most recruits rumour had it that our family backgrounds were being investigated. There was a six week wait at the CH station Wylfa before posting to Yatesbury on 26 November where training was largely split between day and night classes. The tiredness was aggravated as in one part of the huts there were cooks and general duties staff, some of whom got up at 0430 or came to bed at midnight. We also got up at odd times so there was a continuous stream of WAAF's either going to bed or getting up.

From Yatesbury in January 1943 to Prestatyn CHL, which was operationally very quiet. In January 1944 several of the WAAF's were posted to 7000, Katie, 9000 and GCI stations; these names were spoken in hushed tones as none of us knew what they were and rumour had it that the clever ones were posted to 7000 and even cleverer ones to 9000, which was supposed to be the best. I and two more WAAF's were posted to Worth Matravers in the Spring of 1944 for a 9000 course which lasted six weeks and ended about the end of March 1944; I was then posted to Winterton in Norfolk. The site was right on the coast between the villages of Winterton and Hemsby with the living accommodation near Hemsby.

We lived in pre-war timber beach bungalows on the edge of an inner row of sand dunes and the valley in front of us and behind the dunes was mined and stray dogs often set off the mines. The huts were of different designs but usually consisted of one main room and two smaller rooms off with sometimes a sun room also used as a bedroom. There was a kitchen and an outside Elsan, which was emptied daily between 12.30 and 1.00pm by "Sam" the Elsan man just as we were going to lunch. There were six occupants in each hut with electric light and a cold tap, most had an open fireplace with coke available for heating but as this would not burn on an open fire we had to find wood to start the fire.

It was very cold there in the winter. There were no electric power points so electric heating was forbidden but most huts had at least two heaters made by friendly mechanics from a round electric element fitted into a cake tin. These were hidden underneath the floorboards by day and plugged into a light socket and used to boil water to make tea or coffee and filling our hot water bottles as well as providing a little heat as it was very cold in these huts on the sand dunes during winter. (In the summer of 1987 I returned to Winterton for a visit and found my hut 'Rose Villa' in use as a holiday home.)

The ablutions was a specially built block at the Hemsby end of the camp and quite a trek from my hut for a bath, and the best time for a hot bath was when you came off duty about 1 am. The RAF lived in similar huts so I assume that their conditions were like ours except that the girls made their rooms much more home like with a few picture post cards and most of us had a bedside locker made from an old orange box on which we usually had a vase of flowers. Beside the aforementioned orange box we had a bedside rug, a chair and a row of books on the wall and apart from the bed and chair I cannot recollect any other RAF furniture at all. We lived out of our kitbags and most of us had an old ammunition box for the storage of stores and cleaning material.

Operationally, Winterton was the most interesting, the watches consisting of four to five WAAFs with a Corporal i/c, a day staff Operations Sergeant and a day F/Sgt or Sergeant and two mechanics on watch and an Officer and a controller, who was an RAF Officer ex aircrew Bomber Command. During the early summer of 1944 most of the targets were in the Ruhr at night time but D Day operations were covered by Walmer, Worth and Sennen much to our disappointment. Later during the summer we were very busy during the daytime pin pointing V1 and V2 targets in northern France and frequently received photographs showing the results. Another memorable target was the breaching of the sea walls to flood Walchen Island in the Scheldt estuary and softening up before the crossing of the Rhine and continuing with the V sites.

I shall not forget VE day as I was on watch that morning and we were very busy dropping food canisters on The Hague and we were relieved very late by the next watch, who told us that they had just had a celebration lunch but when we got to the cookhouse there was none left, just corned beef and mashed potatoes! The food dropping to relieve the starvation in Holland lasted a few more days and then all the operations were finished and we spent our duty hours helping to dismantle the barbed wire entanglements and other similar tasks. I was very fortunate as about two months after VE day Bomber Command took a few operators on a flight in a Lancaster over the Ruhr, a ballot was held and I was one of the lucky six from Winterton. We flew from Wyton, near Huntingdon, two each to a plane in the bomb aimer's position, an unforgettable experience.

Life at Winterton was much more intense than at Prestatyn although there was a K site opposite Winterton 1 and in the same guarded compound we had very little to do with the personnel, we shared the camp facilities but they were in different huts. Off duty activities were mainly cycling and sailing and I visited dozens of Norfolk churches, went to Yarmouth for the cinema and to Norwich for the day out. There was one part of the beach cleared of mines and used for swimming but not very often. One autumn day I as on my bike ready to leave camp when I realised that I was off it and on the ground and then I heard a loud report. It was an early V2 and apart from a few broken windows in the huts very little damage was done as it fell into the sand dunes between the living accommodation and the sea. In the autumn of 1945 we were all moved to a disused airfield at Ludlum about ten miles away and there I remained until my demob in December 1945.

DAVID C. DAVIES

At the outbreak of the war I was working with an outfit called British McMurdo Silver, which made very high quality amplifiers, and I was working as a laboratory assistant. Then I found myself recruited by the RAF. One day I was a civilian, the next a Pilot Officer, put into uniform and dispatched (in great trepidation) to Manston, in Kent. I spent three days at this fighter station, which at that point in time still had the formal trappings of a nineteen thirties Officers' Mess, very intimidating to a young lad totally unfamiliar with such splendour. However three days later I was moved on to a place called Dunkirk, which was a well-wooded village upon the high ground south of the Thames Estuary and billeted on the local vicar. Dunkirk was the site of a CH radar station. The C.O. was John Ree, an erudite and charming man, who showed me over the station, which seemed to be 'manned' by WAAFs, working away plotting the movement of aircraft both friend and foe. I recall that he took me into his office, opened a drawer and produced a .45 Colt revolver with which he had been issued to defend the station. John Ree had been Chief Engineer of the Logie Baird Company and had been in the forefront of the great competition between Baird and EMI for the television franchise from the BBC.

After a week of these wonders I was posted to the radar school at Yatesbury in the winter of 1939. It was on the Bath road some miles west of Marlborough and a few miles short of Calne; it was on the right hand side some hundreds of yards off the main road and consisted of four long huts. These made up the Officers' Mess, the dining room, kitchens and domestic quarters. Further back were the Officers' quarters and everybody had a batman, who used to run my bath in the morning and lay out my clothes, quite a new world to me. The RDF school was further back about ¾ of a mile off the main road, a high chain linked compound, barbed wire on the top with a 4ft concrete path which led down through the fields. It had two rows of wooden huts separated by some 50 yards and associated with each pair of huts was a 90ft wooden tower, 15 or 20 of these down each side of the site in symmetrical and parallel lines.

In these huts we received instruction in the wonders of RDF. The backbone of the teaching staff in those days was the RAF Education branch and one chap called Bamford, who was rather a tubby, self satisfied, pleasant chap with a sunny outlook, definitely on the podgy side, who also had a similar pug dog. He was known as Bammy and he was a somewhat indifferent lecturer as he used to get the technicalities wrapped round his neck and it took quite a bit of effort to make out what it was all about, so we invented the unit of Confusion, the Bam. I ran into the Bam quite a few times after I left Yatesbury. I found myself on a course with some 25 people. It was really a brilliant collection of people, two or three Dons from Cambridge and Oxford, a lot of chaps from the BBC, various other scientific chaps and others like myself from the radio industry, even a patent lawyer. The course lasted for two months and it was good fun because none of us knew anything about the Services. I remember there was one chap, Blanco White, a KC, who would never walk in step with the other chaps, he always had to be half a pace out because he said that walking in step was regimentation and he was against regimentation.

There was another fellow named Martin on the course who had been in the RAF. He had been on a CH station in Yorkshire. He was a fine engineer and he told us all kinds of stories, one of them about a rigger up one of the 350ft steel towers, a four sided hollow tower and this chap had managed to fall down the inside, was blown against the tower side and was killed. Martin had to go to the inquest and he was amazed at the verdict which was that the chap had died of a heart attack.

We did more or less the complete range of radars then on the go, CH and CHL, learning about the receivers RF5 and RF6 made by Cossor. They had bicycle chains up on one side, sprockets to permit frequency change and were six foot high. The MB1 and MB2 transmitters looked like large pianos and were developed by the Army for GL, Gun Laying equipment. The big CH transmitters were magnificent things, the one characteristic I shall always remember is that they were housed in a large cage about the size of an average dining room and you could look through the mesh of the cage to see all the coils and condensers sitting there. The tuning capacitors were large constructions in steel, some as much as 3ft by 2ft and were mounted in pairs one against the other and articulated at the bottom so that they could be moved in and out to change frequency. Some were moved in as close as 3 or 4 inches and out at an angle as they were pivoted at the bottom and moved outwards like a fan to 18 inches or so at the top. The transmitter changed frequency in a fixed sequence; there were four frequencies and every time you changed the frequency it only changed in one direction, from 1 to 2, to 3, to 4 and in doing this all the condensers had to move in or out. If you were on channel 3 and wanted to go to channel 2 it sequenced 3 to 4, 4 to 1, 1 to 2 and it was one of the funniest sights in the world to see these great big condensers all waving about, going in and out, closer and further apart.

The other thing taught at the school besides the purely technical was plotting to WAAF officers so that they could go to CH stations and become 'Queen Bees' in charge of all the plotting girls – they were an absolute beauty chorus, they were gorgeous. They were all hand picked and highly intelligent and to teach these ladies they had a staff of 1 Wing Commander, 1 Squadron Leader (WAAF), 2 Flying Officers and 1 Flight Lieutenant. The F/O was fat and round, he had been a grocer and was getting on, in his late forties, about 5ft 5 inches, rotund as Humpty Dumpty and the other chap was a F/Lt Garland, an engineer from Mullard and again, an older man. I remember he came into the room one day and there was Jennings, and he was always known as Papa Jennings, trying to explain the difference between CH which sprayed RF energy all over the place, and CHL which had a narrow beam. He had a broom and he had it clasped to his tummy with the handle pointing towards the ladies, with the ladies in a semi-circle, about six of them, in front of him and he was swinging the broom backwards and forwards to describe how the beam took out the aircraft and registered them individually. That was Papa Jennings, he was a great character.

At the end of the two months all these chaps went off to their different jobs, to my surprise I was told "You are an instructor ". Why was this? Because a chap who was due to be an instructor, named Scroggie, was up at the Air Ministry writing text books and instruction manuals for radar stations, and such was his power and influence that he refused to come to Yatesbury and so I got the job. I stayed there for nine months and during that time I learned radar because it was one thing to sit and listen to other people telling you about it but it is was a very different thing to do the teaching oneself.

I had no experience of this at all but by the end of the stint there I knew a great deal about radar because the instructors were all very clever chaps, and there was a great deal of discussion about how these circuits really worked. A tremendous amount of time was spent talking outside classrooms, about how these things were done, how circuits worked even starting with a humble thing such as a time constant, just precisely what was a time constant. Some of the Education officers were really brilliant, I remember one chap became an Air Commodore in the end and was transferred from the Education to the Technical side.

Yatesbury was way out on the Wiltshire Downs, very bleak, windswept on a north facing slope of quite a high range of hills. It really was very cold, I remember the first winter, one of the coldest winters known, I remember the whole place froze up. I had a Morris Oxford and was on leave and when I came back the spark plugs of the engine were out on three stalks of ice about six inches long curling up and down. I remember all the men coming back from Dunkirk in complete disarray and disorder. We found the size of the mess doubled overnight, fighter pilots had no equipment, nothing, just walking about in their flying boots and Silkot jackets, that was all. On one occasion in the middle of the night there was the hell of a swishing noise and some thumps and the next day all was revealed. The Germans had dropped two bombs right across the camp, one landing on either side of the Officers Mess but both turned out to be made of concrete.

I went down once to Poling radar station, it was a CH, just to look at the latest things and either the same day or the day before the place got bombed and when we arrived I remember one of the 240ft towers was standing on 3 legs with the 4th leg blown away and there was a big crater. All the coaxial feeders, all copper, were festooned about, waving about, convoluted but the station was still on the air. I was very impressed with the damage that shrapnel can do because there was a gatepost made of oak, a typical Air Ministry job, all of six inches thick and there it was, sawn off six inches above the ground as neat as anything by one piece of shrapnel. At the end I got fidgety and started to pull some strings. Every two months Air Commodore Hart used to come down from the Air Ministry and give a lecture on each officers' course on the latest trends on radar. The C.O. of the station introduced me to the Air Commodore in the Mess and said that this chap would like to go to the real war and it so happened that Hart was looking for one or two people to head up the new night fighter squadrons and of course amongst other things we had done A.I. instruction at the school. Soon there came a posting and I left Yatesbury for Catterick and High Ercall, to be a radar instructor with 68 Squadron.

RON EASTWOOD

On 15th January 1942 I was posted to No. 4 Balloon Centre at Chigwell, Essex, and had to report to the Walthamstow Technical College. About 60 men were included in the intake and we were allocated civvy billets but had all our meals and indeed spent all our waking lives in the college. The college was built in 1939 and was the largest that I had ever seen and the Army, Fleet Air Arm, etc., were trained there as well as the RAF. The course, which lasted 16 weeks, was on basic electricity and radio; every night we spent hours drawing circuit diagrams on the blackboard with astonishing facility. This was all very elementary but I found it very interesting, much more so than any science I had done at school, I passed the course with credit and was selected with five others out of the original sixty to become a trainee radio mechanic and was posted to RAF Yatesbury.

On 27th May 1942 six of us travelled to Wiltshire via Chippenham and Calne to No 2 RDF School, Yatesbury. This was more like the real RAF. The camp consisted of four Wings three of these being for wireless operators (aircrew) under training and the 4th Wing was for the mysterious radio or RDF. It was a cosmopolitan camp, our intake of sixty was preceded by New Zealanders and succeeded by Canadians and there were a lots of Polish, Free French, etc., in the aircrew wings. We did some basic military training there, drill, physical training and I threw my first hand grenade in the hills somewhere near the White Horse.

The RDF school was about a mile away across the fields from the main site and we marched 'in threes' to it every day. A description of the camp can be found in Arthur C. Clarke's book Glide Path though he disguises it as Gatesbury. Arthur Clarke was the lecturer C, Corporal for our parallel class. The first thing we learned at Yatesbury was that our work was connected with radiolocation as it was then called and of which the public had been told in general terms but which was of the utmost secrecy in detail and we had to swear not to divulge it to any one. All our books were collected after each day and locked in the safes, nothing could be taken from the site. The course was brilliant considering they were dealing with comparative amateurs and I learned how to solder, braze and weld and construct radio sets etc.

The classroom work dealt with the theory of radar, pulse techniques, the Chain Home and Chain Home Low (CHL) networks, cathode ray techniques, strange circuits such as the 'flip flop' multivibrators etc. We learned that 60 Group controlled radar in the RAF and that once we were in it we couldn't get out because of our knowledge made us vulnerable. No one could fail the course at Yatesbury, perhaps that's why they worked so hard on us. Arthur Clarke made quite an impression in the few lectures that he gave us; he always ended up by talking about space travel. The secrecy was so great that I am sure the other Wings didn't know what was happening in 4 Wing and when we passed out we wore the same badge as wireless operators – 'sparks' on the sleeve.

I had already found out that in the RAF each man is posted as an individual and I was no longer with any of the men that I had originally joined up with. At the end of the course we had to indicate which of the ten Wings of 60 Group we would like to be posted to and I asked for Yorkshire. I was less than pleased to be told that I was posted to 70 Wing Inverness. Early in September 1942, three of us arrived in Inverness, the HQ of 70 Wing being at Bunchrew House, a couple of miles outside the town. Only then did we learn our fate about our eventual postings, one was destined for Kendrom at the northern tip of the Isle of Skye and I was sent to Point of Stoer in Sutherland about 100 miles north of Inverness.

A train to Lairg, bus to Lochinver, van to Drumbeg, lorry to Stoer, I came to know the route very well in the next year. RAF Point of Stoer was an AMES (Air Ministry Experimental Station) and was a Chain Home Low unit operating on 1.5 metres. I arrived there on 15th September and found myself something of a curiosity, as all the existing mechanics were Canadians about 12 of them and I wondered if I would fit in. They lived in their own Nissen hut so I was put with the miscellaneous staff but I eventually moved in with our own operators.

Point of Stoer was my first introduction to an operational station and it had taken a year of training to get there, it was also my introduction to the three watch system that I suffered for the next four years, off and on, mainly on. This system went as follows, first day 8am to 1pm, 11pm to 8am, second day 6pm to 11 pm, third day 1pm to 6 pm etc, etc, and was calculated to upset any human life cycle especially the digestive and evacuative processes. The radar station at Point of Stoer was no different from dozens of other units around the coast of Britain.

The advantage of the CHL as against the CH station was that the high frequency used enabled an aerial array about 30 ft long by 8ft high to be rotated on the top of a control room and this provided the beam of energy. In the control room the two operators each sat in front of a cathode ray tube, one measuring range and the other direction. These readings were plotted on a map covered with Perspex illuminated underneath, with a china graph pencil and the tracks reported by wireless telegraphy (W/T) to the Filter room at Stornoway then re-reported to the main Filter room at Inverness.

By 1942, however, the Germans were no longer interested in attacking Britain so the stations in the north-west were fairly useless except for the plotting of shipping. We saw many of the great Arctic convoys sailing up the Minch to Russia having been gathered in Loch Ewe. The only excitement operationally was one incident when we plotted a strong signal moving straight to the station, too fast for a ship and too slow for an aircraft, we were told by Stornoway to take a visual and when we did this we discovered that it was a flock of geese! I thought this very unusual until I read my namesake's book of radar when I learned years later that it was recorded on many occasions. In general Point of Stoer was a happy station, very little friction between the technical and non-technical staff that one found on larger units. I suppose there were about 30 of us with two officers, one technical and one admin. We all had to learn on the job the hard way and I found it interesting work.

The technical site was on the top of the cliff about 250ft above sea level just behind the lighthouse and about 2 miles from the domestic site, we travelled between the two sites by a 15cwt lorry. I suppose all sites near to a lighthouse are unusual in contrasts caused by the sweeping light but whilst this played a part there was some quality about the area that was felt quite strongly by the people who lived there during the war. The perpetual wind on the cliff top also added to the atmosphere but this was found on all radar sites throughout Britain, which were lonely and isolated but few were so far from habitation as Stoer. The considerable number of derelict crofts added to the feeling of isolation. Oddly enough the domestic site, which was a mile towards Clachtoll from the lighthouse, never had the peculiar feeling that the technical site did though it was almost as isolated.

On the technical site in late 1942 there was a small detachment of the

Gordon Highlanders in the charge of a Sergeant-Major and they were responsible for the defence of the site and they actually lived on the technical site all the time in a single Nissen hut. It seems barely credible but these soldiers would not patrol at night as they were so nervous about the atmosphere. They were certainly more afraid of the unknown terror than they would have been for a physical enemy, most of them being young men from the Glasgow area. When they were replaced by Military Police with dogs, night patrolling took place – the MPs were older men and probably less impressionable.

The RAF Police corporals had a lonely task of staying at night in the site guard room, one man on his own and they saw no one from 11pm when the watch changed until 8am the following morning. At least three of the corporals told me that they had distinctly heard a crofter's cart coming up the hill from the lighthouse and driving straight through the barbed wire entrance gate of the site, but when they looked out there was nothing there! They used to ring the technical block on any excuse for someone to talk to! These were hard headed, experienced policemen not normally given to the use of imagination.

One night, when in charge of a watch, I was woken up by the duty mechanic who swore that he had heard someone walking around the operations block and between it and the blast wall; when I walked round the top of the blast wall with a revolver and a torch nothing was there. I suppose the eternal wind, the hum of the technical operations room with its rotating aerial and the mystery which was attached to radar in those days might have all contributed to the atmosphere but it was certainly the most peculiar site I ever served on. I was married on 23 November 1942. I got my leg pulled a lot especially as there was a rumour, unfounded as we discovered later, that the high frequency transmissions to which we were exposed made men sterile.

On Christmas Day 1942, we were sat in the dining room of the domestic site, when an urgent call came from the technical site for help. Canadians Corporal Bernard and LAC Pat Prete and I went out in a tearing rush to find that the whole feeder system that carried the transmitted pulses to the aerial system had collapsed. We spent the whole of Christmas sorting it out. In gales, which were very frequent, we had to lash the ends of the rotating array to the four concrete blocks set into the ground, and this was a daunting task as someone had to climb the array to fix the steel ropes to the ends; the array was only 30ft high but it was disconcerting in a gale. On one occasion when the aerial was not lashed the force of the gale snapped off the dozen retaining bolts holding the array to the main drive shaft, these bolts being each over one inch thick. The replacement bolts had to be sent from Inverness and the Canadian officer and I spent the whole night replacing them.

The Canadians were gradually replaced by British mechanics and I found myself becoming more senior, I was promoted to Leading Aircraftman direct from Aircraftman second class so my 4/9d (23p) a day rocketed to 7/3d (36p). I was quickly promoted to Corporal as I was the only person who knew where things were and I worked under a very good Scottish sergeant from Edinburgh. It was really all bed and work at Stoer, being 12 miles from Lochinver which was only about 200 in population and 45 miles to the railway at Lairg, the nearest cinema at Tain about 80 miles away.

The principal pastime at the domestic camp was beach-combing and in wartime the pickings were plentiful but gruesome – dead horses, strange uniforms and tons of driftwood and other debris from ships. The little loch behind the camp was alive with trout and we had them in the frying pan within 15 minutes of being caught. I really thought that I might be able to sit out the rest of the war at Stoer in peace and quiet but those gremlins at RAF Records caught up with me.

The journey south on leave was always formidable, RAF lorry to Drumbeg Post Office, the Post Office van to Lochinver, the small bus to Lairg and then the train to Inverness. My home was in Halifax in Yorkshire and it used to take me 24 hours to get there, and in October 1943 I arrived home on leave from Stoer to find a telegram telling me to return. When I got back there I found that I was posted immediately to RAF Sennen Cove which took 48 hours via London. I am quite sure that anyone who had been stationed at Stoer would remember it vividly and its deep Gaelic mysteries, but nothing that happened in my later service life could quite recapture the romance and mystery of AMES 108, Point of Stoer and the exquisite CHL radar.

When my wife and I revisited the site, it seemed as clear to me as it did over 50 years ago and was exactly as I remembered, but it was a lovely day for my return, plenty of sunshine and a mild west wind, a blue sea and a clear sky. The real atmosphere of Stoer was felt on a pitch black night with a howling Force Ten ale, pelting rain, a mysterious sweeping radar aerial array and a group of young impressionable men in a totally strange environment.

TOM HATCHER

My introduction to radar was the Operators course at Cranwell that lasted six weeks and was based only on CH but was made as realistic as possible to the extent of working a night shift. However, there were some built-in lighter moments; one of the intimate parts of the CH receiver was known as the 'spongy lock' and on every course some hapless trainee would be sent to the mechanics to ask for the key – laughter all round. I was posted to Worth Matravers CHL in March 1942. When I arrived at Worth I knew nothing of CHL but there was good on-the-job training coupled with regular lectures by members of the technical and other staff.

Part of the training on duty especially for the male operators was instruction on the rudiments of maintenance of equipment rounded off by a test. One at least then felt competent to give a hand with the simple maintenance and so help to keep things going. My recollection, however, is that it never really came to much after that other than the 'winding up' of the transmitter should it trip itself, or helping to lash the aerial when the wind was too strong for the electrical turning mechanism (Wind force 7 or 8 I seem to recall). Information on windspeed came from the Coastguard station a few yards away on the cliff top.

Training was not confined solely to technical matters as Wing maintained at RAF Branscombe (South Devon), a camp that was devoted to less exotic things than radar. 'They' sent us there in small groups of male staff only to participate in what were known as 'Backer's-up' courses that lasted about one week. It comprised a vigorous assortment of P.T., unarmed combat, small arms drill and so on, all designed to toughen us up and the highlight of the course was to fire a machine gun over the field into the sea. It is as well that local folk were kept well out of the way.

Worth main CHL was on the top of St. Albans Head, very adjacent to the ancient chapel of St. Catherine, and additionally there was part way down the cliff and reached by a flight of very steep concrete steps, an older CHL set with a hand turned aerial array. The older set was kept serviceable and was brought into use when the main set was out of service, sometimes for maintenance but more usually when the wind strength on the cliff made it necessary for the aerial to be lashed. I am not aware that the wind ever defeated the old set, the turning of which was very strenuous for the operator concerned.

Plots from the old set were reported through the main CHL, the two working as one station. The main array was lashed on to a pre-determined fixed bearing and the set kept 'live' so that it was possible to read the range of any response on that bearing and it goes without saying that one was forbidden to start the aerial motor whilst the aerial was lashed. Someone overlooked this rule on one occasion resulting in a very bent frame and damage to both aerial arrays. Security at the CHL was a matter of surrounding the site including the Coastguard station with barbed wire except along the cliff top which was presumably too high to present an apparent hazard. There were, however, some slit trenches and entrance to the site was through an entrance manned by RAF police. I cannot recall the detail of the security covering entry to the Operations block itself.

The regular routine of the station may best be described as being in two parts; on one hand members of the day staff, who were the WAAF officer in charge, the senior NCOs and the day staff mechanics, and they between them attended to the administration, training and major routine maintenance of the equipment. Then there were the Operational staff who 'worked' the station for twenty four hours a day, seven days a week on a 'watch' system. I was a member of the operational staff and it is my recollection of those experiences that I relate. Each watch comprised an NCO operator, five or six other operators and a mechanic and depending upon the number of staff available we operated either a three or a four watch system. The night watch was commonly referred to as a 'night bind' and the four watch system was preferable as it allowed a good regular break from the darkened confines of the operations block.

The watch routine commenced with the 'take over' from the previous watch with the person in charge and the operators going on to each separate position being briefed on a one-to-one basis by the off going watch. This most important duty could be a tricky business at busy times when the tube might be full of responses. The watch duties were clearly defined and can best be described in a logical sequence as follows; the operators, two in number, one on the PPI tube and the other on the range tube worked as a team, and were complementary to each other; the PPI had a range of 60 miles later increased to 90 miles and the operator read plots direct from the tube to the 'plotter'.

The range tube operator would supplement the PPI plots with the information as to the number of aircraft and whether or not there was any indication of IFF. For plots under 60 miles the PPI operator then took the lead. The range of the range tube was 200 miles so the operator in that position took the lead in respect of responses beyond that of the PPI and on those infrequent occasions when there was a closer response too weak to show on the PPI tube. The bearing was 'flashed' onto the PPI by the range tube operator, bearing and range being read to the plotter by each operator in sequence.

The radar chain only plotted aircraft over the sea with those overland being plotted by the Observer Corps. The revolving CHL aerial was fitted with aerial arrays on both the back and the front, and switching from one array to the other was controlled by the PPI operator so that it was possible for the station to sweep continuously over the sea whilst the aerial as a whole continuously revolved through the full 360 degrees. This arrangement greatly saved wear and tear on the machinery and my recollection is that the two arrays were not identical, their coverage not the same, the sensitivity of the station presumably being that much increased.

Operational experience gave the operators a very intimate knowledge of the normal appearance of the responses on the tube and the position of the permanent echoes such as the Needles and Portland Bill were all well known. Any new or unusual signals were quickly spotted and promptly reported and all information given to the plotter by the operators was in a disciplined form of words, the aim being to aid efficiency and to avoid misunderstanding. The plotters task as the name implies was to plot tracks on the plotting table using coloured chinagraph pencils.

The plotting table comprised a chart of the area with a perspex overlay brightly lit from below, and the succession of plots from the operators would resolve themselves into tracks on the table thus giving an indication of the direction of travel of the aircraft concerned, with the plotter also able to prompt the operators should it appear that a track had been lost sight of. Following closely behind the plotter was the 'teller' who passed the plots on to the Filter Room together with whatever additional information was available and again, a standard form of words was used.

Experienced operators could produce far more individual plots than could be passed to the Filter Room so there was some filtering of the plots at the plotting table to make the best possible use of all the information available. The Filter Room for their part provided identifications from the tracks, if identification was uncertain then it was classified "X" (unknown) until the position was clarified. The identifications were marked by the teller on our plotting table in chinagraph.

The 'Recorder' used ruled sheets specially provided for the purpose and recorded every detail reported to the Filter Room and the time and in times of no activity this fact was recorded at regular intervals of thirty minutes. Speaking was through telephone headsets, with the operators and the plotter linked together and the teller and the recorder linked to each other and to the Filter Room, so there was thus no loud clamour of voices but rather a gentle muttering which merged into the background hum of the equipment, the spark gap and the outside aerial. There were other duties. Every plot reported to the Filter Room and recorded was later plotted on a large chart of the area, there would thus be built up a picture of station activity and the information was used to monitor for areas of relatively low sensitivity – the chart was replaced every month and was known as the 'Spotted Dog'. The NCO in charge was required to write a report at the end of each watch duty and this report was to be a synopsis of all that had happened thus giving an accurate picture without the mass of detail.

Some of the writers were very articulate, their reports making good and informative reading and even on those occasions when little if anything had come about they managed to breathe at least a little life into their writing. I remember one man's description of fighter aircraft patrolling up and down the channel for most of the night with no other activity of any kind, his words underlining the tedium of quiet nights with nothing to do but watch the moving traces on the tubes – truly 'On Watch'.

Over fifty odd years on, details of particular operational incidents do not come readily to mind, there were many busy times when the tubes were alive with activity but at this distance in time they have merged into a composite picture which will not resolve into its component parts. There are however, two incidents that I have never forgotten and both took place at night.

One quiet night, well to the east of us and over the Channel we picked up a response showing 'broad' IFF, a distress signal and this we were told was one of our aircraft which had earlier gone out on a bombing raid. He had been hit and damaged and was trying to get back but he was going astray. We followed him with every care as he made his way slowly down the Channel. He passed across the front of the station some way out to sea not showing a strong signal but the broad IFF as a large 5 to 10 mile gash in the time base. Our prayers were with him as he struggled on his way and eventually he went out of range to the west and we were later told that he had crossed the coast somewhere in Devon or Cornwall but we never found out whether or not he got safely home.

There came another night when all was quiet, I had been sitting watching the tube for some little while when, there, over the Cherbourg peninsula some 60 miles south of us appeared a faint response and this was promptly reported but no one else had seen anything so it was a matter of "Please watch it closely, Worth" from the Filter room. We did. The response persisted and moved in a northerly direction towards us, there was no doubt in our minds that it was an aircraft. With every turn of the aerial it was closer to us, it was given an 'X' identification and eventually it disappeared into our ground ray (about ten miles) whereupon we alerted the Coastguard station asking for a 'visual' should they see anything.

A few minutes later the Coastguard reported that an enemy aircraft had passed overhead, a fact that we passed to the Filter room. We were told that he had gone on to bomb Warmwell aerodrome and was making good his escape away to the north-east. This incident had special significance for me as I knew Warmwell well, having visited the station on a pre-war Air Day and having been there on a number of occasions as a member of the ATC before joining the RAF. I believe that Warmwell was attacked more than once. On one occasion they overshot and badly damaged Moreton Church, I married a Moreton girl and ours was the first wedding in that church following the completion of the restoration work in 1949, another of life's coincidences.

I left Worth Matravers and CHL in early 1944, and was posted to another type of radar – Type 9000, Oboe. I joined a mobile unit, AMES 9442 that went to France and across northern Europe in a most interesting fashion, but that is another story. Suffice to say that all the unit's radar staff retained a great affection for their previous stations on the radar chain. Worth CHL has gone now; I think it was in 1962 that I went back to Worth and out to St Albans Head. As I understood it, the station had been swept away-pushed over the edge of the cliff and into the sea below.

ALEXANDRIA KEITH

When I reported first it was to Bridgnorth, Wolverhampton. I can still remember our uniform issue, oh boy, one a rather natty dress and one that would have fitted two of me so naturally I kept the good dress but it disappeared at Netherbutton while I was in hospital, one of those mean things that occasionally happened in Service life. We were assessed on our I.Q. and then told what we were most suited for in the way of jobs then on to Morecambe for our physical training, which I thoroughly enjoyed, I was thoroughly spoiled by our landlady at our billets in 11, Marine Road. She happened to be from Scotland as well and as I was the only Scot in the house, porridge and mince and tatties were the order of the day. I was only once placed on jankers for winking at a Red Cap on duty when we marched down the front, needless to say he complained.

My RDF training was at Cranwell and again I thoroughly enjoyed my work. I think that everyone was immersed in their duties with a lot of studying to be done, that once you got a breather you never thought in chatting about what had happened during the day. Mind you we did have our social evenings like dances in the Hangar and fencing or badminton. I think that we all understood the importance of what we were learning and it certainly wasn't something to gossip about.

I was a first class swot and no mistake but it paid off because only a few went to a four way station and I was one of the chosen few from our course. My ambition was to get to Biggin Hill in Kent but as soon as they knew that my husband to be was in that area they posted me to Netherbutton. I travelled up by train to Scrabster where I was billeted for one night in an ATS camp. Thank goodness it was only for one night as no one, I mean, no girls spoke to me and even left me eating in a corner by myself. It was horrible and no help to my nervousness. The next morning I left by boat for Stromness, chained off from the Service men, who were also making for their camps. I remember it well because a lot of the men were sick and I was actually enjoying the journey. It was all new to me and the experience of the big boat and the rolling sea, and I do mean rolling, for I think that it can be one of the worst crossings that anyone can make, I loved it. Landed at Stromness where a truck picked me up for Kirkwall and then on to Netherbutton. When I first arrived I was very nervous and not a little frightened at the thought of meeting, once again, a group of strangers, but I need not have worried because the WAAF officer in charge, Miss England, had done her homework, had found out that I had got married a week before and had immediately prepared a welcoming party in our wee NAAFI hut – there was even a cake with a bride and groom on top. It was a wonderful and a most thoughtful and kindly way to break the ice, but believe me, after the evening I quickly became part of a shift of four WAAF operators.

There had to be four of us on at a time, each at a different position, one on the gonio and cathode ray tube, one recording the plots, one in communication with the boys at Kirkwall and one resting. We moved around when we were working and had to be capable of working all three, then you had a break. At the heart of the secret equipment was the cathode ray tube and I still remember how you kept turning the gonio knob to freeze the trace on the screen then skilfully translate it to range and bearing of enemy planes. It was not always enemy planes as I had been known to plot a balloon, at the beginning of the training course!

Next it had to be recorded and good hearing and clear speaking were essential. I forgot to mention that if you were picked to be a radar operator at all, good eyesight was essential. I used to be forever eating carrots after reading somewhere that they did wonders for your eyes and at 75 years of age I can still read without spectacles so there must be something in it. The information on the recording map was passed to the Signals Operations Room; it was a marvellous system but demanded great concentration hence the break for the fourth girl before she came back to start the sequence again. It gave us early warning of any raids because we could trace them when they were still a 100 miles away giving people time to prepare.

On our off duty times we played tennis in Kirkwall, visited the Church of Scotland canteen, which was my favourite eating place and marvellous walks too of course which we took full advantage of, after spending hours underground, and you can imagine how warm it was, working on such tense work that we were glad of the fresh air. We really had to make a lot of our own enjoyment because it wasn't exactly a place of riotous living. It suited me of course but I can remember walking over the heather on the cliff top and coming across a soldier crying his eyes out, he was really homesick and of course leave was minimal, Orkney was recognised as overseas and therefore leave could not be granted easily.

One of the laughs that I remember was on the RAF boys at Kirkwall, when I first spoke to them on communications they asked what I looked like as they liked the voice, they arranged to have tennis with us and when we turned up they were looking for a red-head with two missing front teeth, a limp and a glass eye, mind you they must have known that I was kidding!

Kirkwall was quite a walk if you were unlucky enough to miss the truck going down, Orkney folk are kindly and made us feel very much at home. The Church of Scotland canteen was by the roadside and had a table tennis table so again if you were lucky you had another entertainment. One thing I learned in Orkney was how to use a rifle. We used to march along the road fully equipped learning rifle drill, up there they were always aware that there might be an invasion by German troops and everyone had to learn procedure in the event of this happening; it never did of course but I often wonder if I would have been brave enough to use that rifle. In case of invasion destruction orders were printed out and were in a glass case by the door of the Ops room, my job was to smash the cathode ray tube with an axe which was part of the general fire equipment. It was very large and a bit heavy for me, then after that get out with the rifle and defend the station.

I'll never forget the finish of my time in Netherbutton for while I was there I had met a Minister's daughter, who was also an ACW1 and a radar operator, the same as myself. We became great friends as we had a great deal in common, in our work, our home ties and our likes and dislikes on the social side. One day a request came for eight radar operators to visit a Naval station at Lyness as new equipment for tracing submarines had arrived, there were no WRNS or radar operators up there and it would give us an insight into another method. Anyway, we were left wondering who the eight would be.

The night before, Sheila Munro, my friend and I were writing letters home and, as we were apt to do, we gave each other an idea of what we were writing. Sheila was always finding things that would interest her father in the way of sermons, I never read her last letter but knew what it was all about. We set off next morning with six others to the Naval base, we had to make it in the morning as we had to be back on duty at 1pm and as we were a small group on the station it was essential to get back on time. However, we never reached there as we had a serious accident. Just minutes before it Sheila changed places on the truck with me and the next thing I remember is waking up in Kirkwall hospital three days after the accident. Months later I was informed that another lorry's girders had got entangled under our truck and Sheila and Gillian, who sat next to me, were killed outright. Apparently, I too was laid aside on the road as being dead but an alert soldier noticed a slight movement of my hand. To cut a long story short I had two years of hospital treatment finishing up at Stracathro hospital, Brechin. This all happened in August 1942 so it left me with a very short service in Netherbutton but a very memorial one.

My return to Orkney many years later (after my family had claimed quite a large part of my life) was sad to say the least. Houses I had visited had changed occupants, Kirkwall itself also seemed changed and yet had still a lot of familiar places but they seemed to be differently placed. I got rather annoyed with myself because they do say that you should never go back to visit a loved place a second time, your memory seems to play tricks. Yet when I went out to Netherbutton a choked feeling crept into my throat as I gazed at the two towers that had been left to decay on the hill and only the bases of our huts remained. I could hardly credit that all the living that had taken place there, the memories, the friendships, the fears, the excitements, the coming together of people from all walks of life had simply passed on like ships that pass in the night. I often think about it and thank God for my memories.

HARRY MARSHALL

The course at Yatesbury lasted three months and finished late in March and then, not at all to my satisfaction, I and about 15 others instead of being posted to operational stations were kept back as instructors for the future. Yatesbury not only trained mechanics it also trained the operators to do the plotting on the operational stations and these people had to be trained the same as we had and to train them there were quite a number of massive consoles which generated spurious signals of different ranges and bearings. A series of rotating cams which rotated 'pots' which made signals move along the trace and other things to simulate interference.

After a few weeks of this we were all posted to RAF Cranwell to open up a new RDF school and I must say that none of us were sorry to leave Yatesbury, it was a bleak and wild open place, miles from anywhere, the nearest place being Calne which was a sausage manufactory and whose products were found very much in evidence in our meals at Yatesbury. We departed in a wagon for the railway station and some of out types looking out of the back of the truck made signs with their two fingers which was not Winston Churchill's victory sign.

We found at Cranwell that the apparatus was not completely installed so some of us set to work to get the operator trainers ready; it was the usual technical compound away from the rest of the camp with great iron railings and a guard at the gate. Cranwell was a very big camp indeed; apart from the college there were two or three flying fields and several schools, and we took over an equipment training section that had been turfed out and some of the billets were brick-built dating from World War One. I found myself detailed on watches to keep the operator training equipment ticking over while the lecture rooms were being prepared for the RDF mechanics when they came along. Everything was ready when it was discovered that there were no trained wireless personnel available in the UK and to meet this situation, apparently, advertisements were inserted in newspapers in the United States for civilians with wireless experience to come forward and help to operate and keep going our RDF chain. A very good rate of pay was offered by British standards but by American standards it was not very bright and it did not attract very bright types at all. In addition some members of the RCAF came along, some as instructors, but three of us, Sgt Cohen and Cpl Goodison were given the task of taking these people in hand when it was discovered that they were woefully behind us in technical ability and out of the great number that came over only enough for one class could be scraped together.

They gave these people the name Civilian Technical Corps and there were some very odd characters amongst them. One 'old' boy of 35 to 40 with a few teeth missing and a shaggy appearance came up to me one day showing a sheriff's badge and whispered confidentially that he was use to investigatory work and that if there was any bother not to hesitate to come along and he would help me out. I suppressed my mirth as best I could and said polite things. Dreadful problems arose over the others, who were given RAF uniforms without the buttons so that they still rated as civilians but they had to look something like the rest of us and they did extraordinary things.

Our Commanding Officer had his own private office at one end of the orderly Room and one of these characters marched in one day to see if there was any mail but there wasn't so he took a short cut through the other side of the room, through the C.O. office, just said 'Hi Ya!' and went out the private back door. This livened things up a bit and caused a bit of light relief in a rather dark situation. They were also known to ride bicycles borrowed from the M.T. section on the parade ground and not a blessed thing could be done about it.

When training got into full swing with regular intakes there were large numbers of men moving in and out of the school and working parades were the order of the day. I remember once in the earlier stages after I had been trained to be an NCO at Cosford that there was a very junior Orderly Officer and a very junior Orderly Sergeant on duty. They were supposed to take the parade state, the unit Warrant officer should have been there in charge and the Orderly Officer should have taken the salute when they marched off back to their classes. Then one fine morning the Station Commander was hovering in the background (this was when the war was going well and time could be spared to brighten things up a bit from a disciplinary point of view) and I saw him in the middle distance; he wasn't so far away from the parade ground.

To my astonishment neither the Orderly Officer or Sergeant took the slightest notice of the great man's presence – an Air Commodore is quite a 'big pot', there are just three above him, an Air Vice Marshal, an Air Marshal, and an Air Chief Marshal, and I rather held my breath and thought there was going to be some trouble and sure enough there was! The Orderly Officer and the Sergeant did not attempt to take any parade state, in fact we had never taken a parade state. The sick went off to the sick quarters without any particular note being made of it, which going by the book was not right, the Orderly Officer just said 'March them to their classes' and it was left to us Corporal instructors to turn our classes individually and take them away which we were proceeding to do when a furious bellow came from the great man: 'STOP THAT PARADE!' So we returned to our starting point.

He called for the Orderly Officer, demanded to know how long he had been in the service, which turned out to be only six weeks, an Acting Pilot Officer on probation. 'Now' he said, 'we will do this parade the proper way, I will take the salute and I want you to take a parade state and the parade state for each flight is to be brought to me'. He called all the corporal instructors, NCOs in charge of the flights and lined us all up in front of him and said 'Go to your flights, I want a parade state taken at the double'. He directed the Orderly Officer to get the parade formed, turn them and march off and each instructor was to take the salute. I looked with some eagerness to the next happening, which was not long in coming because a runner from the Orderly Room called all the instructors to the Orderly Room where the Warrant Officer, visibly shaken and white said 'You all know what happened this morning. The Air Commodore is very annoyed. In future I shall be present at every working parade.' He was not in the habit of coming in at all. He lived out at Sleaford and used to tootle in about 9 am leaving others to do the 'dirty' work for him. Each working parade had to be properly organised; indeed, the Air Commodore was there for two successive mornings to make sure that things were done by the book.

Air Commodore Probyn was a very good fellow. Sometimes the flying field would be in use as an emergency landing field and during a heavy fall of snow large numbers of us had to turn out to shovel snow from the runway. He was an energetic fellow and did not scruple to grab a shovel; we were withered with the cold, but he set an example and when we cleared the runway he took us all back to the cookhouse and insisted that every man had a hot meal: he was a real man's man.

BILL ROBERTS

In September 1939 I volunteered for the RAF when a colleague in the office volunteered for the Army, he was aged 21 and wanted to get into the RASC before he could be conscripted into the Infantry, I was 19 and wanted to be a sergeant pilot ! but I was ruled out as a pilot as I was found to need specs but I agreed to join as a clerk as I was so anxious to serve my country ! I was called up on November 11 and required to report to RAF Padgate only about 12 miles away from home. After four weeks square-bashing I and Harold Taylor from Bolton, who was in the same squad, were posted to RAF Manston in Kent. After reporting to Manston we were sent to a station at Foreness Point, Cliftonville, Margate where we soon learned that we were to be' radio' operators on this unit. I recall two mobile cabins about 50 yards apart each with a wire cage on a pole, so it seemed, sticking out of the roof, but in fact mounted on a large wooden frame over the cabins, all in a barbed wire compound on the edge of a cliff about 70ft high. These wire cage aerials must have been about 12 ft by 4ft by 1ft deep, possibly much more, and turned through about 180 degrees, in parallel when the transmitter and receiver arrays were in unison.

My recollection of inside the receiver van was of a large wireless receiver about 5ft high and 6ft wide with a cathode ray tube about 18 inches by 12 inches in the centre and in front of it. I vaguely remember a trace across the tube similar to the picture seen on screens used in hospital to measure heart beats, etc. It was graduated in miles, about fifty and the first two or three miles of the trace consisted of blips of various lengths, which we all use to call the ground ray, that were really reflections from nearby buildings and possibly Margate Pier.

The radio operator sat in front of this screen winding a handle on his right side which, by means of bicycle chains and gears, turned the vertical metal pole, which in turn moved the aerial on the roof. There was a cable link to the transmitter van where another operator sat with a similar handle and bike chain but instead of watching a tube he watched a meter. When the tube operator was about to search, that is to turn the aerial, he rang a bell that sounded in the transmitter van and, as the receiving aerial moved, the needle in the transmitter van moved either left or right of centre. The objective of the operator there was to keep turning the handle to keep the needle in the centre. It was soul destroying. When a blip appeared on the receiver screen one had to move the handle clockwise or anti – clockwise to obtain a maximum response, and when that was obtained, the compass bearing and the range were read off and passed to a second operator, who converted them to a plot on a chart. I can't remember to whom the plots were passed but it could have been to Dover.

The Foreness unit was an Air Ministry Experimental Station designed I believe by Mr. Watson Watt who was a frequent visitor as were other scientists and high ranking officers. Most days seemed to be spent tracking test flights carried out by pilots of 600 (City of London) Squadron, which was based at Manston and it was referred to as the millionaires' squadron as pre-war its pilots were wealthy part time volunteers. The pilots were frequent visitors to the site as well and I remember one, a Whitney Straight, an American who was said to be a millionaire. I seem to recall Blenheim bombers being used for the actual test flights although I think 600 Squadron was a fighter squadron, perhaps they were the interceptors, I cannot remember.

When I joined the unit in Dec. 1939 it was manned mainly by regulars who had been in the RAF pre-war, wireless operators were acting as radio (RDF) operators as we were then called and electricians and wireless mechanics as radio (RDF) mechanics/ maintenance men. Harold Taylor and I were the first of a huge influx of wartime volunteers with clerical backgrounds, who formed the basis of the new service. The billet for most of us was the Hydrophone Café on the cliff front at Foreness Point and I can remember a room in which 10 or 12 of us slept; the galley or cookhouse and an office adjoining it, but I can't recall a dining room or any other room in it.

The Commanding Officer was a F/Lt. Best, who in peacetime had been a scientist with GEC and when I was demobbed in 1946 he was the C.O. of 73 Wing at Boston Spa near Tadcaster and a Wing Commander or Group Captain. The NCO i/c was a corporal wireless mechanic and possibly a sergeant before I left and he lived in digs. in the town as did another corporal, an electrician. As the weeks went by we were joined by more wartime airmen, clerks for operators and two BBC engineers came as mechanics.

These trained engineers came in as LACs which was rather galling for us who had been in the Services several weeks longer than they had and were still only AC2s. When the C.O. discovered that I was a competent shorthand typist I became the unofficial station typist -all in my off duty hours! I well remember Mr Best telling me that as a reward for the great help that I was giving him, he had recommended me for promotion to AC1, and I believe he did this in all sincerity, he was that kind of man, but what he had not appreciated and I was not aware of at the time was that I was destined to be remustered as a radio operator.

One clear recollection I have of this unit was the unique watch system, the night watch went on at 10pm or 11pm and came off at 6am when the dog watch came on until 8 or 9 in the morning and then we were off duty until the afternoon or the evening. The idea is said to have come from a Corporal Sellwood's peacetime service in the Navy. I was posted overseas about 20 April 1940 and I remember having to be on watch the evening before I left and there was quite a lot of aerial activity, much of it unidentified and low flying. Whenever an aircraft came into the ground ray we always had to go out and get a visual contact and on this particular evening it was very dark and I went out to get a visual of an unidentified object, which had been picked up at very short range, and had moved into the ground ray. I had a glimpse of a seaplane, at least a plane with floats passing within a few hundred yards of the station at about a height of 100ft, the height of the cliff on which we were sited. This caused great panic at the place we passed plots. I remember having to give interviews and statements and it was concluded in the end that it must have been an enemy minelayer but as I left the unit the following day I never did find out.

FREDDIE SMITH

The first station that I went to was RAF Kinley Hill near Seaham Harbour, that was my first radar site, of course it seemed very strange coming straight from training at Cranwell and then landing up there, however we pressed on as we all had to at that time. I was proper flummoxed when I first saw the place because it was nothing like we had been led to believe, I found it quite interesting. We did have various things to do on the site such as to lash the aerials if the wind ever reached a severe gale force and we seemed to have an awful lot of wind that year. We were often during the day up there to lash the aerials down, we had a bearing on which the aerials had to be set. We had to climb on to the platform and on to the aerial itself and attach metal hawsers to it and these were brought down to ground level and pegged down into big stakes that were driven into the ground already prepared.

I got the job of doing this one night about three in the morning, we were roused out of our beds by the station police and told to go up to the site and lash the aerials. This was February 1943 and by jove when we went up there on those aerials it was blowing hard and sleet on top of it and of course no lights, it was a case of having to use Braille and using Braille with your fingers frozen is quite something.

From Kinley I was posted to Fairwood Common, South Wales, for ten weeks and then RAF Church Fenton to do radio work and from there to a CHL station at Easington (East Yorkshire) just above Hull. This was an unusual type of camp to me, all male except for a WAAF officer, who was in charge. My two outstanding memories of it are with one of the officers calling out 'There is a plane coming in very low, go outside and see if you can see it'. I went outside and looked in the direction that I had been told and I saw this plane, limping in, the entire side looked if it had been torn away, and it just limped in about 200 yards above the camp and went out of sight and two or three minutes later there was an almighty bang. I dashed in and told the group and everybody all about it and some of our people went out including our medical staff and we found out later that the aircraft had made it home but had crashed and everybody on board had perished. That sort of put you into an idea of what you were supposed to do and how fortunate you were not to land into situations like that.

One of the other things was that it was very dark on the east coast and I had to look at the trace of the CHL and we had a very, very strange shape. The people in the Operations block had rung me up and said would I have a look and see what we were doing up there as it doesn't seem if anything is getting out, we are not getting much back and we have a strange ground ray. I had a strange trace so I went out and had a look around to find out what it was and I decided that there was only one thing to do and that was to look at the aerial

I opened the door and went outside and oh, the thick fog and the perishing cold. I went back in and put on healthier clothes and went out again and took a further look. I couldn't see anything of interest so I'll have to use my torch so I put my light up where the feeders were and found that they were joined together with hoar-frost and of course this was causing a huge short all along the feeders. I switched off the set, grabbed a brush and went along the entire length of wire as far as I could including up the tower and brushed it all off, came back and run up the set again and got the picture back.

My next stop was to RAF Danby Beacon. I arrived at Danby in January 1944, got there in the dark and eventually went up to the site. Travelling from Danby village is by a winding road, you dip down then climb and climb and climb and I wondered where ever we were going to. Eventually we arrived at the guardroom, booked-in and got allocated a bed and this happened to be where the station police also were and a number of mechanics. The following morning on having a look out, my God, what a view. I was a city lad, I had no idea that there was countryside like this anywhere around and I think that it started from that very first morning, when I saw what we were surrounded by and where we were, just what the beauty of the countryside was like.

I was fortunate in staying there for 17 months and so I saw all the seasons through and it never failed to impress me, every morning was marvellous. If it was getting up to go on watch or it was coming off duty at night on the 8pm shift and coming down the hill, it was a beautiful sight and even to this day, for my wife and I go up there frequently, we sit and reminisce and talk about it. It was quite an isolated place being on the moors like that, all these places seemed to be put in isolated places which

I suppose was the reason for the good echoes that were received on the tube.

The telephone rang and it was the station police at the gate leading into the top site and he was in a right panic bordering on hysteria – would I please do something, go outside and have a look, was it safe? I went outside and had a look and what a sight! all the barbed wire surrounding the site, the four steel towers, the big iron gates at the entrance, the whole lot was lit up as if it were on fire. There were sparks and flames shooting everywhere; it was an amazing sight and the whole thing was lit up, the poor SP was doing his nut, he had gone outside to have a look and seen all these flashes leaping off the fences, you had to see it to believe it! I don't believe anyone apart from the SP and I saw this because although I dashed back in and telephoned the other block when I looked out again it had all settled down, but just for those few minutes it was a hair raising experience.

There also used to be a visiting Wing Commander come called John Scott-Taggart, ST as he was known, he used to write for Newnes Practical Wireless before the war and he was the inventor, if one liked to be so bold, of various models, which were self built.. They were all his own designs and himself was quite a clever chap. I remember that he came up to the camp on one of his special 'treats' as he called them, the treat was certainly for him, certainly not for us and getting out of his transport the fire bell was right opposite the guardroom. He looked at it, it was in a fine black and weathered state, after all who wants a thing bright and shining in a camp that might attract visiting aircraft. He wandered over to the bell and from his pocket he produced, you'll never believe it, a tin of Duroglit and taking a piece he polished his initials into the bell – JST. He then went into the guardroom and 'tore a strip' off the local guard commander and demanded to see the discip. sergeant and chased things up.

He had the proper code number for the day and he went to the receiver block and when she opened the door to him he promptly gave her a right wigging because she had not got a Sten gun in her hand when she opened the door. A fat lot of good she said with a Sten gun in my hand as firstly I don't know how to use it and secondly we have no ammunition. In the Op's block one day they opened the door to the incoming watch and a rat shot in with them, the girl when she had opened the outer door had not closed the inner door, which you were all supposed to do, and this rat shot in to the Operations Room, which was always very dark so that you could watch the tube. The main plot which was the area of the coastline that we looked out on was set out on a Perspex chart on an illuminated desk about 30 inches square and two of the WAAF's promptly shot onto the desk, which collapsed!

Valves in the CH transmitter were continuously evacuated and were demountable, the filaments could be replaced and, having replaced the filament and remounted the valve head the air had to be removed by vacuum pumps. One of the means of testing whether the vacuum was 'hard' was to use a tube encased in a brass outer cover with a terminal on the top to which was attached a very, very highly insulated cable, because this unit from which the tube came from, a square box about 8 inches cube, contained a coil which created an enormous spark. The idea was to hook this wire onto the tube and if the air had been drawn out, and how much, was indicated by striations, or glowing bars, and as the vacuum improved the striations got further and further apart until when the valve was fit for use the striations had gone out.

I was on duty one day and there was a trainee WAAF mechanic sitting cross-legged in front of the pump looking puzzled and I called her 'What's wrong?' and she said that we had demounted the valve and were now trying to get the vacuum but something was not right. So I quizzed her on various points and asking what she had done and how things had progressed when she said. Look I'll show you the vacuum. She was facing the unit and had the spark box in her left hand and she reached for the insulated wire and pulled it round her and hooked it to the brass tube. She switched on and I will swear blind about this, she rose four feet into the air in the cross-legged position. It was unbelievable, almost like levitation.

They must have heard her scream in Whitby; it nigh deafened me and brought the other WAAF out of the telephone booth to see what had happened. What had happened of course was that the thick insulation had begun to perish, probably wartime rubber, and so when she pulled the cable round the back of her it was going round her bottom and when she switched on the cable broke down and as she touched the metal work of the set the spark got out of the insulation and then she leapt up!! An RF burn is a nasty thing and she had to be taken down to the sick quarters to have it attended to and we learnt afterwards that the sparks had put a line of small pin holes in the flesh of her bottom to about six inches in depth. We were in hysterics of course but for the girl it was no laughing matter and it was some time before she came back on duty but, certainly for one thing, she regarded the spark box with a lot more care than she had ever done before.

One of the tests for the correct tuning of the CH transmitter was to check for standing waves on the transmitter feeder lines and to do it correctly we had a long piece of paxolin about 4 foot long with a neon bulb at the end. The idea was to place the bulb near the feeder wires and it would light up and go out at various points and there were marks on the feeder lines to show if the neon should be alight or be out. In the maintenance book SD 0270 it stated '...having done the check [part of the transmitter alignment] take the test tackle and run it along the feeder wires searching for the high and low nodes'.

Because of the pronunciation of 'test tackle' the neon and the stick was called by everyone, even by the WAAFs when they eventually became mechanics, the bollocky stick. An unapproved method adopted by some of the mechanics was to dip a finger into methylated spirits and run the nail across the wire which lit up your finger, it was very, very dangerous with voltages of over 20,000 volts and all that was protecting you was just a thin Pyrex glass basin acting as a condenser.

CHARLES STIFF

I entered the Service in September 1939 just before the outbreak of war as a civilian Wireless/Electrical mechanic at AMES Poling. At that time the station was still under construction and was operating with temporary equipment under W/O Mummery. The transmitter was one of the early type using the Admiralty Signal School silica valves and the receiver a Cossor RF5, installed in wooden huts with blast resisting walls. One feature of the transmitter was the earthing device which was hung onto the aerial feeder when the transmitter was shut down, this was known as the 'Charlie Brinkley' after the boatman at the Felixstowe-Bawdsey ferry, who had a steel hook for one of this hands.

At that time there was little hostile activity and the receiver watch-keeping was rather dull although on one night I took a call from Fighter Command to say that a friendly aircraft would be passing by and would I inform the Anti-aircraft guns. I had the hell of a job to raise them on the field telephone! I picked up the plane on the receiver and followed it into the ground ray and then went outside to watch it go by and then back on the set to pick it up again. This was the first proof I had that RDF worked. After a few weeks I was sent to Bawdsey on a seven week course. There were about 20 of us from along the chain, several of them wireless operators from the east coast fishing fleet and some radio dealers. We were lodged in some boarding houses in Felixstowe. The Research Station had moved to Dundee by that time but AMES Bawdsey was functioning. On returning to Poling I found F/O Dorté in command, he was ex-BBC and finished up as Group Captain Chief Technical Maintenance at 60 Group.

Soon afterwards I was posted to AMES Dunkirk and spent the very severe winter of 39/40 there. This period is remembered because of my narrow escape from electrocution by a flash-over from an anode capacitor, the spare one which was out of circuit but which had retained a charge. It should have been shorted out but the shorting resistor had been removed for some other purpose, I was disabled for a few hours but did not recover the feeling in my thumbs for several days. While at Bawdsey I had applied for a position as an instructor at No. 2. Radio School at Yatesbury, which was to be opened in the Spring, and I was posted there. It was not for long however as one day I was called to Squ/Ldr Tibbett's office and told that I had been recommended for a job at TRE Worth Matravers, this was the old BRS, which had moved again from Dundee. I have no idea to this day from whom the recommendation came from but it was certainly most welcome.

At that time TRE were still much involved in the operation of the chain and were looking forward to the time when 60 Group could take over. I went there to be trained in the production of calibrated plotting charts for the RDF receivers as part of this takeover. I was taken under the wing of two Scientific Officers, a Dr. Cochran and a Miss Rhoda Piri who came from Dundee University. I was soon joined by an RAF Draughtsman LAC T.C.Bernard (Jock) who had been evacuated from France. The main job was drawing charts for the Bainbridge-Bell Optical Converter, which was fitted to some receivers up to the type RF5.

This ingenious device consisted of a glass topped table about 24" by 18" over which was placed a 10 mile to the inch gridded map of the area covered by the station concerned. It was faintly illuminated from below and a small mirror pivoted and geared to the CRT range knob and the gonio projected a bright spot onto the map. A direction-finding gonio does not give a true bearing of the target, so to compensate for this the grid of the map was distorted and the distorted grids were drawn with the aid of an 'engine' of B-B's design.

The optical converter became obsolete with the installation of the RF6 and RF7 which were equipped with electrical calculators known as the 'Fruit Machine'. This employed Siemens rotary telephone exchange switches and was housed in a separate room in the 'R' block; it was a formidable piece of apparatus comparable to a 100 line automatic telephone exchange. It gave a read out on the receiver panel in grid references and letters and heights. The wiring of the calibration into the calculator was a massive job employing special charts and was mostly carried out by ex-Post Office engineers.

Before any of the above work could be done the site calibration had to be done usually by the use of an autogyro carrying a low power transmitter operating on the frequency concerned, which was stationed in turn over eight prominent landmarks some five miles or so in front of the receiving aerials and extended over the angle of coverage. The favoured landmarks were road crossings, church towers, etc., the true bearing of these objects from the aerial were calculated from the 1" Ordnance map, sometimes theodolite sightings were employed and captive balloons were used before the outbreak of hostilities.

About fifty gonio readings were rapidly taken at each position of the autogyro and averaged to produce the error at that bearing. These points were plotted on millimetre graph paper (1mm per degree of bearing, 5mm per degree of error) and a smooth curve drawn from which the optical converter template or the calculator wiring chart was produced. In 1943 I introduced the Manual Calculator Type V, which enabled both azimuth and height conversions to be made on the one device. A similar technique was employed for height calibration using Blenheim aircraft flying on a constant bearing. As a back up for the electrical calculator a manual converter was provided, this was a 10 mile per inch gridded map of the coverage area of the station provided with a radial cursor calibrated in miles rotatable over a compass rose the points of which were distorted according to the angular errors.

When Jock Bernard and I came to 60 Group from Swanage we brought a lot of work with us and we were at first accommodated in a temporary office, which was already occupied by an airman engaged in 'ageing' silica valves. This process consisted of running the valves in a special rig with slowly increasing filament and anode voltages until satisfactory conditions were reached, the snag from our point of view was the terrific din from the cooling fan. We had been at work for a few days when we were honoured by a visit from the C.O., Air Commodore Gregory, "So we have a Drawing Office now," he said, "Good show ". About half an hour later he sent an airman down with a piece of paper with an order to write a notice KEEP OFF THE GRASS. This was the first job we did for 60 Group and we had a good laugh about it !

We were not troubled a lot by the 'top brass' and compared with some units of the RAF suffered very little from Service 'bull', there was a hard core of regular personnel but most of the staff were RAFVR. I had a staff of about four airmen draughtsmen and three WAAF tracers. I realise now that life at headquarters was comparatively peaceful. We occupied the house and grounds of a large country estate on the outskirts of Leighton Buzzard. Administration occupied Oxendon House itself and a hutted camp served for the Technical offices, airmen's quarters, the NAAFI etc. The Officers' Mess and the WAAF quarters were further up Plantation road. It was an idyllic spot, the park was laid out with exotic conifers and rhododendrons with cuckoos calling in the Spring and chaffinches singing outside the Drawing Office windows. A favourite off-duty spot was the Globe Inn on the banks of the Grand Union Canal.

Our operations were very hush-hush of course but security measures were not very obtrusive. I had very few visits to outstations, but two I remember were to Fairlight and Hopton CHLs to prepare vertical Perspex plotting screens for tracking V1s and V2s. It was during the Hopton visit that I spent an interesting evening in the bar of the Star Hotel, Great Yarmouth, with one of the officers, who was very interested in space flight and he said that he hoped to be one of the first men on the moon. I never got to know his name but I have since realised that he could have been A.C.Clark, the science fiction writer. After VE day the closing down of 60 Group was being considered and I obtained a transfer to the Admiralty Signal and Radar Establishment, which was close to home. I was with the Admiralty for some years engaged on the design of guided weapons and then joined the CEGB from which I am now retired.

REG TOWNSON

I completed my Signals training at Cranwell as an apprentice and was posted in Feb. 1933 to the 16th Army Co-operation Squadron, Old Sarum, for two and a half years. I should have gone on a boat to Iraq in the summer of 1934 but I had a medical problem that kept me off the boat and was then posted in August 1935 to the Fleet Air Arm in a cruiser, not a carrier, HMS Shropshire. We had quite an eventful two years, firstly the Abysinnia panic where the whole fleet was at Alexandria and secondly, to Spanish waters during the Spanish Civil War looking after the Consulate at Barcelona, the Embassy at Valencia and pushing merchant ships through the blockade off the north Spanish coast.

In December I was posted to 53 Squadron, which was being reformed at Farnborough, the Flight Sergeant virtually welcomed me with open arms because I was an LAC with one Good Conduct badge awarded after three years of undetected crime. This was a very rare beast indeed and he was trying to keep the station going with Boy Entrants, whose training was considerably less than that of ex-apprentices like myself. The Service had certainly changed during my two years at sea and we were beginning to be treated like human beings, even being allowed a permanent sleeping out pass on request while the old tunic with a choker collar had been superseded by one with a cut away collar and shirts and ties. This may seem a small concession in the light of present day eccentricities of dress but it came with shoes instead of the infantry style boots and slacks instead of winged breeches and puttees. When the signal came from the Air Ministry posting me to RAF Felixstowe the Flight Sergeant said.. 'Oh No! I'll soon put a stop to that.' but to no avail, and I arrived at Felixstowe late one Sunday evening in early December 1937. I detected a somewhat unusual note at the guardroom where they directed me to a special billet, the rest of the course were already there and I was much put out because none of the people there, most of whom were friends of mine, would tell me what the exercise was all about or why we were there. All they would say was that we had to go to work in plain clothes on Monday morning and the silly thing about it was that we went from Felixstowe in a RAF marked lorry!

The first stop was the ferry across the river Deben and we were piloted by a Charlie Brinkley, who became quite celebrated among the radar personnel. He had lost his right hand in a boating accident and it had been replaced by a hook and the description of an earthing stick that was used on all radar transmitters, the brass end of which was semi-circular like Charlie's right hand, entered the RAF Stores Vocabulary under the entry 'Stick, Earthing, Brinkley.' Quite who christened the earthing stick a Brinkley was never revealed but there was another piece of test equipment which was a spherical neon lamp on a Vulcanite rod which was used to detect the presence of standing waves on a transmitter feeder line and rejoiced in the nickname as the 'bollocky stick' and, needless to say, that name did not get into the Vocab. (The list of RAF Stores).

Once inside Bawdsey Manor we were initiated into the mysteries of aerial theory, spongy lock pulse circuits and I do so well remember my horror at the thought of putting 230 volts A.C. onto the grid of a small triode even if through a blocking condenser. The courses were run by a Flight Sergeant Ridley, who later became a Group Captain and Flight Sergeant Leslie Bourne with a Sergeant 'Tug' Wilson. Security was tight, very, very, tight and we were absolutely forbidden to breathe a word of it to anybody unconnected with the course or with the subject. Life at the Manor was very pleasant, working in plain clothes. The main thing that I remember is that we were introduced to very up to date aerial theory, which we certainly had not covered at Cranwell, and there were demonstrations of open wire feeders and practical experience on the working RDF equipment in Bawdsey.

On the Service side at Bawdsey, Squadron Leader R.G.Hart was in command, who subsequently became Air Chief Marshal Sir Raymund Hart. I make no apologies for saying that he was an officer and a gentleman in the very best tradition and as I know from personal experience, Raymund Hart never forgot any of his Bawdsey airmen or NCOs whenever or wherever he met them. His accidental death soon after his 'retirement', Air Chief Marshals never retire officially, was a tragedy of the first order for he was not only a man of sterling personal qualities to whom the country owes a debt of gratitude for his technical and operational drive, but also had fantastic stamina and a first class brain. Rumour had it at the time that he had studied radio in a French University in the French language, which was no mean feat, and we knew from first hand experience that he kept going for three days and nights during one of our operational exercises with only cat naps and a quick dip in the North Sea to revive him.

On February 8th 1938 I was posted to the Air Ministry Experimental Station at Canewdon and set off in my faithful Morris 10 APC 359, which was my very first motor car. My colleagues were Corporal Davy, 'Trixie' Pearson, Joe Goddard, 'Lofty' Weekes, 'Gibbo' Gibbons and at Canewdon already there were Jack Evans and Jack Colquhoun. Evans was promoted to Corporal while we were there and I was also promoted to Corporal in March 1938. The officer in charge was Warrant Officer Tommy Scarfe, whom I was shattered to find as a Wing Commander when I returned from Malta in August 1941. Life was very easygoing at Canewdon. We did not work week-ends and in fact the first week-end that we did so was the week-end of the Czechoslovakian crisis when we were all busy filling sandbags and sticking them round our wooden huts in which the equipment was placed.

While at Canewdon I had the great pleasure of assisting L.H.Bainbridge-Bell, or as he was known to us from the Bawdsey days with some affection, 'B.B.', in the installation of the Optical Converter that he had designed. Connected by strings and pulleys to the range and gonio controls, the converter produced a spot beam of light which indicated exactly the range and bearing of the echo on to a ground glass screen, and giving the exact map reference required for transfer or 'telling' to the Filter Room which in those days was at Bawdsey. 'B.B.' always used to turn up wearing a tatty old sports jacket, a pair of flannel bags at half mast and drove an open M.G. which was absolutely full of gadgets-he was a most interesting character and a delight to work with.

He was no fool as an engineer, was technically inventive and, rarely, also intensely practical and the beginning of radar owed much to him not only for his energy and utter devotion to the job in hand but also for his original work on ionosphere research. He required a universal bearing to be fitted on to a block of wood and I used an old piece of timber from one of the towers, which being Douglas Fir was rather coarse grained and to make holes for the screws I used a bradawl and split the wood right in front of 'B.B.' who said... 'tut, tut, tut, laddie, next time use a drill, drills were invented after bradawls!' He was that sort of chap, delightful to work with. I can't remember that we had many visits from civilians. Watson Watt came in once, he was VIP stuff, we always regarded him as the politician and 'B.B.' as the practical man.

I was not there when the 350ft towers arrived, in other words the towers had not arrived by January 1938 and I did not see those until I came back from Malta. Canewdon certainly had crossed dipoles and the goniometer. The crossed dipoles were at the top of the tower with the sensing reflectors mounted on the outriggers, and this was a bit of a pain in the neck because it frequently stuck and it was a rather hazardous undertaking to stick a plank across the outriggers and free the reflector relay. 'Lofty' Weekes was rather good at this although he was the biggest and the heaviest of us; he always used to get up the 240ft tower and do it.

We had civilian riggers for most of the tower work and they never ceased to amaze us as they used to go up the towers in all sorts of weathers and certainly scorned the use of the internal ladders. There were platforms every 40ft with ladders in-between them but the riggers would just shin up the outside. I well remember clinging to the ladders especially near the top where the tower sections became much smaller but we soon got used to the height and ran up and down the ladders with abandon, though never with the aplomb which the civilian riggers displayed – one tough character never wore anything more than slacks and a shirt, winter and summer alike.

When we arrived we all had to live out, three of us in the Rose and Crown at Rochford until Mrs Baker became very ill – our lodging allowance was 25 shillings (£1.25) a week on which we lived like fighting cocks with three cooked meals a day. The wooden huts were completely unprotected until that weekend when we put the sandbags round them and that was the first time that I was not allowed to go home on a weekend pass. I can remember at that time being sickened because we had to attend a church parade in Canewdon and thanks were offered to the almighty God for deliverance from the Germans or something similar and we had sacrificed the Czech nation for the sake of our own skins. About that time an Army guard was put on the site from the Honourable Artillery Company and we were very pleased to see them as we had hundreds of sand bags to fill.

Whilst at Canewdon we did have a system installed there of using ourselves and the Dunkirk CH station to get range cuts on a hyperbolic grid map and this was the first time that hyperbolic navigation, which in fact it was, was actually used. We had two traces on our tube, our own and Dunkirk's, and we used to take the range of the target from us and the range of the same target from Dunkirk and check them off on the hyperbolic grid and get a much more accurate position than we could get from the range and bearing readings that we took, which was pretty low at that time. We got quite good at it but the hyperbolic method of using Dunkirk always gave us better results. The system was invented by a Corporal Chapman who was at Bawdsey and it was certainly introduced to Canewdon and Dunkirk and I never heard if he got proper recognition for his efforts. It was at Canewdon and Bawdsey that we met for the very first time professional radio engineers and we were very, very impressed with all of them that we met They were the nicest of people, never looked down their noses at us because quite frankly we were only half trained, that we were the users rather than the originators which they were. In January 1939 I left Canewdon to be part of a group taking the very first Mobile CH to Malta.

LEN WITTER

I joined the RAF the back end of May 1942 just a couple of months after my 21st birthday and went to Blackpool, was there for eight weeks doing initial training, squarebashing, etc., then posted to 73 Wing, 60 Group at Malton, Yorkshire, along with nine or ten others. The next day we all had an interview by a Squadron Leader. I told him that I had just finished a seven year apprenticeship on lift construction and he said "I think you are the type of person that we are looking for ". He asked me if I could climb and I said that I had been used to climbing up and down cliff faces, steps and stairways. He said that we want men that can climb and he explained the situation regarding aerials at many stations along the east coast that involved a lot of climbing.

The next day I was packed off to Staxton Wold CH station, which was not far away. I caught the bus and met the aerial party there who consisted of a Flight Sergeant, Sergeant, Corporal and an LAC and they were quite pleased to see me as most of their crew had been posted overseas. Within two or three months more were recruited and we finished up with a crew of nine or ten, some obsolete barrage balloon men so they were quite capable of rope splicing, tying knots and rigging in general.

The towers at Staxton consisted of four transmitting and four receiving towers, the receiving towers were all wood and the transmitting towers all steel with a tapered base 350ft high, the receivers 240ft high, The transmitting towers were all in line about 40 to 50 yards apart with three cantilever platforms on each side of the tower, one at 50ft, the next at 200ft and the top one at 350ft, The top one was not a platform, more like a catwalk 3 ft wide with a handrail supported by angle irons, very, very open and as you walked along the catwalk it was very springy and in windy weather the towers swayed. In between the 350ft and 200ft platforms and the 50ft platforms there was an aerial array stretched between tower number one and two and between towers three and four. There were two curtains, the exciter and the reflector; there wasn't much to the reflector curtain but the exciter curtain was quite a complicated affair strung together by small wires of ⅛ inch diameter. Our job was to maintain and repair these curtains as they did need a lot of repair especially in winter time when many gales blew on the east coast.

It was quite a job getting these curtains down, rather dangerous and very exhausting having to climb up 350ft carrying ropes, block and tackle, spanners etc. To get the curtain down we would climb up the tower carrying a light rope, about ½ inch diameter, right to the top of the tower then lower the rope and then pull up a heavier one inch diameter rope and believe me that needed some pulling up. Once we got that up we anchored the rope by a pulley block, there were no proper anchorage points for a pulley block, we just used the hand rail and tie the rope to the curtain. The curtain was anchored by a couple of eye bolts, which were fastened to a one inch diameter bar one foot long with tubular spacers, the eye bolts about ⅞ inches in diameter and these were fastened on to the bottom flange of the 6 inch by 3 inch channelling base of the cantilever.

To get to these bolts we had to lift up the trapdoor then lie flat on your tummy and there was just enough room to get your arms through to undo the ⅞ inch diameter bolts. The rope was tied to the bar and the blokes down below would take the strain while we undid the nuts all done simultaneously with the other riggers across the next tower, then gently lower the curtain down on the rope pulling it out from the bottom. The Flight Sergeant was always down there and he would pull out the curtain, very careful not to bend the copper wire and spread it all over the ground on the long grass, we would then start examining dipoles that had broken, repair them and then, before the curtain went up, grease all the wires to keep out the elements but I am sure that it did not stay on for very long. The damage always came after the gales, a heck of a lot of gales on the east coast with broken wires and broken insulators keeping us quite busy in winter time going from one station to another trying to keep the stations on the air. I worked on three curtains, complete renewals, one at Danby, one at Staxton and West Beckham. There were drawings to work to and involved hundreds and hundreds of splices with very small wire and we were stuck out there often in very bad weather. One curtain was done with six inches of snow on the ground for a couple of weeks, just splicing.

We did have flying suits, they were quite warm and we had plenty of mittens but even then the fingers got very very cold! Once the curtain had been repaired the next job was to hoist it back up again and this needed a heck of a lot of strength with two blokes pulling on each of the two ropes and, obviously, the higher the curtain went up the heavier it got and by the time it was reaching its destination real brawn was needed! It was the heck of a job reconnecting again as you were lying flat on your tummy trying to guide the two eye bolts into the two holes in the bottom flange of the channelling.

You were shouting instructions to the men below – up a bit, down a bit – and it was quite nerve racking as you looked down 350ft into fresh air more or less and we had to be careful not to drop the ⅞ inch nut that was in your hand or a couple of washers once you got the eyebolts into position. When you were tightening up with your spanner you had to be careful that you did not drop the spanner and hit some one on the head, and with somebody having to run down the tower and pick it up, but on the whole we were quite free of accidents, a lot of near misses but no serious accidents.

A common fault on the main curtain was 'arcing', this was a flashing blue light due to a dirty insulator or a break and could be seen very clearly at night. We would look at the job and probably decide that it could be done without taking down the curtain so we do a 'bosun's chair job'. This would mean stringing a rope across from one tower to another but doubled for strength, sling a bosun's chair from this rope, fastened above the 200ft platform, about 250ft, and that was the heck of a job, put the smallest guy we had in the chair and hoist him up and there he would be, 100ft to 200ft in mid air pulled up by half a dozen blokes holding him there while he did minor repairs, which even if it took a couple of hours was easier than taking down the curtain, which could take all day. That kind of job was done quite often. There was also a lot of ground work to be done. On the bottom of each curtain were four concrete blocks that ran over a gantry used as weights to keep the curtains taut and these had to be removed.

There was a lot of work maintaining feeder wires and also helping civilians to do matching and phasing, a job we were not happy with as it would take hours looking for a spot where we had to sweat more copper wires that went into the ground – there was a lot of experimental work and guessing in that job. On the receiving towers the maintenance was mainly finding leaks in the pressurised tubes that ran up the towers. A series of copper tube about ½ inch diameter and in these tubes was a copper wire with small insulators and these copper tubes ran up the tower into the dipoles and right into the R block.

We had quite a lot of problems with leaks at the soldered joints causing loss of pressure. If it dropped completely that gave a very bad reception as it kept out condensation, our job was to find the leaks, a very boring job done with soap and water and a brush looking for bubbles at every joint. We would look for leaks like that for days on end, there would probably be only one or two from the top of the 240ft tower to the R block and it was always found in the end as we were not allowed to go until we found it. Then it had to be repaired and that was a tricky job for any solder that dripped down into the joint and got wedged in the copper wire and the tube caused havoc with the picture.

We certainly did some travelling, we used to travel in any old van or wagon that was available usually from the station that we were leaving as they provided the transport to the next station; we spent hours and hours in the backs of vans. We were quite happy when we had a long job such as renewing a curtain because we would be settled for five to six weeks and that was when we could catch up with shoe repairs and laundry business and get kitted out for some new clothes. We used to walk around like tramps or gypsies, nearly always with dirty boots or scruffy clothes, it just couldn't be helped.

To make things easier for travelling we disposed of all our webbing, kit bags and gas masks and got battered suit cases from home, which was much more handier for travelling. I remember once when two of us were sent to Stoke Holy Cross and an officer there said that we would only be there for a few days so all we took were side packs just for shaving tackle, etc. Then he found a second job at West Beckham on a receiving tower fixing frames and brackets which took over three weeks. We never had a change of clothing, we were really stinking, no socks, shirts or collars, we just turned the shirts inside out; I was very disappointed with that job having been without a change of clothing for five weeks!

Another job that I remember was on the last day of the year, New Year's Eve 1943 and we had an urgent call to go from Staxton Wold to Danby which wasn't all that far away to repair an R/T aerial and we were told that we must go on that day. We eventually got back to Staxton about seven at night and found out that all the rest of the crew had gone out on a binge into Scarboro' and I was left with just the Fl/Sgt. We went into Scarboro' to try and find them but we never did, we went into every pub and we knew that there was a liberty wagon back at 11pm and saw it in the distance just pulling away. We finished up walking the six miles back to camp and as we got half way at Seamer we heard a clock chime twelve so we sang Auld Lang Syne, just the Fl/Sgt and myself.

The Fl/Sgt was a real character, we never guessed his age and we looked on him as an old man really, he had been in the Navy in World War One as a Petty Officer, very noticeable wherever he went, you couldn't mistake him. We always reckoned that he must have been about fifty, a tough old man about 5ft 6 inches tall, a good strong build and his hair almost snow white, we used to call him Snowy, not to his face of course as we always respected him and his rank. His skills as a rigger such as rope splicing, knot tying and general application of rigging was very, very, good and there was no doubt that he was top class in that respect. He was a very likeable chap, wasn't the usual discipline type that was usually required in the RAF and we appreciated this and never played on it.

Wherever we went we were a necessary evil as on small stations like Staxton and Danby there were not a great number of people, but very close knit. There were some very educated people in radar and some of them knew it as well and when we stepped into the camp we disrupted their general way of life. They had to find us accommodation and in these small camps it was difficult to find, we used beds vacated by bods on leave then looked around when they returned. We would generally arrive late at night when the storekeeper had to be found to provide us with blankets and then be supplied with meals. It had its advantages as well as we were never called upon to do duties such as fire pickets, fatigues,

KENNETH R YABSLEY

In May 1940, just as the air raids were beginning to be aimed at the mainland of Britain I thought as a patriotic citizen, young and able-bodied to offer my services, so I travelled from the small town of South Brent to my local recruiting office which was staged in the Museum and Art Gallery in Plymouth which had been requisitioned by the War Office. I received a warm welcome and did not get beyond reception as when I mentioned my age, almost 18, and my civilian occupation, I was told that as I was apprenticed to a local builder as a carpenter and joiner I was in a reserved occupation even though air crews were in such demand. I left there feeling quite humiliated and was told to wait pending my age group to register. This I duly did in the following April, 1941 and was called to a medical in the following August which I passed A1. When interviewed later by a 'frosty' looking major I was given no assurance by him just what sort of regiment or unit I was likely to join, as of course with a few years of trade training I felt that I may be able to maintain some degree of continuity by being allocated where my past trade experience would be useful. Once again I left that same establishment feeling not a little frustrated.

As I had not received my call-up to the Army by the end of October, I volunteered for air crew with the Royal Air Force. I followed almost the identical procedure, interview, medical, intelligence, etc and was told that I would be summoned at a later date for the purpose of attestation which I did at the end of October. Of course if the Army had sent my call-up papers before being sworn into the RAF I would have been a soldier, however I was notified quite soon after being accepted into the RAF that I was to proceed to No.3 Recruits Centre, RAF Padgate near Warrington on 8 December 1941 as 1702534 AC2 Yabsley. This was quite a significant date as while on the train going north we learned that the Japanese had attacked Pearl Harbour – how nice!

After arriving at the recruits centre it was quite a busy three or four days particularly as we had to be kitted out and subject to aptitude tests, which was likely to test anyone's patience, as there were times when squads were summoned to parade often for a period for three hours at a time before anything happened! In the end after exhaustive Morse tests in which I proved an absolute dunce, I was posted to private billets in Blackpool as an ACH/GD pending a further selection test. It will be appreciated that the streets of this Lancashire town were just teeming with RAF blue. I was billeted at North Shore in a guest house owned by an elderly spinster by the name of Miss Annie Dickinson. I shall never forget her concern for us young lads as there were 15 others besides myself and everyone without exception with a healthy appetite.

The headquarters of the RAF in Blackpool was situated on the front at the Lansdowne Hotel (Central) and the A.O.C. at my time of service from early December 41 to the end of April 42 was Air Commodore E.L.Howard-Williams. Square bashing and PT often happened on the sea front which also gave the few visitors that were there to watch us drilling and not least the drill instructors, who had ample opportunity to display their prowess. There did not seem to be a great shortage of cafés and eating houses as except for pure luxuries the places we patronised for tea breaks were well stocked; also we were taken to the range on one or more occasions for rifle drill and grenade throwing. One of the most amusing incidents happened one morning when we were visiting the Derby Baths and someone, somewhere, got the syllabus mixed and a squad of WAAFs arrived to use the pool at the same time, imagine then to their chagrin while they were filing in to change we were already occupying the self same pool, about 100 of us in and around the pool with nothing on but our birthday suits!

I was posted after a very memorable stay in the seaside resort of about five months to No 1 RDF School, Cranwell as a RDF operator U/T. Having arrived at one of the RAF's most noble domains I was billeted at West Camp, which was on the opposite side of the road to the Staff College. I think if I remember rightly we were using RM4 receiving sets whereby the range and bearing of aircraft both friendly and hostile were converted to plots by a goniometer. Prior to the completion of the ten week course we were asked where we would be desirous of being posted for operational duties, and I opted for the south coast and was posted to 78 Wing HQ at Ashburton in south Devon for onward posting to a coastal station which was RAF Branscombe, near the town of Sidmouth around the end of June 42.

This was a Chain Home station and we plotted high flying aircraft and also at long range, our other stations on the coast adjacent to us were CHL involved mainly with low flying aircraft and shipping. Instead of fixed aerials like CH, the CHL used a gantry which rotated but only plots which were seaward or immediately on the coastline were reported as of course any aircraft proceeding inland whether hostile or friendly were plotted by the Observer Corps. Having arrived at the operational station of course there was a greater feeling of achievement as we were then dealing with the real thing.

Basically the equipment was the same although we did have an electric calculator which was quite akin to the computers as we know them today. On occasions when the north of England, like Liverpool, were raided, the raiders coming from north-west France would pass directly overhead. Great interest was attached to our own aircraft on special missions as they were heading for enemy territory, particularly photo reconnaissance for on their results would determine the location of the next raids on the continent of Europe. The history books tell us that the reason a lot of coastal radar sites escaped attack was because of the complex nature of the aerial siting, to fly at anything like low level or dive bomb was most hazardous if not suicidal.

Our Operations Room was under many tons of earth but nevertheless well ventilated and pleasant to operate. In the corner of the technical site were mock-ups which from the air would appear to be watch-crew quarters and some times we were told to take a walk to simulate a well worn path. However knowing the inventiveness and technical brilliance of the Germans this probably failed to fool them! During the time I was at Branscombe the Dieppe landings were staged and although we were on the periphery of the area there was more than the usual aircraft traffic that night.

Our domestic site was about a mile away, sometimes we were ferried there by van or very often prepared to walk, the personnel of the watch comprised of WAAF as well as airmen perhaps all the more reason for preferring to walk. The Commando raids on Dieppe did in fact promote the possibility of a reprisal anywhere along the south or south-east coasts but happily none occurred. I did visit the Filter Room situated near Box in Wiltshire where the plots were assessed as they were received; it was a manor type of house such as one finds in the countryside. This one was called Rudloe Manor, HQ for No. 10 Group, and while travelling in the vicinity of the camp a couple of years back I found to my astonishment that it still operated and it was an 'Open Day'.

I also made a visit to Sectors Ops where mostly intercepting aircraft were controlled and based and sector maintained close liaison with all the radar camps and Filter Rooms in their respective zone of operations. We operated a three watch system and also having had the privilege of enjoying some seven months on the station and the second Christmas in the RAF I was posted in early January overseas. I had during the time I was operationally involved lived only some 40 to 50 miles away from home, a privilege I guess few would claim in wartime. Having obtained 7 days leave and around half way through it a telegram arrived ordering me back to the unit to 'proceed on overseas posting' and although I received the telegram almost within a couple of hours of dispatch, I didn't arrive back at camp until 24 hours had elapsed with the ready prepared alibi – I was away from home when the message arrived!

Ex-CTC narrative by James "Jim" S. Farrior

In June, 1941, I was 21 years old and working in Atlanta, Georgia, U.S.A., as a radio telegraph operator and technician. My job paid well, the work was interesting, but life was rather dull. I wouldn't have dreamed that I would soon cross a submarine infested ocean to work in a war torn land. A newspaper article mentioned that Americans with technical radio experience would soon be able to volunteer to help in operating and maintaining a British advanced warning radiolocation system. I wrote to His Majesty's Consul, who sent me an application and a booklet describing a new organization, the Civilian Technical Corps (CTC). Corps members had to have a certain level of experience, pass a background check, and also pass the RAF physical exam.

Although my fellow workers considered me insane, I completed the application, and found myself on Sept. 21, 1941, in Montreal, Canada, where I was officially enrolled in the CTC. We were issued the standard RAF uniform, but with black buttons and a CTC insignia. After processing, I was sent with others on a troop train to Halifax, where after a few days, we boarded a crowded troop ship, the HMTS Andes. Together with some other troop ships and escort vessels, we made a zigzag crossing, arriving safely at Liverpool on Oct.17.Upon debarking, we marched to Lime St. Station, where I was amazed by the large train station, and the diminutive steam engines and passenger coaches. Later, however, I would become impressed by the reliability and dependability of the British transportation system, even in wartime.

Our train was loaded mostly with people in uniform, and after passing areas in Liverpool that had suffered extreme bomb damage, we moved out into the most beautiful, picture book scenery that I had ever seen. It was a beautiful day, and farm animals were grazing on bright green, well-kept fields separated by walls and hedges. I was captivated by the beautiful vistas that opened up as the train made its way to Bournemouth, where CTC headquarters was located. To our surprise, we discovered that Bournemouth had a mild climate. At that time, Bournemouth had not yet received much bomb damage, and it still gave the appearance of the holiday spot that it had been in peace time. We were billeted in a small hotel that had been taken over. At Bournemouth we discovered such things as warm beer, bread made of various grains that resembled cow feed, hot tea without sugar, porridge, and cabbages boiled until they disintegrated.

On Oct. 23, we were marched to the Bournemouth Pavilion where we were lined up and told that we would be reviewed by King George VI and Queen Elizabeth, and that we were to stand at attention and look straight ahead as they passed by us. They soon arrived, and both of them walked by our ranks, but not together, and spoke warmly to a number of us. The King spoke to the man directly in front of me. Also there to be reviewed were some newly arrived airmen, mostly RCAF. After it was over and the King and Queen had returned to their car, we broke ranks and everyone ran closer to the car and gave three cheers. They waved as they departed. I felt that I had been a part of history.

Five days later, we passed through London on our way to Cranwell, where we were assigned to the huts we would occupy while attending the RDF School. Some of the men complained about the military lifestyle imposed on us, which didn't go over well with the officer and sergeant in charge of it, but the majority of us felt that the almost constant marching, drills, parades, etc., were offset by the excellent quality of the school and the instructors. One RAF instructor told us that things would be far better at a station, and that was indeed true. We soon discovered that a few men among us had somehow been accepted by the quick selection process, but were not suited for the training or the work. I was pleased when they were culled out early on.

On Nov.13, we met the King again when he entered our classroom accompanied by Air Commodore Probyn, the Cranwell C.O. He remembered having seen us at Bournemouth, and spoke in a relaxed way, adding that he was in Cranwell for some additional flight training. On Dec. 7, the Japanese attacked Pearl Harbor, and the United States entered the war as a combatant nation. We all worried about what affect that would have on our future. The first impression by some of the men was that they should join the American forces immediately. On Jan 10, I had my first and only brush with English law when I was riding my bike shortly after dark on a deserted road and an irate 'bobby' came up behind me on a bike and charged me with riding a bike without displaying a red rear light as prescribed by law. An extreme embarrassment occurred on Jan. 17, when a 'bobby' from Sleaford came into our classroom while we were taking our final test. I was called up front to face him while he read, in a very officious voice, a summons for me to appear in court. Later, I wrote to the Justice of Peace explaining that I would be posted before the date of the trial. Perhaps I'm still a fugitive from justice! It was a happy day when we were given our final scores and were told where we would be posted. Our principal instructor, Flt. Lt. Bond, told me that my posting to RAF Scarlett on the Isle of Man was the best of all.

After a few days on leave exploring London, I traveled to 77 Wing headquarters at Liverpool, and on to Fleetwood, where I boarded the boat for Douglas, I.O.M. The scenic views as the boat entered the harbor and as I traveled to Castletown on the Victorian steam train were like fine paintings. When I arrived at RAF Scarlett, I was assigned to a hut, and was given a warm greeting by the RAF, RCAF and RNZAF Radio Mechanics. After talking with a few of them, I knew I had nothing to worry about. When officially checking in the next morning, I met our C.O., Flt. Lt. Walters, who welcomed me cordially.

Scarlett was a typical "West Coast type" CH station. Over the next few days, I worked with two of the most experienced men, Harry Wooding and George Ashley, both of whom soon became Sergeants. We did routine maintenance on the MB2 transmitters, the RF7 receiver, and cleaned some insulators on the receiving dipoles on their 240ft tower. What a view! The CH equipment was well designed and built, and very reliable, but it was necessary to keep all parts of it in excellent condition for it to do its job. Soon afterward, I assisted the Wing Maintenance Team when they came for the quarterly maintenance that we at the station always referred to as the "quarterly sabotage".

In the days that followed, I made many friends at camp, and also a number of friends among the citizens of Castletown. They were very fine people. I developed a strong interest in the history and quaint culture of the Island, an interest which I have to this day. I read a number of books, visited the Manx museum many times, and explored many of the historical sites on the Island. In April, two more CTC men, George Fulton and Jack Boor, who finished at Cranwell in the class after mine, were posted to Scarlett. They were both good men with considerable electronic experience, so they helped our staffing considerably. Our goal at Scarlett was to get on a four watch system, but we seldom had enough men to do it. Typically, new people would be posted away shortly after they arrived, and some of the more experienced men were also posted. As a result of that, I soon became one of those with the most tenure, and a few months later, Jack, George, and I were all "old timers" at Scarlett. We often had gatherings in the Common Room, and Scarlett was also noted for occasional big parties, which we called "shaky do's", to celebrate this or that. Great fun! We didn't need much of an excuse. By now, we were used to warm beer from the world famous Castletown Brewery. We would sometimes have a small orchestra and visitors would come from the CH stations at Bride and Dalby, and from the CHL station at Cregneish. I had a nice WAAF girl friend, Vera Bradford, whose presence made life much more civilized and pleasant.

Having been a commercial telegrapher, I enjoyed standing in for LAC Dick Haslam, whose job it was to send plots by W/T to Preston during drills or when the phone connection was down. I had also had experience maintaining relays, so I helped Sgt. Fred Harvey burnish relay contacts in the noisy "Fruit Machine", the coordinate calculator for which he was responsible. In return, he spent a great deal of time teaching me the finer points of trigonometry. In early Oct. 1942, the camp became crowded, and some senior mechanics, including, George, Jack, and I, were billeted out in private homes. The three of us rented a large bedroom in "Merton Croft", the fine home of Mr. & Mrs. Fred Cooil. We had the best of all worlds. We took our meals at Vernie Vanwell's small restaurant, Anne's Supper Bar, and at her home on Sundays. We slept in beds with springs, mattresses, and sheets, and also visited our friends in the huts and in the common room at camp.By that time, we had received several promotions and our work assignments reflected our higher status. Through the Cooils, and others, we met many more Manx citizens.

In early 1943, the U.S. Armed Forces, the U.S. Embassy, the American Merchant Marine, Lockheed Overseas, and some other organizations began actively to recruit CTC members. Through attrition, the Corps began to shrink, and there were rumors that at some point the Corps would be disbanded. There were three CTC men, Floyd Harkcom, Harold Wright, and Paul Hand, at the CH station at Bride, I.O.M., and we exchanged rumors with them. Harold Wright, a senior man at Bride, liked his work, but told me that he planned to make a change before something else decided his fate. My work at Scarlett continued to be interesting and rewarding, and I dreaded the thought of leaving the Isle of Man. However, on May 19, 1943, George, Jack, and I decided we must make a move and, after obtaining approval from CTC Headquarters, we traveled to London and joined the American Merchant Marine as radio officers. Those days at Scarlett had been days to remember.

ABBREVIATIONS

AA	Anti Aircraft
ACAS	Assistant Chief of the Air Staff
ADEE	Air Defence Experimental Establishment (Army)
ADGB	Air Defence of Great Britain
ADR	Air Defence Research (sub-committee of CID)
ADRDE	Air Defence Research and Development Est. (Army)
AM	Air Ministry, now Ministry of Defence (Air)
AMES	Air Ministry Experimental Station
AMP	Air Member for Personnel
AMRD	Air Member for Research and Development
AMRE	Air Ministry Research Establishment
AOC	Air Officer Commanding
ARP	Air Raid Precautions
BBC	British Broadcasting Corporation
Blitz	German Air Raids (colloquial)
BMHQ	Base Maintenance Headquarters
Bowen	Dr E.G.Bowen
BRS	Bawdsey Research Station
BTH	British Thompson-Houston
Bullock	Sir Christopher Llewellyn Bullock
Cabinet	Top policy making committee of government
CAS	Chief of the Air Staff
CID	Committee of Imperial Defence
Courtney	Air Vice Marshal C.L.Courtney CB CBE DSO
CTC	Civilian Technical Corps
DCAS	Deputy Chief of the Air Staff
DCD	Director/Directorate of Communications Development
DD of S	Deputy Director of Signals
DERA	Defence Evaluation and Research Agency
DG of S	Director General of Signals
Douglas	Air Marshal W. Sholto Douglas MC CMG
Dowding	Air Chief Marshal Sir Hugh C.T. Dowding GCVO KCB CMG

DSIR	Department of Scientific and Industrial Research
DSR	Director of Scientific Research
EMI	Electric and Musical Industries
Ellington	Air Chief Marshal Sir Edward L. Ellington KCB CMG CBE
FBI	Federal Bureau of Investigation
Freeman	Air Marshal Sir Wilfred Freeman KCB DSO MC
GEC	General Electric Company
Hart	Squadron Leader R.G.Hart MC
HMSO	His Majesty's Stationery Office
I/G	Inspector – General
IWM	Imperial War Museum
Joubert	Air Marshal Sir Philip Joubert de la Ferté KCB CMG DSO
Lindemann	Prof F.E.Lindemann, later Lord Cherwell
Londonderry	Marquis of Londonderry
Ludlow-Hewitt	Air Chief Marshal Sir Edgar Ludlow-Hewitt KCB CMG DSO MC
Marconi	Marconi Wireless Telegraph Company
MAP	Ministry of Aircraft Production
MetroVick	Metropolitan Vickers Electrical Company
MI.5	Military Intelligence
MRAF	Marshal of the Royal Air Force
NAAFI	The Navy, Army and Air Force Institute, a shop where tea, coffee, meals, sweets and cigarettes, etc, were purchased by ranks lower than sergeant
Newall	Air Chief Marshal Sir Cyril Newall KCB CMG CBE AM
NPL	National Physical Laboratory
Peirse	Air Marshal R.E.C.Peirse CB DSO AFC
Portal	Air Chief Marshal Sir Charles F.A.Portal KCB DSO MC
Post Office	General Post Office whose telecommunications functions have been transferred to British Telecommunications (BT)
PRO	Public Record Office
RADAR	Radio Aid to Detection and Ranging
RAE	Royal Aircraft Establishment
RAF	Royal Air Force: in the text also refers to Servicemen
RAFVR	Royal Air Force Volunteer Reserve
RDF	Cover name for radar, no specific interpretation intended
RFC	Royal Flying Corps
RNAS	Royal Naval Air Service
Rowe	Mr A.P.Rowe

Salmond	Sir John M. Salmond KCB KCMG DSO
SAT	Scientific Adviser on Telecommunications
Signals	Air Ministry Signals Directorate
SRS	Stanmore Research Section, later Operational Research Fighter Command
Swinton	Lord Swinton
Sykes	Sir Frederick Sykes GBE KCB CMG
TISC	Treasury Inter Services Committee
Tizard	Mr H.T.Tizard, later Sir Henry KCB AFC FRS FRAES
Trenchard	Sir Hugh Trenchard KCB DSO
TRE	Telecommunications Research Establishment
YMCA	Young Men's Christian Association
WAAF	Women's Auxilary Air Force: in the text also refers to Servicewomen
Watson Watt	Mr R.A.Watson Watt, later Sir R.A.Watson-Watt CB FRS
Wilkins	Mr A.F.Wilkins
Wimperis	Mr H.E.Wimperis CBE
WO	War Office, now Ministry of Defence (Army)
Works	Air Ministry Works Directorate
WRNS	Women's Royal Naval Service
2.IU	No. 2 Installation Unit at RAF Kidbrooke, London

GLOSSARY

AI	AIR INTERCEPTION: Equipment fitted in fighter aircraft for the night interception of enemy aircraft.
ASV	AIR to SURFACE VESSEL: Equipment fitted in aircraft for the detection of ships.
CD	COASTAL DEFENCE: ground equipment for the location of ships approaching the coast, ports or harbours.
CH	CHAIN HOME: Ground equipment for the location of aircraft approaching the coast. 10 and 5 metres.
	ADVANCE: Hutted equipment with 90ft guyed masts. One channel.
	INTERMEDIATE: Hutted equipment with two 240ft wooden towers. One channel.
	FINAL: Permanent buildings with four steel 350ft towers or 325ft masts and four or two wooden 240ft towers. Two channels.
CHL	CHAIN HOME LOW: 1.5 metre ground equipment for the detection of low flying aircraft approaching the coast.
CHEL	CHAIN HOME EXTRA LOW: 10cm equipment for the detection of shipping and very low flying aircraft approaching the coast.
CMH	CENTIMETRIC HEIGHTFINDER: 10cm ground equipment for heightfinding
CRT	Cathode Ray Tube.
CW	Continuous radio wave.
DIPOLE	An aerial that gives the highest transmission and reception efficiency, the length of which is half the wavelength.
D/F	DIRECTION FINDING: A land based system that uses three spaced stations for finding the position of ships and aircraft
GCI	GROUND CONTROL OF INTERCEPTION: 1.5 metre equipment for the placing of an intercepting fighter on the track of an unsuspecting enemy night bomber.

GEE	Navigational aid for Bomber Command using pulse transmissions from the ground.
GL1 and 2	GUN LAYING: 7 metre equipment for AA guns.
GL3	GUN LAYING: 10cm equipment for AA guns.
Goni	GONIOMETER: A device that electrically 'turns' fixed aerial systems to obtain a bearing.
HF	HIGH FREQUENCY 100 to 10 metres (3 to 30 MHz.)
H/F	Heightfinding
Homing	Bearings provided by a single Direction Finding station that enables aircraft to fly back to base.
IF	Intermediate Frequency of a receiver after conversion
IFF	IDENTIFICATION FRIEND OR FOE: equipment in aircraft and on the ground to enable echoes of friendly aircraft to be identified.
LAA	Light Anti-Aircraft
LOS	LINE of SHOOT the direction of maximum transmission and reception of an aerial.
MB	MOBILE BASE A mobile CH station with telescopic masts.
MF	MEDIUM FREQUENCY 1000 to 100 metres. (300KHz to 3MHz)
MRU	MOBILE CH STATION with workshop, accommodation,etc.
PPI	PLAN POSITION INDICATOR: A cathode ray tube display with the range line rotating in synchronism with the aerial.
PRF	PULSE REPETITION FREQUENCY The number of pulses transmitted every second.
RF	RADIO FREQUENCY The frequency spectrum that can be transmitted and received in space.
R/T	RADIO TELEPHONE A voice service using radio frequencies.
UHF	ULTRA HIGH FREQUENCY 1 metre to 10 centimetres (300 - 3000Mhz)
U/S	UNSERVICEABLE The Services word for faulty equipment.
VEB	VARIABLE ELEVATION BEAM: Equipment to measure height using a 1.5 metre wavelength.
VHF	VERY HIGH FREQUENCY 10 to 1 metre (30 - 300Mhz.)
W/T	WIRELESS TELEGRAPHY The transmission of information with Morse or other codes on a radio frequency.

BIBLIOGRAPHY

DOCUMENTS IN THE PUBLIC RECORD OFFICE

1. AIR2, 8, 10, 12, 16, 19, 20, 22, 24- 29, 33, 37,41, AVIA7-13,15, 17, 22, 26, 44, 46, 51, 53, CAB102/640-643, WO33/1822
2. Volume 4 and 5 of the *Air Ministry Signals* Series, AIR41/12 and AIR10/5485.
3. *Army Radar* compiled by Brigadier A.P.Sayer, published by the War Office. Is in the form of galley proofs plus interesting correspondence. (WO32/11625)
4. *The Story of Radiolocation* by the Ministry of Information.
                                                                    AIR20/1494

RECOMMENDED READING

BATT, Reg., *The Radar Army,* R.Hale, 1991

BOWEN, E.G., *Radar Days,* A.Hilger, 1987

BROWN,L., *A Radar History of World War II,* IOP, 1999

BROWN, R., *Boffin,* A.Hilger, 1987

BUDERI, R., *The Invention that Changed the World,* Abacus, 1998

BURNS, R., *Radar Development to 1945,* P.Perigrinus, 1988

DEAN, M., *Radar on the Isle of Wight,* Historical Radar Archive, 1996

GOUGH, J., *Watching The Skies,* HMSO, 1993

JONES, R.V., *Most Secret War,* H.Hamilton, 1978

KINSEY, G., *Bawdsey: Birth of the Beam,* T.Dalton, 1983

KINSEY, G., *Orfordness: Secret Site,* T.Dalton, 1981

ROWLINSON, F., *Contribution to Victory,* Metropolitan Vickers, 1947

ROWE, A.P., *One Story of Radar,* Cambridge University Press, 1948

SCARTH, R.N., *Echoes from the Sky,* Civic Society, Hythe, Kent, 1999

SWORDS, S.S., *A Technical History of the Beginning of Radar,*
                                                      P.Perigrinus, 1986

WATSON-WATT, R.A., *Three Steps to Victory,* Odhams, 1957

ZIMMERMAN, D., *Britain's Shield,* Sutton Publishing, 2001

The Origins and Development of Operational Research in the Royal Air Force, HMSO, 1963

The Journal of the Institution of Electrical Engineers, Vol 93A, 1946

INDEX

Ellington, Sir E. 21, 23, 54, 173
EMI 307, 314
Escape of German ships 279-281

Fair Isle 175
Ferranti 141
Fighter Command 54, 160, 171,
    205, 220, 232, 250, 279, 304
Filtering 196-199
Fleming, Dr 69
Forbes, Jane K.T. 154
Fort Wallington 221
Franklin, H. 188
Freeman, Sir W. 54-5, 63, 66-7, 69-
    70, 74, 91-2, 95, 99, 125, 136,
    175, 180, 202, 209, 224, 250,
    291
Fruit Machine 196

GCI – First used 233
GEC Ltd 103, 121, 186, 189, 239,
    262, 265, 314
GEE 249, 282, 304
George, David Lloyd 5
Gill, D.A. 283-4
GL – First used 80
GM – First used 161
Great War 4, 9, 34, 64, 165
Grouse and Siting 89
Guerlac, H.T. 143

Harris, A.T. 254
Hart, R.G. 63, 94-5, 115-6, 122,
    134, 138, 141, 166, 168, 173,
    194-6, 228, 233, 267
Heidelburg 308-309
Hill, Prof. A.V. 20-2, 64
HM Signal School 45, 136, 148,
    262
Hitler, A. 16, 108

IFF 113, 116, 126, 132, 141, 150,
    153, 155, 172, 234, 249, 283,
    314
Inspector/General 173-4, 218-9,
    223-4, 229, 265
Isle of May 161, 164
Isle of Man 171

Jamming 102-3, 225-6, 259,
    279-280, 287
Jefferson, S. 320
Jones, R.V. 300
Joubert de la Ferté, Sir P.J. 58, 61-2,
    72, 137, 160, 163, 165, 171,
    175-6, 177-180, 183-185, 187,
    190, 209-211, 224, 227, 229,
    231-4, 237-8, 242, 245-7, 250,
    252, 254, 257, 262-263, 267- 8,
    270, 274

Kidbrooke 100-1, 110, 119
King George VI 152-3, 202, 296

Lamb Experiments 114, 168, 232
Larnder, H. 142, 153, 171, 173, 233,
    236, 318, 320
Lee, Sir A.G 177-8, 190, 201, 209
Leedham, H. 67, 69-71, 75, 240,
    249
Lindemann, Prof. F.A. 20, 22-3, 57,
    209, 224
Line of Shoot 60, 98, 127, 129, 133,
    144, 153, 165, 167, 187, 199,
    230, 257-8, 279, 288
Londonderry, Marquis of 22-3
Ludlow-Hewitt, Sir F. 218-9, 223,
    265

Magnetron 188-9, 287-8
MB 116, 202-3, 253
MAPRE 202

NOTES

NOTES

NOTES

NOTES